HOW WE FIT?

By

GODFROY BOURSIQUOT

After all, I remember.

THIS STORY IS DEDICATED TO MY family, my friends, my son **Madyuf,** my daughter **Mayud**, to all those who have plunged into nostalgia. And if there is a breath of gratitude beyond silence to tickle hope from the future to the past, that breath will remain in my memory. And always at your door, to sing first the sublime honor of your efforts by my side.

Thank you to everyone I have met on my way. Thank you for the lessons you have taught me. It is not just a matter of drinking from the source, but of distributing wealth, starting by saying thank you, to you my children, my family, and my friends. How would you react if one day you saw your name written on the walls of your city?

Contents

Introduction

No one has ever imagined that I would spend my life abroad. Haiti has always been present in me, with its share of good manners inherited from my father and my mother. Leaving an old life is not easy, it calls into question commitments. Especially when you leave for the first time to join other cultures, other families.

To settle in another country is to adapt to the tempo to dance differently to the musical rhythms of the drum of life. One has the impression of having left the dreams where one still exists, where one is powerful, to go to swell the crowd on the other side, to live another life in the opposite direction.

There was a great temptation to turn back, but the people I encountered daily gave me the strength to resist. They have given me back the confidence, this essential element which, when it is reciprocal, allows to give balance in everything.

Here in the US, people have arrived unaware that they could not live at the same pace as in their country of origin. They come from America, Asia, Europe, Africa, and the Caribbean. They are of different culture, different nationality, and different language. As immigrants, they act every day to reduce exclusion in all its forms: social, economic, and cultural.

I have advanced in this world by considering it as a great school, and where each country is a classroom. When you meet strangers, you are in the playground. If you behave badly with someone in this space, it is the school, your school, which will have problems: in other words, the world, our world. People have their difficulties. You can take someone's hand to make them cross the street, and yet shock them more than anything else; violate their rights, because that will prevent them from identifying their strengths. Also, you can teach them the same thing without holding their hand. And if the confidence is there, the suffering disappears, we can no longer break the rules, rob each other. We must respect people in their values and capacities.

The challenge is that people from all walks of life can meet, find meaning in their lives together and mobilize for a just and noble cause. By climbing mountains of differences every day to work together. During the first two weeks, I suffered to the point of forgetting my first name, stressed that I was adapting to this form of multiple culture. Yet I have met extraordinary people, wonderful people. As I have not stopped doing it since my childhood, I silently watch for any sign of hope, this hope that connects me to this eternal dream of seeing everyone immersed in an atmosphere of joy, and of living a story of love and peace.

I have never ceased to be a dreamer, misunderstood, whipped by anxiety, oppression, and contempt. This story always comes to my mind, and my forgotten first name is with me. This is how, in a dream, I started to detach myself from the world to follow this girl...

I have the impression of being the stake of a fight between the physical world and the spiritual world, a kind have back and forth: when I am depressed, I only turn my back on this physical body. I have to reinvent every day what a day could be, as well as my first daily duty.

It is not about isolating myself from the reality that evolves and changes every second, but rather adapting to it. To understand my presence everywhere; to look for me and look at me in everything.

It is not about trying to find an answer to everything, but rather to commune with yourself, and to fight your frustration. Take the opportunity to take the time to grow, transform and detach your being from all that is visible. Use each situation as a compass to find the direction of the crossing and open another path to success.

To the unknown I am the unknown man, unknown on my way. I know so little about myself that I sometimes have to beg another stranger to teach me things about myself. I live at random; I look for myself among the abandoned: I was born Haitian and I will die for my cause, I am a poet and I will die for my words. I expect all this because the criminals are there, and they live among us. I expect all of this...

Let me kill me for my creation and my words, I expect all that; let me take my life for my ideas, I am like that! I am waiting, alone, and I don't know when, but I know that death is there and that it awaits me, too. Everyone knows it, even those who already violate my confidence know it.

I come from a country, an extraordinary country of incomparable purity, a country of war without reason and end; a country lost in the dust of its miseries; a country of extreme poverty which is engaged in a struggle without me and you; yet he has been calling us for a long time, under this sun shines for centuries in this land of dreams; a green nature, a country of happiness and peace, a country of law where speech is free; right to housing and life, right to actions, right to promotions; a country where life appears as a vision which is reflected in a beautiful painting offering power for all...

A country that awaits us all, for a new morning, all for a new life, a new fight in a thirsty country: thirsty for justice, thirsty for life and peace. And if one wondered what is this country...

This country is Haiti and I cannot stop believing in everything that painfully inhabits us, since I am a lonely man, an unhappy poet. I recognize that for some it may seem a little odd: wanting to live first for art and others.

I have, after having devoted my time for a long time to art, to children, to the community and after having suffered many disappointments, experienced the adventure of several pages of history. But now I am going back to the other homeland as we would go to a hospital supported by people, like a prisoner. I cross a corridor like an invisible man. No one sees me; I go into the rooms and sit on the illusion beds I find there. I am lying on the sealed back of the reunion.

The white walls of life, the gray curtains of uncertainty on the glass windows of doubt hide from me the real nature of things. The door is open. In front of me, the big corridor, the opportunity to cross the big barrier, is there. Passersby watch me cry and laugh at the same time. I combine the past of my verbs where my suffering nests, but where chances smile at me. I look at eyelids closed like windows, like forgotten days.

By simple politeness, I speak in an affable tone turning my back on my fundamental doctrine that is to be reserved, and yet I do not smile! I have suffered too much. Too often I lie to myself, mocking the emptiness of these sad times.

I look here and there, without smiling, without strength: children and orphans without help bent by hunger pass in the large corridor, set out on the same path as me. Everyone is looking for a hand to get bread. I look at them and they too cast their eyes on me. I have a nightmare in broad daylight. What does a man look like when a nightmare is constantly watching him?

A suffering, which others ignore, is inscribed in me to return in the evening to disturb my sleep. At what is this life of sensations, this power to bring about a silence that worries, haste, indifference should have masked?

A poet who, morning and evening, takes the same route, is bored, exhausted, exasperated. The path of anguish, redone day after day, for years, remains an ever-new adventure, although it has always been started again. So, on the bed of my adventures, I still look at children and orphans. A story that I may not have time to explain, to write.

My imagination makes me discover the other nature of things; another sense of life in this homeland, where I wait like in a waiting room. I reduce the world to despair, and let it be ruled by memories. I look at the world and it hates me, I become ashamed of myself: I have too many friends converted into enemies. I want to be alone, alone, without friends, without anyone by my side; because nobody in this world wants to understand me, I wonder why...

Finally, I realize that I ask too many questions in a single life, silence is always the answer of my hell.

Isn't it silly to seek life in the various ways of living it?

I said to myself yesterday in the silence of the night - but no doubt, I may have known it well before childhood -: "All we should know today is that we have no power if you are not able to look in the mirror." A form of life behind each of us, crippled, with laws from a pyramidal source, crosses the threshold of our thoughts.

I strive to be myself, a man of firm character, but adopting a simple attitude as always. An insider who allows others to easily find a new path, without savoring the pleasure of being in the first place, but rather that of being able to stay the best.

There is something that we can always do better than the others. To get there: stay true to yourself, listen to your inner voice and above all never stop on the way when you are facing obstacles. Have the courage to measure your limits and do the things in which you feel great. Never want to impress anyone in his life to avoid living an arrogant life.

It is the way you throw the ball that allows you to reach the goal you dream of. No one will make you happy before you decide to take the first step yourself which will lead you to be happy. You exist to find the path that you want to chart for yourself to lead the life that will make you happy.

It is the existence of everything around you that creates the life you seek. This life manifests itself in looks, forms, movements, attitudes, formulas, and ways of thinking to form, transform and define every morning the parameters of a power that will make you live sumptuous days and evenings.

It is not the skill of your hands that forges the performance that others admire, it is rather the quality of heart that produces the embalming spark of perfume that makes you similar to those with which everyone wants to foil. Do not give another image to what you need to develop, rather paint a partial picture of reality. Joy is a mind game to score points. In this entertainment, you must paint yourself the picture of what you aspire to, while remaining within the prescribed formula.

You are a transparent board that must be repainted day after day with a motivation that you must support until the end. And you can do better than everyone you look at, and people applaud you. Do not grab the big head when you are in the limelight.

To be conquered without danger, we triumph without glory... If, in your space ritually occupied by your spirit of creativity, you are already qualified for a gain without having had to face a rival, that you reach the objective without having forever bow your head in front of the door, you will always have the boon to sound the alarm to break in a door in addition to the one opened by this crystal clear picture, visible to everyone. Surround your name, your character, and your personality with secrets to finally find what you feel valuable or elegant in your social connections.

Your expectations will never be fulfilled if you do not remain like an empty container ready to receive the new morning with all that it contains. And never forget that you have the hook in your hands to catch your seconds, minutes and hours of joy, a chance that everyone hopes to have in their life. Always stay happy without forgetting that even if the river joyful is on the road to your heart that does not prevent it from mixing with the quicksand of your daily life.

What you are is reflected in your skills and especially in the motivation you have to achieve the goals you have set. What you want to do does it now and with determination as if you were accessing a simple staircase that would be one kilometer from your room. When you get there, make the world see you differently, prove to the world that you are unique in everything you do, and don't hesitate to worship every new thing that brightens your life every day.

Motivation is like the amount of water you can get. Let us say it is like a river or a river from which you must receive powerful water, but which flows drop by drop. If you want to live a productive existence, the source will not dry up, and you will transform yourself day after day into the creator of your own life.

It's how you think and act that will determine how successful you are. If you do not change the way you see things today, you will be the barrier to your development and tomorrow what you expect will not be yours. Never be afraid of being an adventurer in life because life itself is a great adventure that should not be taken for granted. The people who promise you the moon never hope you can be free for one day to do what you want with your life. Those watching you now are not the insured protectors of tomorrow. You are stronger and more intelligent than all those who accompany you. Coaching is just a temporary chance for you to guide your actions, but it makes you dumb and dependent.

Like me... What I have become today stems from voluntary missions carried out since my childhood. Each of the faces I meet increases my knowledge, all the poor neighborhoods, and each of the people who are part of it, all the young people and the children were first of all a source of imagination and creation.

My life is shaped by physical and metaphysical adventures. Everything I do is success. I've never experienced chess in my life, so adventure is a safe road for me, a school without rival. Adventures train me. A great man is one who meets nature in an impossible world, without a family circle and who runs daily after time with ease.

I cannot let my dreams die; I feed and protect them by internal and external journeys. I feed them in my sufferings and my rejoicings. I always have a positive image of my travels: trips often to unknown places and without a road map. I always cherish the madness of reaching the goal...

I do not believe in chance, but the fulfillment of a commitment. Everyone has a gift from somewhere, you just must guide and feed it with the madness of being happy and natural.

I never drop a commitment; I have a vision of things that I do not give up easily; I don't let anyone make decisions for me like I never take someone else's place.

I do not pretend to say that the ideas of others cannot complement mine and that what they think is not right. On the contrary, it is important to consider the opinions of others.

When I was younger, I always wanted to have my own space, it was one of my first goals: to be lonely and free. I always had the spirit of a traveler, always had an image to discover in my head, whether it was a celebration or a distress.

I seek to live in depth the mystery of my existence, that of others too, as well as the full reality of things. Thinking back to the story of my childhood and my life of adventures, I realize that for a very long time, the Supreme Being has staked my life with experiences that prepared me for the different activities that I would have to exercise as that of motivator with the most deprived.

I have no special words to speak to young people; I just speak to them like a friend, like another part of my being. The need to travel often manifests suddenly, when sometimes we had something else in mind; I'm there and suddenly, I want to leave, without preparing anything; whereas two minutes before, I didn't even have the idea to go for a walk.

The beauties of nature, the music of the birds, the simple things, the accompaniment of others: this is above all what drives me to travel. At home, the need to work arises especially in front of nature shows. I feel that my job, my mission since I was 12, is to simply throw myself into the world of children.

I learned to travel alone, no doubt thanks to my thirsty for nature, listening to birds, watching flowers, serving children, playing with them. For me, a traveler is not only an adventurer, but also a dreamer and a motivating messenger, but above all, he is a human person in touch with nature and Man to weave bonds of human solidarity and foster a deeper understanding between adults and children in their environment.

During his travels, one has the feeling of reality, of space that changes, of time that moves and of society that changes every day. There is the song of the birds, the music of the water, the growing plants, the transforming flowers, and the clouds dancing in the sky. Children who play and transform themselves into real creators of another world.

We have everything we need to be happy on a trip without having anything: a hat, a pair of boots, a bag, books, a pen, and sheets of paper. Nature is your gain and your endless playground.

So, I focused on the children so that they become full actors in their own natural life. I wanted to make them speak as well as all those who have no right to speak. It is a big Experience. I have been fortunate enough to travel and meet many children. From them, I learned a lot. I think it will help me later, even after I die, to exist in some other way. I do not know how many times I can say it, but they are exceptional.

Most of the time, when foreigners think of Haitians, they think of voodoo, not as a religion, but as it was defined at the source, as witchcraft; they think of poverty too, yet each of us has a wealth to share, a unique, original wealth. If you come to my house, you must not believe, because you are rich, because you are a foreigner, that you are going to be accepted as a god. Being rich, foreign, means absolutely nothing to me. You are a human being, a student in the same school as mine: this world!

And we drink this atmosphere from the same glass wherever we are. That is all! As my way of working is not very formal, often people think that I am not a classic educator and yet, sometimes, after several weeks spent with the children, the parents consider me as a parent, as a member of the family. Confidence and creation of existence is another dimension of the wealth that we have in ourselves.

One of the temptations that I have always tried to avoid is not to destroy this stable wealth that is the heart, it is the power of money and never to undermine my dignity. You can really welcome someone when, humanly, you have established a contact, a friendship, a mutual, sincere interest.

In this life, we often work in the shadows, silently, ignored by public opinion. I sometimes go to a group on the street, in the countryside or in the Bateys in the Dominican Republic to offer entertainment with a few children. It is a spontaneous action that comes from the heart. I play with them without necessarily belonging to a group or an organized movement.

I usually meditate alone every day, but I have many opportunities to meditate with others when I play with street children, young people and during meetings. My job as a motivator has allowed me to experience extraordinary moments. I suffer from loneliness too; it is part of this job. Family is my strength, my balance, and my energy. His moral support is essential to me. My father and mother's advice reassures me and gives me the energy I need.

I use the richness of the heart, which already pays off in the underprivileged when they acquire the certainty of wanting to succeed in their lives. Many people come to me and ask me what my secret is for being so calm. At first, I did not know what to answer them, because this calm side is natural in me, it is I.

In fact, I understood one thing: you cannot be motivating, reinventing movements over time without finding harmony, balancing with yourself and identifying your own wealth. I am motivating because above all I like to practice self-mockery, to look for myself in another way and find others. I always dress very simply, and I have a positive outlook on everything around me.

Many people think that I am a rich man. In fact, yes, they are right, because having a heart awakened to everything around you is not understandable for everyone. I believe in the richness of the heart, in the power of thought, in human value. For me, the most important wealth is in the one in front of you. I never understood these people who say: "I want money to live", without ever saying: "I want love, attention, human value, spirituality and I won't keep this spirit of sharing to exist ".

Children are sincere, intelligent, and frank, honest and mysterious, creators also of their world, always occupied by adults. And the most important thing is that they have a family. Unfortunately, many of them do not live with her or at least they live in an incomplete family unit.

We work, we are tired of the judgments sometimes made about us, but when we are with children, we receive tons of love all at once. Now, so many children who love you at the same time, it is something huge!

I am hiding, it's true. I mostly hide what I think deep inside because I never wanted to tell anyone what I felt inside this heart that is sometimes pierced with insults and violations. I am a very reserved person. I remember the first risk I took was when I started working on the street with the children. I slept outside with them so that I could understand their inner life. It is something I can't explain, it's too sensitive.

The Drum Dance

August 17, 2007: Port-au-Prince airport in Haiti, heading to New York JFK airport in the United States. We spent almost a quarter of a normal day to join the other family members. On the plane, I remember, to my right are three people, another Haitian family. We share our different points of view on how we are going to settle in another country. A West Indian, sitting not far away, mingles with our improvised conversation.

"With us, we never worry about what we will meet elsewhere," he said. To settle in another country is to adapt to the tempo to dance differently to the musical rhythms of the drum of life. "The pleasure of this trip was the meeting with this West Indian.

Besides, despite everything, there are more and more people who want to settle in another country. One always seems to want to leave the powerful dreams of an existence to go to share the vision, which one has of that of the others. There are at least five or six generations of families who too, over the centuries, have become slaves, paid for their entire lives in territories semantic.

Do not judge anything, everything makes sense. Little by little, those who accept succeed in moving away from their deep maternal roots. Only a few victims among us fight to the end, and some continue to forcefully cling to life, however hard it may be, while still having nostalgia for their homeland. For a second, a minute, a day, a week, a month, a year and a lifetime, millions of thoughts strike the memory, and nobody understood anything!

Absence teaches me a lot about my life and the lives of others. The existence of each thing is not a coincidence; one is often the complement of the other. This is the biggest abandonment ever recorded in the hallway of my life. The death of mom and the disappearance of my daughter on my way.

Funeral, abandonment, disappearance, uncertainty, doubt, fear, nightmare. And nobody knows the reason, and nobody has an answer. Would there be several hundred excuses, and will I be the only victim? Shame settles in me, heavy like lead. And this shame, I felt it everywhere, to the glances that blink, to the point of also arousing animosities.

The day's pass and the sufferings are still there. We hear, we watch, we listen, we meditate, we observe, we wait, and everything becomes time. And everything is space in a cross of glances at the hidden objectives. All around me, the space is transformed and the passages to cross are these painful looks and complaints.

We do not have time to think except that we hear cries of pain. It feels like we are living just to find time to transform life. I imagine a smile mixed with tears in my life as a father. This is what I ask for the weight of time that weighs on me every day.

Like a drum, I hear the beating of a heart, a voice like that of a bird singing in my head. Sometimes the rhythm is light, sometimes it is gentle and groped on the flowers to open petals and give scent to the morning sun. In the meantime, the bees are working.

The doors always open with a soft voice, a tender glance to offer a postcard, an invitation to take the road of adventure. But we are like at the foot of this volcano of fire that does not stop spitting lava of pain from the bottom of his mouth. Hope, upheaval, hatred, relief, punishment for days like in a fictional forest. Offended by each look, we have no sun in time. We have so much to share and transmit all around us: distance is not a concept to know, not even space where we are. Until then, I manage the suffering and I transform it into a pool of purity where I invite everyone to dive.

No need to worry about my behavior, the time has transformed me so that I can think of other things, preferably positive, rather than having bad thoughts. With you, huddled in memory, it feels like you are living just to find a physical body, to feel a breath. There is a time to look in the face, watch sleeping, watch eating, watch growing, watch running, watch singing, watch dancing, and finally watch and feel everything as if by magic to transform a life together.

A life lesson that I can never forget. Naivety plunged me into a pearl of wisdom that gnaws at my heart and causes more suffering than years of prison could have imagined. Obstacles after obstacles, a pillow drowned in tears, a tortured memory. Eyes are closed, we become invisible, but we must always hope, never forget actions, mornings, nights, and we then observe the shadow of the steps of a holy presence.

We are always on the same path by going back and forth and completing thousands of kilometers per day. Always the same route with always the same hope of finding the road suitable for skipping space and time. Obedience, service, teaching, resistance, many things strengthen my ability to regain a taste for life. The existence of everything is the true witness of its cause, there is no chance. Life is not as you look at it, but as you transform it and protects it to transmit it and see the fruits that reflect its reality. The day's pass and the silence are still there: we wait, we hear, we watch, we listen, we meditate, we observe, we absorb, and everything becomes time and everything is patience.

How we Fit?

WHENEVER I COULD, BEING THE GOOD old journalist that I am, I would write about what I have experienced and what I have observed. Being an immigrant who did not speak the language of my new home, but was instead educated in my native country, I know first-hand about being misjudged and dismissed. Ever since I was a child I have always loved to write. I grew up reading and writing sentences from essays, poems, and stories. I had always dreamed of becoming a writer and a journalist.

Immigrants try their best to fit in, going against the reality of exclusion in all its forms: social, economic and cultural. The challenge for newcomers is not just to find a job, but also to find purpose in this new life. Looking for a way to contribute. People immigrate to America from around the world with a preconceived vision that is far from the reality of their evolving new life. I thought I could write about what happened in everybody's life and as well as my own. Many things have happened in my life from my birth to now. I've seen, I've heard, I've lost, I've gained so much that I wanted to share a lot of these happenings with others which include my love, my culture, my successes, and my failures.

I am one of them. Leaving our native countries for whatever reason and trying to make it in another is not easy because the culture, language, and traditions are all so different. Unfamiliarity, the sense of being alone away from loved ones always feeling the desire to go back home constantly permeates your thinking. Knowing that it is not feasible is heartbreaking. The overall theme of my book is to talk about how my life was in my country and what it became since arriving here in this welcoming country, how many steps I have needed to take before being accepted. I had to start from the beginning as if I had not been born or had a life someplace else before I immigrated to this country.

It is the people you meet along the way that can unknowingly give you the strength to continue. Each new person you meet brings something to the table, each one is like a piece of a puzzle that altogether forms a beautiful picture, each one trusting that whatever they contribute is unique and important making the way go more smoothly. This realization keeps you going, especially at work, performing tasks that you have never done before. The overall theme of this book is how you can grow up seeking to know everything about your surroundings and everybody who surrounds you. First living in a place where if you stand in front of your home people will come by and say hello to you using your first name.

I wrote this book to explain how I then became invisible by moving to a place where nobody knows who you are and what you can do. (HOW WE FIT?). I wrote this book to share with you who I was in Haiti to who I became in the United States. My eyes are closed and my pen struggles to release memory to share the experience of climbing the stairs of life's lessons. If you are climbing, it is always good to look back without asking others to pity your struggle. Climbing the stairs of life requires courage to take the steps one by one with peace and love. The main characters of the story are my parents, my brothers and sisters, my son and daughter, kids that I have educated and deal with and myself.

They are the main character in my book because they play an important role in my life and who I grew up to be. The main characters are my family, my organization because they are the reason why I am who I am today. Finally, the main character of my book is all and nothing at a time.

The days go by and the silence is still there: we work, look, listen, meditate, and observe while there is time. Being an observer is like a lesson of wisdom with flexible rules, allowing you to become invisible while you learn and grow. I think this book will appeal to others because of the urge to learn something new different. Because this book talks about family, about struggling in a place where you are invisible to others and I am pretty sure if not all, many of us humans have struggled during a part in our life. I think this book will appeal to others because I am human and so are they. I am talking about my everyday life experiences, cultures. A way to learn about a different culture and experience is by reading this book, my book, that maen: your book.

The more we know each other: I toll you the more we connect... In all history, I love the courage, the compassion and the passion of people I can feel so much love of people around me the experiences I have shown the way I come from all those combinations make me special every day.

I started my first job in the kitchen, carrying the food as well as washing dishes. Under the quiet gaze of my supervisor, while performing my duties, I observed and reflected on all the people around me? Coworkers, supervisors, and the clients we were there to serve. Sometimes life? Circumstances force us to stay behind the curtains, but this becomes a place of observation that is enriching.

They always talk about being a different individual in society and I am one of those individuals, walking in the streets, talking to strangers, living life in an unknown world. Yes, there is. I have heard of nationality differences in the news, how different we are from each other. And since I talk about Haiti in my book, this will be a way to show that we are not that different.

Of course, there is. They talk about cultures from different countries and I do talk about my country's culture Haiti. My book is different from other books because I have read a couple of them and from what I can tell the way they were written is from research, from guesses, from talking to others. However, my book is from experience, firsthand experience.

My book, unlike others, is from real-life experience and consequences. It is from the heart. I wrote this book with tears, sweats, anger, and love. I have put real feelings in this book and that is how different it is from others. I want readers to learn about our culture. There are many lessons in this book and one of them is no matter how much you struggle, no matter how invisible you are to society those close to you are aware of your existence and just take it one step at a time.

I want to share with you some of the experiences in my life that I have had since living in the United States with my family and friends. Socially this year was interesting for me. I had improved my skills of communication through further development of the English language. I was able to improve on my knowledge of computers and by the steps I took; I was able to cultivate my computer skills by attending workshops and classes given at the local schools. Day after day I learned more and more about the American culture and political system.

In the United States, I have met people who have come from many different countries other than my own. Through this experience, I have learned a lot about their cultures, and I believe that it is a great opportunity allowing us to learn from each other, and to share our diverse lives. I will remember all the good things that these experiences have brought into my life.

In this country during those first few months, I believe that I had learned and progressed a lot about the concepts of the English language. The most important thing that I have learned from my life is concerning the value I place on my self-esteem and my creativity. I will never forget my first month. I was determined to carry on with my initial dream. I resisted through moments of adversity and continued to stay focused on the goal.

I will also never forget what so many had told me, statements such as, "this is a country where there is little patience for your acclimation to the American way of life, your orientation will be short, forget what you know and take time to think about a new way to reconstruct your life with your same dream but with a new objective."

At this time, I can say that my attitude and my determination to prove myself have taken me a new way. I am really at a loss for words to explain my experience spiritually and socially. Life is like a big school that teaches you about your existence. Believe in yourself, and yet be open to the different ideas that develop through communications with your peers, including those from a culture different from your own.

Through experience, you can remember the things that you have learned and therefore avoid making the same mistakes so that your next experience will be better. I have discovered a lot of things; I have many stories to tell of my life's lessons. I did not have time to look at myself until now. These days I see the change inside myself because of what I have learned and so I have made a new projection.

Many people still do not know how you can gain experience and progress to a better life in this country. The big message I have to share is this, when you have a good education, when you give yourself time to write, to read, and to share your work, it may give you more possibilities to speak English and the ability to find your way.

Always a new beginning! It's my life! Every second of the day one sentence at a time. I think about my past. Every morning of every day I look at my face in the mirror and I want to make a new life. I look at my father and mother. I look at my son. I look at my wife and my whole family. Then I think about it, is it possible for me to transform quickly.

Thinking about my existence up till now, because I am a young man who only has 38 years in this life. Yet, I have much experience in my work but now I feel lost. I just came to a new country not paying attention to what was happening suddenly sadly I realize I now live in another country apart from the home I have always known! The same sun rising daily in a different land. Yes, I am sad, but I decided to go for it all to make the shift. This country teaches you not only about your life, and culture. This country transforms your mind it is an interactive life with your family, your friends, your community. Where people from many nations come together.

I remember when I spoke about my special situation here in America with someone who soon became a good friend this person offered me so much support, he gave me ideas and took action to help me. This dear friend helped me attain my first job and even opened doors for me as a journalist and social worker. I always remember my work with the children in the street even now as I work as a dishwasher at an assisted living facility here.

However, at the same time, I go to school to perfect my English because I know education is the tool to surmount social problems. I believe socially, spiritually, emotionally, and mentally you need knowledge through communication every day of your existence. As students from other countries, we are like a family. We come together without questions about faith or nationality. Often at school, there are many people from the same country, even in the same area!

I believe it is a fact that when you write, read and speak in English every day, which by constant practice you can communicate with people without any problem. When you have the moment to meet somebody new use that time to practice the language. Soon you will have no problem applying for work or helping your children with their homework and exchanging important information about healthcare needs.

I remember all of my interactions with my teacher about my homework. I recall the many challenges I faced with a diverse group of teachers and counselors. With great effort, I worked through many obstacles such as computer lab, English class, student consul, GED class, PRE GED class, workshops, and conferences. Everybody in this center of learning is my teacher when I communicate with them, I am learning something new.

In this school, there is deep solidarity. So many experiences have proven to me that an interactive approach to education and engaging the student as an active participant is a better way to teach. For example, if you view learning to change a life, you will transform the social situation of the learner for them in better.

After a few months, I see there is a big difference between my country and this country. I simply do not have the time nor can I put into words a way to explain this. I can only say that this country has shown me a new way of learning. It is a new beginning for all people. I have learned that you can use all the opportunities that your environment offers you to change your life, your way.

Like a new plant, before it blossoms it must have the care of its environment and the time to grow. As with people, I have found it most important to know that one can not grow without the education and support of those around you. For example, if you want someone else to talk with you take the time to talk with them and to listen. Naturally, you will find that when you put together your ideas you can realize that there may be a common goal. If you choose to go further, if you wish to evolve you must take to the road an move forward with your ideas.

Remember that life is made up of many experiences and communications. You can develop your life when you share your ideas or participate in some activities and as your community gives you their time without limitations. Your main objective should none to focus on the types of activities that interest you most. Through reading, writing and speaking you learn how to look at yourself to familiarize yourself with your style in your way. With your knowledge gained from your experiences, you are a source of multiple streams. Believing in yourself is the way to change your life.

When was facing the new beginning of life in America, a new plan for new steps in my native country happened. I had been promoted to lead an organization. My community in my country of origin has real charm and hospitality each encounter with the people there has spiritual power. Imagine you leave there, you come to this country where you now have your mother and father every day in front of you suffering because I tell you there is something nostalgic about our original home.

I am tired! I am sad! All my life always fighting for the betterment of my people. I want to make a change in my country. I want my country of origin to be better. It is my native land where my roots are. Believe me when I say, if you want to go anywhere, you need freedom. When you want to communicate, you need freedom. You may want to explain yourself by speaking your truth, you need freedom.

I see my people living in slavery! Here I bring you my spirit. I share with you my heritage. I may be poor in material things but I have my freedom, my friend! If you want to change your life, your country, your world, your land then you must share your time, your skill, and your friendship. Everyone needs freedom, peace, and love.

My dream is your freedom. My dream is your peace. My dream is your life. My dream is of you my people living as you wish to live! Freedom is when you can create, freedom is when you have a way to go. Freedom is when you believe in yourself because then you can transform yourself. It allows you to renew your world this world is yours! This world is your house. You are supposed to create your freedom.

You are supposed to care for your world. In a life of freedom, you are meant to share life as you are meant to create yourself. Believe me, you can transform yourself. The capacity to ask yourself you have one part in your freedom.

Freedom is when you can help others Freedom is when you are confident in yourself. My blood is my flag, it does not matter what country I come from. It does not matter what language I speak. It does not matter what color my skin is. It does not matter what symbols are on the flag from whatever country you originate from. You must discover your way. You must learn for yourself to see your future and to create a new life experience for yourself. Once you have a clear idea about yourself you will realize that you are a part of the flag and all of those that it represents.

Your life is better for your flag flys. It may fly with a loud wind or along with a silent breeze, but your flag flies freely. As you expand your knowledge your flag fly on a powerful wind. Your life is like that flag. Everything you do in life becomes your Flag. Your hopes and dreams, the way you engage people, your determination to reach your goals are all part of your Flag. A major component of the flag is to protect your life. Another is to create happiness for yourself and others by being kind. Life is too short. Always know that when you leave, your flag remains.

We are all connected by the same flag. Your blood and my blood are the same color. Red. We bleed the same! Our blood circulates through our bodies the same way. What affects you affects me and also has affected everything surrounding you.

Never forget your roots! Never forget your culture! Never forget your Native Language, Never forget the source from which you come from. Without you, there is no blood. Without you, there is no flag. After all, We are the same flag! We are the same blood! We are together only one flag, only one blood. My flag, your flag. My blood, your blood. All for One! You and I are We forever!

There is always darkness after a long day. Before the moon is full I see my mom she is sewing the clothes that I wear for school. Thank you, mom. I remember to time in life, it was at the noontime of the day my father working He works and sweats and works and sweats as the sun rises in the sky. After my coffee I go to school I make myself a collector of words. As a word collector, within a short time, I go forward looking for a new way in life. In this new way, my eyes are opened to many possibilities to move forward. When you look at me you may see me as unfortunate. You do not see enough of me to know that Now I look to a brighter future.

Day after day my English gets better. Early in the morning, I like to sing when I see the sunrise. I love my son and so I sing to him to wake him in the morning. He likes my song. Butterfly, butterfly Wake up Take your power on the flowers. The song is about my English I am a butterfly with my words I share my words everywhere I go, to the classroom, in a newspaper, on the television, or the radio with you my friend Ha! Ha! Ha! I'm a butterfly. They ask, what is your secret? Secret! About your ability to speak English so well? I tell you this, as it is no secret. All-day I read, I write, and I speak all the words as if serving them on one platter. I believe that the teacher is a tutor. The teacher is a guiding light, but you must practice on your own. You must be like the butterfly, butterfly, butterfly, butterfly, butterfly.

Who is this book for?

THIS BOOK IS FOR ANYONE WHO thinks they can never improve or change their lives, their families and their communities. It may sound obvious, but if you don't set goals in life, then you have no good reason to exist. You have to know how to take responsibility for yourself and others. If you have no goals, the course of your life may be just a long, hazardous crossing. You will be less likely to succeed than those who have found motivation to move forward. There is a path already laid out for all those who want to leave now. Stop asking yourself too many questions about what can happen tomorrow; step by step, step by step, don't be afraid to go for it. Open and go through the doors in front of you. Success: you have it with you and in you. The light that you seek to light your steps is at the bottom of you. No need to follow the same path as others.

On the contrary, make sure to leave your fingerprints so that others follow in your footsteps. Turn on the light within you that will light your way. Measure your power in all its forms to reduce fear and get to know what makes youstrength, your expertise. You will have to relearn to live your life, but know that we never stop learning thanks to our past experiences. We are all born creative and very good at inventing new things to impress those around us. Deciding to move forward and clear the past to become useful to the community is a lonely and sometimes a little crazy choice, but one that guarantees success in the long term.

It is not that difficult, especially if we are trying to learn something from our mistakes. Life is to remember something good from our blunders. Unfortunately, some people fail to move forward for fear of being criticized by the very people who stand still. Others just don't care about the inner voice that speaks to them. Start today, don't wait, because time flies by and you will be too old to dare to take bold risks. As a creator and defender of human value, you have to be enduring to get good results and to go beyond appearances. Without the blind belief, endurance and persistence of the craftsman, no work is possible. Therefore, we can admit that to live better, it.

It is essential to recreate a new adventure every day, a new route that adapts to environmental pluralism. Your first job will be to défi the idea that it is difficult, if not impossible, to change your life path. Notoriety matters little. What matters is adding a new creation to your path every day. Let me explain how I learned that my name could be the title of a great story and how I became the heir of a great creator. I will also teach you how I have managed to impose my signature on others, to transform small steps of children into miles traveled as adults. All the experiences that we live help us to be fully aware of our existence, to regain self-confidence to transform the small problems of everyday life into unshakeable success. We all have an interior world within us and constitute for others a riddle to be solved. We all have a path to follow, but we can choose to fork at any time.

Whatever strategy is used, each choice is respectable. He never condemned someone who decided to change course to find that brilliance in their mind. Quite the contrary. If you are not looking for life, others will not be waiting for you to achieve their clarity. No one except you can make you want to progress. Remember that your neighbor is not there for you, but with you. If you disappear, he will still be there, but with someone different. Each word or glance coming from a third person must enter you like a breath.

Do not judge what you are experiencing or seeing. No need to ask yourself too many questions. Instead, let your imagination run wild and try to analyze the power that each moment can have over you. Time flies too quickly to understand yourself. Whatever questions others may ask, you are the only one who has the truth. Don't question yourself, just answer. Life is a learning site guided by each vibration and each heartbeat, it is the language of silence of each of the eyes around us.

Observations From Behind The Kitchen Counter

PEOPLE IMMIGRATE TO AMERICA FROM AROUND the world with a preconceived vision that is very far from the reality of their evolving new life. I was one of them.

Leaving your native country for whatever reason and trying to make it in another is obviously not easy because the culture, language, and traditions are so different. Unfamiliarity and the sense of being alone, away from loved ones, plus the desire to go back home, constantly permeate your thinking. Knowing that it is not feasible is heartbreaking.

It is the people you meet along the way that can unknowingly give you the strength to continue. Each new person you meet brings something to the table, each one like a piece of a puzzle that all together forms a beautiful picture; each one trusting that whatever they contribute is unique and important so things can go smoothly. This realization keeps you going, especially at work, performing tasks that you've never done before.

My eyes are closed and my pen struggles to release the memory to share the experience of climbing the stairs of life's lessons. If you are climbing, it is always good to look back without asking others to have pity on your struggle. Climbing the stairs of life requires courage to take the steps one by one with peace and love.

The days go by and the silence is still there: we work, look, listen, meditate, and observe while there is time. Being an observer is like a lesson of wisdom with flexible rules, giving you the opportunity to become invisible while you learn and grow.

I cannot help but admire those with whom I deal on a regular basis at Rogerson House:

"Good morning," says a woman who everybody call here **Mimi Petrino**, like a flower, greets us by opening its petals. Her every breath indicates "I am here for you." As you come through the door she is the first form of therapy in this place. Originally from Italy, she has been here for many years, gracing others with her presence five days a week. What a wonderful gift she offers to everyone crossing the threshold of this place regardless of skin color, country of origin, or gender.

So is the way the receptionist receives us, advises us, and counsels us with her warm smile. "Welcome, welcome!" "May I help you?" "Looking for someone?" "Looking for something?"

She always has the right question, the answer always satisfying. Her smile and kindness adorn her words: "Would you like some coffee, tea?" "Take your time." "Sit" "You will find newspapers there," she says of the waiting room, with a serene look.

Her desire is to help. You can find an answer, or at least hope for an answer when you come looking for work, as I did. With her indelible smile, she will hand you the form that will mark a new stage in your life.

"In this place, we offer the best there is for our clients. They really like being here and do enjoy their stay with us." With these words, she shares her peace, and one cannot help but be moved by it. Despite the pressures, many times, with patience and love, she has managed to overcome the smallest details that might disrupt the day. The welcoming smile of a receptionist reflects to the visitor what is behind those long corridors. She represents this place well.

With each encounter, she only brings out the positive, making it easier that day to walk through the doors, regardless of what may be happening in your life. Around her, there is no room for negativity. She possesses the key to make life easier in this special place, surrounding you with hope and joy.

Many from diverse backgrounds come looking for a job here, regardless of how simple it is, but hopefully enough to sustain life in this new country away from home. No job can be beneath you, when you must take care of your family.

I started my first job in the kitchen, carrying the food as well as washing dishes. Under the quiet gaze of my supervisor, while performing my duties, I observed and reflected about all the people around me – coworkers, supervisors, and the clients we were there to serve.

One may assume that those who work in a kitchen are just doing a menial job. But preparing, cooking, and transporting food is an essential role in the survival of our clients.

The work can be hard – but it's made easier if you have a boss who understands everyone's value to this dance of life. He knows how to communicate with a smile, is thoughtful, always available to listen and exchange opinions, and makes a schedule that suits everyone the best.

His wisdom sometimes hides behind reserved behavior. But one can get a glimpse of his eloquence when he talks about his favorite baseball team, the Boston Red Sox. Posters of the team adorn his office. You know he's real, and he makes you feel that he is there for you, open even to critique in order to improve the working surroundings.

"Why do we have to work so hard?" What is the meaning of our work?" For a newcomer in this country, working in a field foreign to him, these questions many times instead of eliciting an answer, bring on even more questions: "Why this kind of job at this stage of my life?" "Why not another, somewhere else?" Us, human beings, eternally unsatisfied.

But caring about the job that will provide for you and your family is simply respect for yourself and for everyone around you.

Imagine a woman who only gives her best. She works all day without respite. Like many others, she left Jamaica in search of a better life. Her days start with much that has to be done at home before she goes to work.

It is an honor to work next to **Carmen Porter** such a courageous woman of great character who makes decisions taking into consideration all who are involved. Chatting with her during breaks, one is mesmerized by her broad knowledge of the history of the Caribbean, its people, the history of black people, of all people.

For some, the fact that we work in the kitchen may mean that there is nothing profound in our dialogue. A kitchen may bring to mind images of dirty dishes and repetitive tasks. However, if you had a chance to eavesdrop, you would hear someone who personifies the love of family, integrity, character. You would catch her beautiful smile when she speaks of her only daughter.

We understand the real purpose of society in the dedication of this smoothie woman. Her job is to empower families to make their children happy by building bridges in the community through a solid culinary education: she is a food specialist. Going to people and taking into account all their spiritual and physical dimensions, knowing a little about their history, is already a path to success.

Inform, train, participate and involve people in concrete actions. Keep people informed of what we are doing, and especially people who are very interested in the cause we are defending. Talking without doing anything and doing without saying anything are dangers that can bring down any organization.

Act with an open heart and tell people what is being done, demonstrate respect for the opinion of others, and at the same time state their views and reasons for doing so. It's about being ready to listen to others. Optimism must be the weapon of the kitchen. The amateur cook is not there to provide answers to problems, but rather to listen, discuss, accompany, always encourage creativity.

Discover people and their lives through a simple dish or a glass of fresh fruit juice. Part of his job is to believe and make people believe in the value of man, to give the assurance that we can transform everything. Each person has hidden talents that must be discovered. Build a common destiny while respecting the freedom and autonomy of each person in relation to other decision-making powers. You cannot develop yourself without working to understand others.

To be a respected, responsible person, you must be able to understand the life of a community and to integrate it. Each person has his reasons for living and he must choose his own principles to base his style and his personal conduct. Continuous research to find out why we exist and what meaning we should give to our lives; how we see the world; the people we meet have the same goal: to succeed in their lives, even if they are not walking in the same direction.

If we take the example of a plant whose purpose is to give fruit: this plant must go through many stages. Each phase has its own rules that give it meaning and allow it to reach real production. It is important to seek the goal of one's life to guide each action.

The joy of existing lies in the ability to create. You are alive, and your existence is an instrument to build the life you want to live. Your capacities as a responsible man will mobilize your resources to build with others. You must constantly recreate your life so that it is adapted to the reality of your environment.

You should know that you are in the presence of a multifaceted community, of different profiles who seek each other to be, each in its place, a useful instrument, animated by a feeling of responsibility towards elements that surround you. And each person alone represents a multitude of characters.

What you say, do, see, or think is the product of your own reading of things and the environment in which you live. The faces you see are a reflection of your being. The worker, according to this woman who works in schools to promote a society in the behavior of well-being, must refer to morality without being moralistic, but also to common sense to remind all those who share the same space the duties and rights of their clients, as well as the consequences that would result from bad behavior. Describe the social evolution of the company in thirsty information and training communities. This evolution also affects the transformations of the society in which it evolves through practical actions visible to communities.

The work of this woman is based daily on the search for values, focused on the existence of each. Studies and research are carried out for integrated development. Available, she is a faithful listener of homeless society, from the point of view of ideological orientation. We have gathered documentation totally focused on the cultural study of this category of inhabitants, because without these social studies, we could not be effectively operational.

It is deeply exhausting for a person in charge of the direction of community development to invest himself in claiming the universality of an entire population which has been directly involved in its own social destruction for years. To respond to such dysfunction, this woman recommends social orientation workshops for culturally diverse communities. We must work on new approaches to social classes and on movements.

Among all the things that we remember, we remember this young African from Senegal to whom his mother had instilled a mysterious force, like a divine heritage: he always has the desire to make his preparations of typical dishes well following the standards imposed by the society.

It respects the structural pyramid strictly dictated by the supervisors. As soon as he crosses the threshold, he becomes another person: the one who goes back and forth to serve customers, the one who will tell stories to fill the void. As soon as he walks through the door, with his face similar to that of our Haitian compatriots, he adopts the gait of a real remote-controlled robot and he looks like a young lion just out of the jungle.

"When I was young, I lived like a machine, like animals in the jungle," he says with a smile. "My mother always said to me before coming to America: "My son! You should never lower your head," and she gave me a ring that I wear as a road tracer and in whose protection I believe. This gem is very important to me. When I wear it, I imagine it's like my mother is holding my hand!"

31

A smile does not leave his face when he tells the story of his origin, where he comes from, he is proud of himself.

He crosses the door and his step draws a movement straight out of Africa. The frame of his body forms a silhouette that carries chapters of history dating back hundreds of years. And history is also written with the memory of the one who wore it for nine months. As soon as he arrives, you can see a bright light that opens before his feet and floods his feet.

He never ceases to say that it is not easy to live decently in a foreign land. It seems that time does not advance like this little drop in a physiological saline infusion that would not want to fall. One has the impression that the hours do not generate new mornings, but all this is especially when you are nostalgic for your native land and that you are tortured by impatience to finally reach age of retirement.

His mother is omnipresent in every action he undertakes in this country. His mother's name is his lifeblood "Mum, mum! Mom said, mom did, mom told me ... And he works by humming Zulu songs, which, he says, give him strength. He moves his upper body in rhythm and, still smiling, he adds: "I like it when it moves!"

Activity! Yes! ... I like this ! Finally, they did not understand anything my brother ... He has a playmaker capacity, people can easily follow him, he is exceptional. His gaze, his gait frighten the world at the same time as they attract it. He always has a story to tell and the influences of his roots never leave him. In words, in gestures, he speaks like a king of Africa and one cannot control him. When he speaks, he has an eloquent speech filled with emotion. "When I'm somewhere, I control everything," he says. And the tireless kitchen workers are always revived with survival techniques to work out life-sustaining everyday, like in laboratories.

Bars, tables, foods, all have a heart that pulsates. The degrees of imagination of each combine as in any musical group in search of a harmonious rhythm ... In the kitchen, we reveal ourselves in the gastronomy or the desired composition of a salad, except that we are all invisible compared to what we are. And no one is afraid to mingle with others. This mixture exceeds everyone's nudity. And the emotional wave that you can't see flowing from everyone's eyes can flood an entire city.

Memory has no suffering. Technically, the charms have no colors and life, musician, plays on the heartbeat thanks to the thousands of liters of blood that she constantly pumps. The liters go back and forth like a singer doing his vocalizations, the days go away under everyone's footsteps.

We're here for a new morning. When you look at the clock on the wall, you get the impression that every second, every minute, every hour is part of the recipes for each dish.

Let me take a moment to present this story that I am writing through everyone's eyes, through the competition that everyone is competing in as everyone is on earth to play the game of life. I go through the door, move around in space and infiltrate activities. In the aisles, I mingle with customers up to the back of this large space, in the warehouse corridor where I make my way to the heart of the kitchen by following the path of the shelves where the products are located.

I walk with peace, I walk with calm, I carry silence within me. I'm one of the people who work to solve the problems of those who wander around the store shelves looking for some product. Like many others, I also participate in this commitment, in the know-how of a kitchen that combats stress, the cause, and effects of which we know...

This reminds me of all the childhood stories where dreams have escaped, drowned in nostalgia.

But you cannot cry when, in this same alley, your self-esteem is enlivened by the good humor of certain people who cross your path. And if everything goes well, there is no one who is as successful as I am. Except for all those around me, although it is the result of a long journey filled with passion. And what it is in this collective game does not matter, everything is built with courtesy. Truth be told, we are not just a player, we're also an actor and a winner. You have chosen dishes to satisfy customers who are looking for a special place to have a special dish. And this image of player and winner lives through each of us.

And this image of player and winner lives through each of us. We are content to pull the strings of the game, those of human value which bounce between realities and illusions, in a kitchen of communion where the invented recipes are the result of an inevitable sharing of know-how between collaborators.

We lived in anonymity and the suffering of a nostalgia that we thought was incommunicable. People, victims of a "value crisis", remain silent or disappear forever as public figures. When you can finally express yourself through a book, and then share the story with others, existence can be transformed. I have followed life in this kitchen, day after day, with a rare curiosity of extrapolation which is not often found in this world of contradictions.

It is not allowed to quote the name of this place without being able to quote everyone's name. This kitchen is classified among the best classified concerning the choice as regards food, education, but also in the field of preventive health and the protection of the family, but as we have never been to visit whom either by writing this story, we are unfortunately not able to produce testimonies to confirm our words.

The desire to share with everyone is essential for everyone to participate in this collective game. And that doesn't mean that we don't know anything about all this family wealth since to discover the true face of these thousand subjects, you have to go deep into this story and master it as a whole.

I didn't say anything too ... I just took a subtle look at the space of this large hospital corridor to get an idea. It was like pulling a dry rope and traveling the full twelve months of the year while enjoying this pleasure from start to finish ... It's been years today ... There is a time obviously when nature intoxicates all the trends that are not organic. This society did nothing but seek the face of perfection, day after day, without ever leaving its movement and its reformist surfaces in particular.

On these kitchen tables that are no more than two meters, people invent with their hands the culinary waves that will link all the people around them around food. I didn't know if the community was good or bad, I had no idea where I was, I only knew the entrance to this store. All the people move in a single corridor which shows that this kitchen was not made for predators.

However, there were people who should not be approached, who should not be spoken to or touched at the risk of becoming an isolated person, invisible to the logistical or domestic needs that each consumer creates.

My mother would have been happy, if she was still alive, for her boy to participate in a new stage of training where, in less than two months, he had rebuilt himself thanks to his integration into a movement that summarized his objectives. In fact, time, shared experiences tell me the story of each.

I also want to know the challenge of living with the young recruits in this kitchen. And now everyone has experienced the day differently as in a good game of cards, sitting opposite each other. The addition: objective, know-how, and dream as a gift on behalf of all those who cook. Everyone's inspiration combines to create a sumptuous culinary work. There is nothing more important in this kitchen than clinging to everything that exists all around, without neglecting the evolution of everyone's behavior in their feelings. Very concerned about the mind of each individual.

You could never really imagine if something good or bad was going to happen in this unpredictable life. So, basically, cooking has always been present in everyone's life. Even when one lives very far from one's own space, one remains perfectly attached to the fundamental of the actions which one performs successively. Whether inside or outside this kitchen, there is an intimate harmony between everything that exists and that evolves. There is a common objective in each of the actions combined with each other to go elsewhere, leaving a whole life behind. And in the goal?

Run after the unpredictability of a daily newspaper. Finally, wherever we are, there is always this feeling of uncertainty and we cannot detach ourselves from the tombs that some people dig to bury humanity. These people use their weakness or strength to make others suffer. We find ourselves forever and irreversibly in perpetual struggles. So, to face its differences, I take everywhere I am the wisdom of my roots. This is what makes me a better observer and I apply this law of silence to resist and remain invisible in a fabulous universe.

Basically, we never felt that we had to escape from a situation that was happening all around us, that is to say, that we never suffered from exclusion because that since ancient times. As you know, there has always been a kind of social breakdown to overcome.

Everyone is attached in some way to this notion of exile, invisibility, and nostalgia. We are always behind a back door, we are attached to this notion of adventure and discovery. And we have never known this kind of existential discomfort due to moving to where we are, because we take with us, wherever we go, our own home. My choice to exist differently has always accompanied me, my native place is part of my nomadic life, so to speak.

I know this is very difficult to understand, but I often repeat that if you are able to state a problem, whatever its nature, then you are able to solve it. As of 2007, I categorically changed my way of seeing things, my way of thinking. I have relearned the sounds of new music, another form of life without adding the epithet of my former life to it. In my opinion, the elements of my life have totally changed the way I speak. I feel freer to express myself despite the immigrant races and colors. The worsening of unemployment has created a disruption of equilibrium because of the average salary generously touched by a certain category while my native people are suffering.

I for my part oscillate between unemployment and politics. Personally, I wanted to build a more egalitarian society. I believe that everything that we can put together to change the world is really important and opens a door. We must admire all those who want to change the destiny of the Cité du monde.

It's like a dish that we would all taste together and whose ingredients, if you can say, have contributed to this exceptional life that everyone shares. It was for me first a fusion of spirit which delighted me with veterans tired by the arduousness of their life and students, young people of the street of which I was part, and in particular young people of the community to which I belonged. I suffered a lot during the first two weeks. Until I forget my first name with the stress caused by adapting to a new form of culture ...

I suffered to forget the person I had become, the person I had been in the past. However, in this kitchen, I also found extraordinary people, wonderful people. From the edge of the table where I sat, I constantly observe this room where everyone works, shares a look filled with love on their monumental metamorphosis.

We keep wondering about the thousand and one stories that can be read on each face. On each of them hides a sign of hope that catches my eye in silence. This hope confirms the dream I cherished since childhood: to see everyone happy and to be able to live a beautiful story of love and peace.

Thinking of my childhood sometimes rekindles the spark of the soul of the misunderstood dreamer that I was, a slave to my vision of a suffering people, sensitive to the misfortunes of others, a victim of the gaze of the other, whipped by anxiety and oppression, treated with contempt ... This is a story that always came back to me in memory and this forgotten first name that accompanies me.

My heart is bleeding and I am in pain. I suffer from not having had time to tell the world about this love that is shared in the minutes of silence, simply disturbed by the monotony of the routine ticking of the clock hands which run non-stop, singing the hymn of good days loaded. I got lost like a tender old man watching his grandchildren, I got lost in the ability of these men and women, with their holy hearts, to transform each of their breaths into a wind of good humor. I smile and surrender to an ambitious wish.

Ha! If I were a doctor, a doctor of myself, a doctor like this young man who arrives and who goes away like the lightning that tears the sky, without saying a word. If I were a doctor of my ills, would I remember my first name? And what would I say?

Ho! A first sigh, maybe nothing ... A second sigh, another nothing ... Nothing perfect ... And everything to say ... And everything to do again ... It's difficult to talk about yourself ... So, I meditate under the purring of the kitchen vacuum cleaner. So, I write so as not to lose history and also to forget the cultural differences that I experience daily. The pen is my outlet. Thanks to her, I don't forget anything. How bad I would feel in an office! I would be too easily distracted.

I wish I was somewhere else! Write, create poetry, theater, cinema, play with children! But I had to go to companies several times to ask for work. Seeking employment in this host country has caused me far more hassle than mingling with this culture pool. I visited all the websites that came across my eyes. I had no preference for this or that job, whether it was compatible with my job or not. I no longer knew how to present myself or prepare my CV to convince people to hire me.

I don't know how I got the urge to write this authentic story, which is my story. I wrote everywhere, at all hours of the night and even in the dark, just so as not to lose the ideas I had, and above all I wanted to be able to share with everyone this vital race to my quest for extraordinary love.

However, it was not easy, no! Because ... I fight daily to find time and space to write. It was only a few weeks after I was hired that I started attending training meetings to discover the many facets of the position I held and to follow exercise sessions to deal with daily stress. The simple fact of having taken part in these sessions changed my life socially, as well as the vision that I had of my job, because they opened up new horizons to me. Since then, I have been much more demanding of myself, because it is truly an extraordinary satisfaction to give my maximum to what we do.

This is the major lesson that I learned from these training sessions, not to mention that everyone being required to participate, it added yet another new dimension to my life, that of being able to meet people from different cultures dedicated to a common cause.

Sharing knowledge is an incredibly rich experience. I also think that having competed and having gone to draw deep within myself has helped me a lot to build my life as a food preparer and guide, because I learned that in this profession, each person is, daily, a company for the other. I am very pleased to have been able to continue to participate in the operations of this company to prepare food for different nations and different cultures. I am not the only man, and even less the first lost on the way, unknown to all. And no one among us knows the way better than another.

We are sometimes so limited when it comes to knowing that very often, we are forced to beg a stranger we meet on the way to teach us things about ourselves. We live by chance and I cannot stop believing in these painful things, since I am a lonely man, an unhappy poet. I recognize that for some it may seem a bit odd: wanting to live first for art and children. I have, after having devoted my time for a long time to art, to children, after having experienced several disappointments while looking for work, known As the adventure of immigrants.

Now I work for a company where I work in the kitchen. Accompanied or supported by other people, like any other new recruit, is an experience like no other, but another bell rings in my life. I don't want to talk about conflict right now, because I'm in a transition phase. I only speak of conflicts if I have to engage my being in parallel things. The advantage with cooking is that it is - without a bad pun - a food choice, that dictated by the obligation to survive.

At midday, the darkness of stress and loneliness invades you so much that you immediately want to abandon everything and leave to flee space. We must always think of the one who drives us and who goes away and does not come back. He was the first to receive me and entrusted me to more or less patient men and women. I wonder if he was sick ...

The humorous youngster became one of the kitchen supervisors after a few months. Also, we often asked ourselves questions about him: he always had a note to respond to a complaint, a request or simply a look.

Are you happy to work with us? Do you feel good as a food preparer? However, the principle of everyone who works in the kitchen is absolute secrecy. You should never know anything about the lives of others. As far back as memories go, we are always satisfied to see the face of a father and a mother, a brother or a sister at the one who works by our side and it is so every day since the first day.

Weeks go by and we see again all these people endowed with the power to have beautiful faces made up of a smile and never leave your eye. It's as if we are all gathered under one roof to destroy humanity's greatest pain, that of being hungry. We cannot allow ourselves to think only of ourselves and to forget all these values that are conveyed around us. We share the same world. One mission unites us to save humanity, that of doing everyday things by uniting our actions.

Anyone who takes the time to understand the words hidden in the silence lodged in a look has a chance to understand the invisible being who lives in each of us. And the strength of this silence is everywhere. Whether you are first or last, lower or higher, it forms a language that you cannot translate or decline with words. And time doesn't allow us to put anything off until tomorrow, every minute gives us a shot of energy.

We cannot close our eyes at the risk of losing this call to live in the early morning when we meet this young man from Connecticut in the United States and share with him the love of a job well done and with respect to each one. He never closed his door, either to his co-workers or to customers who approached him. And that's how a person from the kitchen who working in the renewal of life has a gift and benefits others.

Nothing escapes this young man. It's like he's playing a drama scene that varies throughout the day. He is still inhabited by a very protective feeling. Occasionally, he shares a cake or pizza which he buys on his account just to tell others that they are welcome. It goes far beyond what a normal employee's normal life should be. He is always ready to help anyone to work conscientiously. And even if the one he motivates is already indoctrinated by another belief, he goes to the bottom and always with the humor that characterizes him. The kitchen has a prominent place in his mouth. Methodically, he talks, he eats, he drinks, he tastes everything. Even when he takes a heavy look at something, he is far from constraining it for anything.

Whether in the kitchen, at the cash desks, near the other bars, next to the seafood displays, on the few meters of tables filled with meat, without forgetting organic dairy products, cheeses, liqueurs and coffee aromatic, finally everywhere, I always had a tender eye when I realize that my place is forever in these aisles filled with products of all kinds ... While this young Connecticut brought part of his being in this perimeter, he has the power nestled in his heart to treat everything with humor. Yes, it brought joy where all fantasies take power ...

This is what makes it in fact in permanent communion with everyone, like the bee which forages the flowers and transports the pollen from the flowers they visit, then deposits them from flower to flower: it connects people to each other at a glance and with his humor.

So I took advantage of his gaze from the first second he smiled at me. It was the day of my interview to get this job in this intimidating and strange universe where you can easily be hurt by another person just the way they approach you.

Thanks to him, I never had the feeling of being illiterate, that is to say, that he never left me aside and, on the contrary, he explained everything to me with respect day of my hiring just before leaving, because he had to leave early. I found myself then in the misery of the insults uttered by my new guides. Also, I learned, day after day, to anticipate difficulties ...

Attracted by everything that exists around me, even the most elementary thing that nobody necessarily notices, I develop my know-how for exhibit mon talent de AàZ. Ilyaeuunesortede dialogue between the glory of my self tinged with lyricism and the notion of existence in general, like all those who plunge into nostalgia. Like a tireless soldier, I am welded to my daily observations.

I have never known a person as comfortable with his colleagues as this exuberant and sensitive young man, irresistibly natural and original! His humor is omnipresent and his enchanting character unconditionally smiles on the popular world. Become invisible.

The experience goes beyond anything that can be found in a simple monotonous life. And I fully understand that the values that bring light are unique. The ambition of any true value is to always start again in another direction. This experience, where it was mainly a question of protecting my love, my knowledge, and my value, changed my whole life and my vision of things.

In this part, I will mainly try to explain how each man has the power to become invisible and what must be most important for him in matters of existence. Because to exist is not only to be there physically. To accomplish the great mission of existence, one must recognize the different dimensions that makeup man. The spirit behind this book is much larger than the book itself if we consider individually the historical evolution of each life in its time and space.

And I wish for you to understand that I could never have written a single word if I had not been guided by the spirit of the heart that the Divine has sown in me to faithfully fulfill his will without going further than myself. Now I'm going to start a real conversation with everyone who wants to read me or listen to me in their deep silence. I would not have made this love trip if you who read me now did not exist. It's been a few years now that I have been reinventing life through the love of sharing my vision with others.

I really want to see you, to chat with you to tell you the mystery of the love of cuisine to which you cling daily. In every bite of food, you have the power to convert your world into infinite luck. I want to tell you about a world where men and women transform everything that happens in their hands into food.

I want to tell you about a world full of grace with water, fire, and air. This world, you do not see it, but it is both on your plate and at the same time in your life and opens the doors to a new day, a new world to create, build and transform.

There are so many things around us that call for a critical look, that we cannot be content to be confused. We are observers, and this behavior requires the use of consciousness as a motor, in order to allow ourselves to be absorbed in the daily evolution of the multidimensional existence of men and women all around us. Whoever we look at becomes our own image, reflecting the same aspiration, projecting the best in us. Thus, everyone becomes a source of innovation, like this young man with a creative look.

He remains attached to his studies while working behind the counter of this store where he takes a few seconds to create something new. The silence is such that his breath is heard in his little red beard: his name is Alex. He asked me to mention his name if I ever wrote a book to talk about his character in this kitchen.

He becomes an admirer of the shows made by his comrades and his impartial clients, some of whom are loyal, show up day after day. Each day for him represents a new challenge.

What does she expect from her work? Like many immigrants, she sees it as the hope for the future of her family and those who were left behind. Taking on whatever life brings, the joy as well as the sad moments, performing the delicate steps of an intricate, dignified dance. Dreaming that those who make the same journey will accomplish the dreams they had when leaving their beloved country, in spite of all the isolation and difficulties.

Like other immigrants who came before her and will come after her, she continues to engage in life, staying strong and silent in the face of adversity. They pay a dear price in a new world, trying to keep a sense of self.

In some respects, this woman is just like the fire from our stove that brings life and nutrients out of the food that will feed and sustain our clients. This bright light from the kitchen cannot lose its brilliance, even among the disdain of others.

It is over a year now that I have worked as an assistant cook, and I see that each day can be a new battle in the vacuum of a time filled with the presence of a prejudiced co-worker. All that happens in the workplace can influence the individual, and the collective. Small unconscious gestures or words can sometimes damage if one does not stand strong.

One operates in a reduced space for movement, very limited sharing of words and all that is music, light, whispering corridors, as chorus and drama games fill daily lives. And so you must build relationships of trust with residents, families, fellow workers, and the institution.

Each one of us who work here can become a source of inspiration, much like one young white man who graced us with his presence. Humble character with multiple faces, his eyes radiate a contagious passion. He plunges his clients in a light universe of dreams. He sees them a companions, traveling together on a highway of merry adventures. Being able to bypass their suffering, he is seduced by the expression on their faces that speaks volumes about their greatness.

As an altruistic being, he lives in devotion. He becomes a traveler who knocks on every door with his magic wand to revive the soul of the inner child of these old men and women. He engages himself without ulterior motive. It is all about them.

Working behind the kitchen counter, you cannot escape observing, even for a few seconds. In a profound silence where you can hear yourself breathe, you become a fan of the poignant play that he and his troupe of intellectuals present day after day in front of you.

Their everyday lives are a challenge, far from the clichés of the streets or journalistic reports. Observing this allows you to discover an ambivalent world. On one hand – spirituality, on the other hand – lack of acceptance, in a place where scattered pages of men and women's diverse life histories undulate in a limitation imposed by the executioner that is Alzheimer's.

He approaches me with his usual dreamy gaze. When at work, he is constantly thinking about how to make his clients better. Like a troubadour, he uses his guitar to serenade them. He invents music and songs whose lyrics are sighs that penetrate the soul. The young man does not see these people with the heavy load of Alzheimer's as being sick. Born of the wisdom coming from behind the faraway look of these seniors, a remarkable intergenerational relationship is established – intertwined by a song, a poem, or even a simple musical note.

Despite the disease, weakness and fatigue, they cannot help themselves from being transformed. All these men and women become, in his eyes – visitors or spectators, peers and friends, guests and fans, even art critics. Each one occupies a position in the spontaneity of the whole. With his audience, every day, he puts together a great performance inspired by his imagination. Through his music, he becomes the creator, entertainer, therapist, comforter, and supporter.

Working with the arts can often help those who are suffering from Alzheimer's to transcend themselves. A simple gesture can become a work of art. The goal of each day for him is to create a space where his clients can be creative – and to let them know that they are.

These well-educated people often act like children again. Some refuse to follow rules. But he lets them know that they can sometimes say NO, these men and women who go about this big room with their dream to live happily make use of the movement of each one to invent a form of musicality. They are able to create – so they are. You can feel the flexibility he has within as he works with the notes. It is with this flexibility, and with respect, that we can find a voice for every person around us.

With keen observation faces are studied, one by one, according to the provisions of the moment. After a lifetime of achievements, these seniors have come to a stage where society sees them at a standstill. But each one brings much history – and mystery. Sometimes life's circumstances force us to stay behind the curtains, behind a counter. But this becomes a place of observation that is enriching, where you can see that such a group, the gathering of octogenarians and centenarians, can forget loneliness and find comfort as a caring soul interacts with them.

He is able to communicate his spiritual vibration. Being a therapist is for him a sacred mission, and perhaps a search for self. He is seeking his alter ego. Together they become travelers who take different paths but with one goal: to live by looking in the same direction.

Some people make an effort to have others to look at them, seeking attention instead of being wholeheartedly interested in others. Without question, he lives and breathes how necessary it is to devote time and energy to others. By working with seniors suffering from Alzheimer's, he knows how vital it is to establish relationships based on respect for who they were, and who they are right now.

He sees meaning in their lives; the renewed discovery of free will, and freedom. In acknowledging the quiet spirituality of these minds now rendered still and silent, he must know why he exists.

It seems that we walk more than a thousand kilometers a day in the corridors of this building to give our best serving the residents, who are often frustrated, metamorphosing from the strengths of their pasts. They reach their final stage of transformation before becoming butterflies, light and fragile.

I am reminded of a young man from Liberia, who is not afraid to explore their world. To him, these residents are like family. He bravely challenges indifference and decorates his time working with a mischievous look in his eyes and a brilliant smile that brings joy to the heart. Passionate about his work, he became a teacher of himself, and continues his routine with many small gestures of kindness for the residents, authenticating their lives.

Those we interact with give us a chance to reflect ourselves, and we can choose to project what is best in us. Our existence is built by and for others. It cannot depend on limiting barriers imposed by society.

One may never realize how difficult it can be for those who find themselves on a new path where everything has to be recalculated to fit into their present situation. As life changes, it is not unusual to feel the lack of many familiar things, but it is also an opportunity to notice and appreciate the people who make a lasting, positive impression.

And so I've been privileged to observe, from behind the kitchen counter of a very special place, many important life lessons for new immigrants to learn at work… and perhaps also for those who work with them. The journey continues!

There are so many barriers; it's like in a lonely raid, always taking a new step to escape suspicious looks. Even when you walk straight, that you are kind, helpful and serious, you are not spared from the indifference of some people around you. People whose names I remember and with whom I spent my first few hours of work ignore me today. It is like there is no one by my side.

When you are new, you want to fight loneliness, but you can't speak. Fortunately, I still have the night as my only hope to change my tomorrows. Even when you refuse to believe it, the clock is there, dominating the whole room until the arrival of a new morning that reminds you that you are not alone, because, that we are alone or not, loneliness leaves and returns constantly in our little world.

Each one has its own unique suffering! One morning, a woman from the management, responsible for education for this store, comes to visit us and wants to meet everyone in the kitchen to talk about food safety and hygiene. She has gray hair, a compassionate polar look, and is dressed in a black shirt and navy jeans that day. Very quickly, you realize through her speech, her gestures, and her way of being in general that she has a certain class. The store becomes the real theater of a lifetime.

People come and go like spectators who would travel to attend a session and then return home. Very few of them understand the difference between coming to the store and rushing elsewhere to have the opportunity to be in direct contact with the farmers.

There are those who come for friendship and to consume and others who come to pass the time. I take advantage of their presence to try to better understand my role in this cuisine and the antagonism that exists in each of them, even if it does not often stem from an ideal ideological current.

I am very tired! On the immigrants' coastal path, I am still hanging on the back of an animal of circumstances. I control all the drops of saliva that can make you want to live fully. No matter how boring it is to meet others, I learn many things that allow me to discover myself.

Take the time to enjoy life and share lots of unforgettable stories or interesting sources of information. We must be skillful, burlesque, talented and daring to lead an entire people in one and the same direction and to understand the different facets of the parameters of our life. With another colleague who comes from Salvador and whom I call "Chiquito", I speak, tell and analyze everyday reality every time we have the chance to close the bars together. He talks about the injustice of justice, he talks about loneliness, selfishness, revolt, oppression, and about immigration and tolerance.

He talks about everything! It is the migratory release and sometimes silence creeps in and then gives way to the stories of his friend tackling a great subject that only politicians repeat: it is we who do not know the splendor of our potential in the economy of the world, but the others, the intransigent ones know it. Chiquito connects conversation on the conversation!

And this is one of the paths of this source of immigration, it is a common problem. Between each dialogue, a lot of water and saliva has passed. From morning to evening, people of all cultures train, invent and in the meantime whisper ... the first immigrants initiated this art of pleasing others. And it is fun to still be able to share this pleasure. We spend nights joking like those who play cards to pass the time...

And that is true! Chiquito and I are just kidding to kill the savage time of imperatives, pecking memory before putting it in a fence. I am sometimes humiliated, bored. I play hopscotch in the sun; I look out the window in the future. Prudence tortures the time we spend waiting for the poor moment of retirement.

"Whose fault is it today if we live life as a culprit?" asked Chiquito. In our country of origin, we are king! My parents have hundreds of hectares of land to work and keep animals. But there! Now we stay on the bench of the last of the cursed. Ashamed, on this bench, to look at the eyes that look at us as a stranger, a lost, a deserted of our language, our culture, and our origin. When you are an immigrant, there is always a moral and relentless void to fill. You never have the right to live happily; the heart is always hurt by disappointment. We always feel isolated and loneliness pursues us everywhere, even in the middle of a whole.

Other occupants ... and each morning, the faces combine the verbs of suffering. And also, by looking at people who have not been able to understand how the daring existence exists teases them every day because of status, like a child with dreams whitened eyes who has just had a new family. The lucky ones, on the axis of a reverse role or the pitiful ones, shouting in the silence. These people who look at each other do not know the true value of the initial being buried in each of us. We are like zombies in front of them! For them, we are not alive.

It's infinitely sad, but it's true! We do not have much money, but that doesn't stop us from having a secret vision. Despite everything, we must say thank you to this superior force which removed us from this limit of territory reduced to alms, but if we were to write a letter to the whole world to let him know this state of survival in which we evolve all, it just looks like we are all lost, as if plunged into a nightmare. Faces covered with scars, suffering from nostalgia, little escape maneuvers clung desperately to the news so that we could live differently.

Passing through the large corridor, at the time of my break, I crossed the kitchen door, passed between the bars and in front of one of the store's cash registers, next to a corner reserved for children sometimes accompanied by their parents. I went to the refectory where I sat at one of the small tables.

A few meters from me, almost opposite, a young and pretty girl has almost finished her meal. The young lady is indeed exceptionally beautiful, slim and brunette, very elegant, looking quite like a high fashion model.

I decide to go have a coffee and while it is being brewed and I'm waiting to pay, I don't miss the pleasure of admiring its shape. Our eyes meet, but to remain discreet, I pretend to observe a hanging garden inside the building as well as the passers-by that we can see passing in front.

I rest my eyes on her and realize that she is looking at me, giving off even more magnetism. Also, I wonder how to approach it. We do not use the same jargon to communicate. She gets up, looks at me and gives me a broad smile. I let her go without saying a word. Her lips in the shape of flower petals give off the scent of jasmine-scented ice cream and poison my eyes. I cannot control my urge to introduce myself. The candles of emotion put me in front of her. It was a Friday evening. I approach and ask him: - Where do you come from? - Me? Replies the girl ... I don't know my father yet, I come from a world, blackened with lies and confusion, which plunges me into an old dream generating speculation of all kinds. This tall brunette hides a look that thrills.

Seeking to unravel the mysteries of such a morbid encounter through the vowels and the syllables of the words, I advance to put myself beyond the reach of the captive waves of the charm of his body dressed in a white shirt that brushes against an innocent canvas leaving guess a generous chest. She turns to go towards a corridor, which will take her in front of the exit door. I continue to follow her, observing her legs like two cigars lost in the smoke of her gestures. She comes back to me with a necklace, which she caresses with a gentle hand, and which reminds me of the Buddhist confession. She gently points her index finger at my hat, the idol on my way. And this is how twilight settles over the whole city and the sun turns towards the horizon! She then crosses the door in an ecclesiastical approach drawing her buttocks under a long skirt draped in indigo blue jeans. Her breasts panic over a white scarf that serves as a bodice, her natural black hair falling to her neck.

She walks almost barefoot, carefully and rhythmically throwing her long brown legs in a half-ray of sunshine, the victim of a dark evening. I leave quickly to work. I did not even have time to say a word to him.

We write and it is as if we were looking at each other on this same table arranged for a party that we remember, tasting, misunderstood, the boredom of gray days. However, in all this silence, they remain in my memory, those who followed me the last nights in the corridor of midday parallel to that of midnight...

Another memory ... The memory of the girl and my daughter to whom I want to send a letter explaining who I am, how I saw her on the street like all the other children...

And I would love to be a writer without an alphabet, a poet of poems without words and if I were ever given the mandate to create another world, I would build it like a corridor at the entrance of a path where I could meet my girl. Just enough to answer hundreds of thousands of families looking for a loved one. At each break, wisely gathered in front of this store, time is spent listening to children, men, and women digging their identity buried in sequences of new stories...

These stories are always told in a corridor or on a bench, or even in front of a table installed in another corridor. We tell stories as if it were a long bohemian poem. Informally, the meeting space begins to take the form of a sanctuary where everyone connects to his or her word as a ritually respected prayer. I listened, with a particularly attentive look, to this little boy:

— We knew dark moments. My mother worked day and night in an assembly industry; we only saw her once a week. I was always alone, and I had a blue fear of the company of other people, so I was constantly curled up on myself. In my thoughts, I kept thinking about my mother, my family. I am here, but I would have preferred to be in a large forest with plants and animals.

Here we live as in a cave where the errors of time are fatal. In the neighborhood where I live, there are always night's upset by alcohol and forgetfulness, destroyed by the dream and the shadow of desire that makes us slaves. Sometimes we are too immersed in the daily slump to penetrate reality. I've just arrived and mingled with the heat of the old city, it's like a world apart, almost another planet. In a corner where the sun doesn't shine as usual, in a swarm of people dazed by ghost lights.

Life is like a riddle hidden in a fairy tale; my birth was a difficult birth. Every morning, inevitably, I find this frail young girl installed in the same place. She suffers from a deep sense of absence and abandonment. She always feels like she is going through her last morning. It is as if her life is told through the stories of everyone she meets on her way or when she is upset in her sleep by nightmares.

Some people on this bench smoke drink coffee or tea; next to it, a small group of saleswomen swarms in a morning mock. In a corner, a little more lit by the rays of the sun, a bearded man with the face of an old man drinks his hot drink and recounts his dreams of last night.

It's like he's talking about issues that affect people, and this girl too. In fact, the stories told by this elder are always closely related to the lives of the people who live here or pass by. Anyone would always like to start their day by listening to their confessions. As for her, she is looking for a special person in her life, a person who could give her the secret of her birth: her dad...

It's in front of this door that the whole story takes place. So, it seems strange to listen to an old man telling stories that are both imaginary and real. Do not be surprised if even today someone invites you to listen to it and if its stories inspire a series of amazing reflections on the existence, life, mission and total commitment of human beings. If you do not take responsibility for bringing something in your own life and in your community, you cannot get out of poverty. This is the wound of the whole world and you must heal it without taking away the dignity of the one you help and while treating your own scars.

You cannot help others if you do not recognize that the wounds of others are your scars. And if you do not help yourself, you will be unable to help others. You have to learn to discover yourself before you go to others, until you look at your face in the mirror of others and you realize that, very often, the problem of the one in front of you is reflected in your gaze.

The man we affectionately call the old man begins the day with a story about people's daily commitment. "The engagement in general is for everyone," said the 58-year-old. Some people get involved without realizing it. For example, in a country like Haiti, a shoe shiner takes a lot of risks. In the morning, he leaves early, he rings his bell everywhere in the streets, he does not know if he is boring people or not. Some people feel disturbed, but he is there to clean the shoes. Some people say to him, "Don't make any noise!" But that does not stop him, by reducing the noise just a bit, from continuing his engagement with his jingle bells to reach as many people as possible to earn more money.

Another example, again, is happening in Haiti. Mrs. Sara, who is a trader transporting goods from one point to another across the country or even from abroad, travels every day between the capital and the provinces.

No one is aware of the weight of his commitment. She suffered breakdowns on the road; she takes a lot of risks to bring food to Port-au-Prince to feed a maximum of people she does not know.

Some women have spent six days on the road, and when the President goes to buy food in the supermarket, he does not realize what she has done for him. However, if the road is simply redone, this trader could have even fresher food. If he thought about it, he would see that it is a service, that it is a sharing, that the one who owns a shop stays there all day to render service to others. If what we do, we did it with mutual respect, we would cultivate trust in others daily... The more people feel that they have value, the more they have the strength to commit. People who engage without thinking about them end up devaluing themselves. It's like with a business: you buy it, you sell it, if you don't make a profit, you can't eat. But if we manage to eat thanks to this business, we will get up early to continue our commitment to make it work.

In engagement, if you are valued, if you feel good about yourself where you are, you do not need to create another character, you do not need to create a father or mother to be comfortable. More committed, we will also be much stronger! Someone like Mrs. Sara can be proud. She spends her life on trucks, but she can also say, "My son, he's a great doctor, a great mechanic." Yes, she can be proud! It is a great success because it worked well.

I often say that if your job is to move the table, whatever the obstacles, you must move it, but you don't have to move the chair: that's commitment. Commitment is essential in life, and I look for ways to engage with people every day. But experience has taught me that we do not necessarily know the meaning of the word "support", and we now realize that when we engage, very often also, we accompany people. Support goes better with commitment than coaching.

When you accompany someone, you give them a chance to be free, and to know that they can commit themselves to another. All the time,

I congratulate myself: "What a good job! "If someone is not already committed to himself, he will not be able to engage with others.

It is because I care about myself that I am committed to defending the rights of children. Everything I do for children is for me first. If you don't see yourself in others, you don't commit. All commitments are different and will grow like a small seed that grows. True engagement leaves people free, and when they realize it, they move forward. I can talk about what a person's commitment is. A committed person, if they really are, must be spoiled. She no longer speaks for herself, but speaks all the time about the community, about people, about how they are by their side. It's like a drug running through his veins ...

It's as if an inner voice is telling this elderly man something besides the dreams he's telling, to provoke debate and give pleasure to everyone he meets on the highway. His advice is as follows: if a young animator works with adolescents, he should never forget that he is above all a human being and that he has not necessarily had other examples of value. Always try to understand it well, and not let it get lost in the trap of illusions.

One of the women who sell coffee speaks with the girl: - Keep quiet, little one! When you have an elder of that age in front of you, and he takes the time to talk to you, anything can happen in your life.

— Is that so! replies the girl in an almost dizzy voice. - I sell my coffee and I am silent, said the woman ... On the left, the old man moves as if to hold his blue jeans pants.

— I repeat that you are my daughter, it is true, it is an observation ... - How? There are those who imagine that some are born with the chance to find what they are looking for on the highway while others are only there to seek, listen, watch and accept.

— Give me time to have my coffee and then we can talk. I'm going to talk and too bad if you don't believe me! And too bad if they hate me in the village for what I'm going to say!

People never liked the truth. They always prefer lying. The vendors whisper to each other, the old man asks for another coffee, and he starts talking again without being able to interrupt him. This time, he is a little moved.

— How old I am, tired, exhausted even, when I speak, nobody believes me! The girl comes closer and responds with imperial calm to make sure she won't offend him. - Everything I just heard and what you just explained about being old doesn't mean anything. I, too, do not trust people who roam the streets. Often they tell anything.

— Anything, what does that mean? I'm just telling you what I found. We'll talk more after, let me finish my coffee. The girl wonders if this old man is constantly on the move.

— But why can't you always stay in one place? The whole village only talks about you walking and telling stories, interpreting dreams, predicting the future of young people. So why all this? Today your story is clear and fair. It happens to me like in a mirror and the things I see look like mine.

— When you understand, you will see how you look like me and you will know that you and I are on the same road. Men usually know the road to the fields and women know the road to the river, but that doesn't stop it being the same road.

— I do not deny it, but the problems are not the same. Your story is so hard to believe that only an elder like you could understand yourself and take the time to listen to yourself. However, despite the work I must do today, I take the time to hear from you. - And I don't want to shut up, not until you understand. It is especially tormented people like you who take me seriously and put my advice into practice.

— You too, you seem tormented, answers the girl. You have lost your smile and you don't see yourself with your real face. I feel you when I look at you, but I don't see you. It's like wearing a wrinkle mask that tells years of painful stories. You live more in a dream than. Is it loneliness, the absence of any person that puts you in this state?

— We have almost the same gift: I interpret the dreams and you interpret the faces. The prolonged absence of my daughter does not allow me to stay in the same world as the others. I find it hard to admit history. It's like a dream. Finally, I realize that my intention was not to write a book, but rather to send a letter to my daughter to tell her the true story of her dad.

Like a Prisoner

SUPPORTED BY PEOPLE, I CROSS A corridor like a prisoner. I go into a room and sit on one of the two beds I find there. I lie on my back. The white walls, the gray curtains with the glass windows hide nature from me. The door is open. In front of me is a large hallway. Passersby watch me cry laughing. I relive the suffering of my past. I look at eyelids closed like windows, like forgotten days. By simple politeness, I speak in a pleasant tone to my doctor. I do not smile. I suffer too much. Too often I lie to myself, mocking the emptiness of these sad times. I look over there. I look here and there, without smiling, without strength: a child, an orphan without help bent by hunger, passes in the large corridor, sets out on the same path as me. He is looking for a hand to get bread. I look at it and it's like I have a nightmare in broad daylight.

What does a man look like when a nightmare is constantly watching him? A suffering, which others ignore, is inscribed in me to return in the evening to disturb my sleep. What does this particular life of sensations look like, this power to bring about a silence that worries, haste, indifference should have masked?

A poet who, morning and evening, takes the same route, is bored, exhausted, exasperated. The path of anguish, redone day after day, for years, remains an ever new adventure, although it has always been started again. But, on the bed, I still look at the child. I do the math thinking about a thousand things that I may not have time to explain, write ...

Give a ramshackle house to a wealthy nude, to any private individual, he'll leave it in a corner, like a mausoleum. Give the same house to a group of underprivileged children, they will make it their palace, and of their life a joyful story ... A good example to follow: the cultural activity which revives the grace of reverie, the leisure which is characteristic of childhood. Each of the faces of poor children is proof of this. With emotion, any being endowed with sensitivity can easily observe a source of love between children despite conflicts, despite wars.

I become a slave in my spare time. I am still plunged into darkness. Alone on the bed, nothing moves. I surrender myself entirely to the hope of tomorrow, like a madman wandering the streets giving birth to nights in broad daylight. A nation, a family, a religion. All these elements form an invisible chain of slavery. Thus, the word freedom becomes for me the song of dreamers ... I write and all of a sudden a power outage changes the look of the room ... Total black, I fix on the mirror hanging on the wall the still image of this poor evening ... Still in the same mirror, I look on the other side, like an infinite poem ... The rays of the moon are reflected, like a bouquet with light tones ...

With a candle, the light comes back and the ghost who accompanied me leaves, chased away by the sage who gives the room another face. The illuminated left corner looks like a sliced cake. My imagination makes me discover the other nature of things; another sense of life in this hospital room. I reduce the world to despair, and let it be ruled by memories. I look at the world and it hates me, I become ashamed of myself: I have too many friends converted into enemies. I want to be alone, alone, without friends, without anyone by myside, because nobody in this world wants to understand me, I wonder why ... Finally, I realize that I ask too many questions to a single simple life, silence is always the answer of my hell. Isn't it silly to seek life in the various ways of living it?

I said to myself yesterday in the silence of the night - but no doubt, I may have known it well before childhood -: "All we should know today is that we have no no power if you are not able to look in the mirror ". A nurse, with pyramid-shaped eyebrows, crosses the threshold of the room where I am. Another, in front of the entrance, looks strangely like the one who carried me for nine months. With a smirk, she leaves the door of the room ajar. His approach reminds me of that of my young mother. Each nurse becomes for me the mother of a new family. However, I never stop telling myself that it is not easy to live well on a hospital bed.

Time does not move forward like this little drop in the saline infusion that seems not to want to fall. One has the impression that the hours do not generate new mornings. I feel the presence of nurses, laboratory technicians. With mother's words and gestures, they speak to me, they control everything: tension, heart, serum, everything ... At the hospital, I discover myself in the invisible sand of sleepless nights that fill my memory with suffering.

The charming technicians and nurses leave, and return without hope; like a singer who sings without a chord, the days go by under my feet. I'm here again for a new evening. When I look at the iron rod that holds the serum tube, every second lasts forever. In the middle of a night singing the darkness of loneliness to the edges of my eyelids, I think of the doctor who leaves and does not return. He was the one who received me first and entrusted me to patient women and girls. I wonder if the doctor is sick I also ask a question to my brown straw hat looking at me on the sideboard: "Are you happy to see your boss lying down?"

Poor hat, who could answer: "But ... But ...!" Even in the wild silence, the great secret of the nights is never knowing how life will end. As far back as I can remember, I have always seen my father and mother working in the first morning of spring. I see them again this evening in these beautiful, smiling, make-up faces that I look under this hospital roof in this new season of 1994. The greatest pain is to think only of yourself and to forget all its values. We, the inhabitants of the Earth, we share the world. Who then will come to save humanity? Will we have to roll up our sleeves?

I've heard this many times, but I don't believe that others can heal our wounds. My father and mother sacrificed almost everything they had to pay for their children's education, but they were unable to predict what the future would hold for the world. Mom and dad did everything in their power to stay together and live happily within their community, in harmony with their culture and their traditions. However, they ended up in another space where they didn't understand anything.

The peasant has been considered a commodity for some time. We manipulate it to make it poor despite its wealth. The ill-treatment of this class of workers lasted a very long time, too long ... The other arrives with a hopeful song to make him believe mountains and wonders. Ultimately, his goal is to control everything and rob him of his possessions. In the end, unfortunately, the land is abandoned by the primitives who have lost faith in their values. The poor worker, abandoned by civilization and overtaken by modernity, succumbed.

A few years ago, I wanted to denounce the evil to start on a healthy basis. Because of the terrible invasion of donor gods into communities, people are no longer working. They no longer believe in their values. Many have lost their lives, even though they could have been treated with their own traditional medicine. They also hardly eat sweet potatoes.

Due to a lack of training and protection of natural resources, millions of people have been diverted from their true path. Throughout our history, nature has always been an open door which has deliberately accepted all the people. When I saw nature abandoned by men, I felt a sense of dread. So I decided to look into this reality and engage in a process of community renewal. Conceived ! It's like we all have incurable cancer and we're just waiting for death.

My brothers and sisters have all suffered from displacement. My father and mother were also victims of migratory cancer. We have all witnessed how the illness slowly brought family members, and even neighbors, to death. I guess it is not too risky to say that this is an experience that very few have had. To fill the silence that is within you, you must speak aloud in your time and allow time forsilence. By its strength, silence is greater than anything. While we can sometimes guess the language, we can't speak the words of silence.

To counter insomnia, I am given a valium bite. Two minutes later, my eyes close. Too bad if I don't wake up. Life is just a return to the morning. It's the best reward time has for a patient: a sunny morning to understand that a doctor's smile is as important as a liter of serum. Far away in the darkened space, through a half-open window, the reef of solitude, the stars, the moon and the fireflies stare at me.

The sacred words of poetry soothe my pain just as they soothe my memories. Not without a certain sadness, I look at the doctor without knowing why. Finally, I let express my great silence. When I look at it, I see a small mark on the edge of his nose, similar to a bean seed. She approaches me, caresses my left cheek with a soft hand and speaks to me as if to herself. Through words, she seeks to understand the cause of my ills. She smiles, then leaves. It's crazy how I hate the silence of doctors ...

She realizes my discomfort and comes back to tell me that I have nothing very serious. Although happy, I cry. Tossed in nostalgia, I can't help but think of my mother. I then start to eat, amazed by the pleasure it gives me provides! I almost died! I still remember ... A simple fried banana, and yet what a delight! Out of breath, I am again passed through a new crisis.

Fortunately, quickly, a man joined me and it was like a breath of fresh air. He's so stiff when he walks that he reminds me of a disjointed puppet hanging on a wall. He is kind and patient. I remember his name: Michel. I had spent the first few moments irreparably alone on my bed with no one by my side. Now, to overcome loneliness, I talk all night.

I refuse to believe that there is another patient in the room until the arrival of a new day. No matter how well I know I'm not alone, loneliness keeps coming back to haunt me. My only suffering. One morning, a nurse from the clinic came to see me. She has gray hair, a pale, compassionate look, and is dressed in a white dress. Very quickly, I realize through her speech, her gestures and her way of being in general that she is a good mother. The bedroom becomes the real theater of a lifetime. People come and go like spectators who would travel to attend a session and then return home.

Very few of them understand the hell of this suffering. Some among them come by simple friendly duty and others to pass the time. I take advantage of their presence to try to escape my anxiety, but they do not often give me the courage I hoped for. I feel like a bitter taste, a taste of vinegar. I'm not looking to turn around, although it should have been. On the bed, I am lying on my back, still very tired. I control my drip. With the other patient, we tell each other everything. We talk about the loas (the spirits in Haitian voodoo), the springs, the inhabited trees, but also the brutality of the people on the people, injustice and justice. We talk about loneliness, selfishness, revolt, oppression, but also tolerance. Finally, we talk about the community.

Treatment for community disease has not yet been found, but there are effective ways to control the invasions and influences we experience from all sides. The problem stems from the friendship given to this big brother, once considered a breath of fresh air when he arrived in the area and who was greeted with all honors as a little god. The factors that contribute to this increase in production at the human level can be compared to recognizing the value of each. Poverty has a significant impact on power. This means that it is often difficult for community members to interact with each other to find a common solution. If you love the community and are ambitious, you should consider becoming an independent person. You can't just sit by the window watching the time go by. You will have to be focused in order to face the many hours of physical and mental work that await you. If you want to offer yourself secure stability, manage your life as best you can, whether or not you gain a certain reputation, you need to understand the culture around you to make the transition smooth. However, studies have found that this lifestyle may be associated with interconnected culture issues. Indeed, this often produces in families high phenomena of interconnection. No word prevails on this question of culture. Everyone comes together and no one is alike.

If you feel good on the path you have chosen, it is either because you have traced your course in the past, or because someone else has done it for you. A prayer was heard and answered for you to be able to have a good day.

Sometimes you meet the unexpected. You only need a minute in the morning to control your daily steps. Sometimes you forget your neighbor and you no longer manage to rub shoulders with people properly. This is why, during mediation or during a new course, I recommend that you think for a minute of all the different people crossed in your path. But above all, make sure to balance human and nature and stay connected to reality.

You also need to be attentive to put yourself in the shoes of those most affected by the problems, especially in the most remote areas. Remember to connect intimately with everyone you meet. You can for example offer to take a bath. This will allow you to break down the barriers that keep you away from them. This is how you will avoid putting distance between you on the pretext that you do not belong to the same class or the same family.

If you spent the whole day trying to understand your neighbor, make sure that in the evening you take a moment to solidify the relationship. Unexpected and impromptu passages without real understanding are of no interest. Do not hesitate to tell others about your new projects to integrate them more effectively. This condition represents a risk factor for certain communities, given the difficulties they sometimes encounter in conceiving their own social and economic development. The enemy eventually turns out to be a friend, like an illness that arises when big dreams start to take shape on the way out of darkness. This disease leads to a lack of communion and social culture, but also various community consequences.

The community enemy can be easily dealt with by the contributions of healthy communication. But there are other types of enemies against whom communication is not enough. The latter represent a threat to the development of community life. Everything becomes subject to negotiation. The goal is to find a normal balance to decrease the number of enemies in the community. It's like reducing the risk of the human body getting sick. The lack of drinking water is considered the main cause of misery.

But with a well-organized community, this is an issue that can easily be resolved. There are many other reasons behind the increase in misery.

Among them are lessons that are poorly assimilated and poorly transmitted. It's unhealthy release and silence creeps in after each conversation. I'm still in the same dream ... In November 1982, something extraordinary happened in my life. At the time, I was very young. In any case, far too young emotionally and physically to be able to make big decisions. My existence had turned into a steep slope, I was too vulnerable to act ...

Since I was ten, I used to take part in meetings with young people where I never dared to express myself. I preferred to analyze my environment and understand the way of thinking and acting of those around me. I kept everything in mind and at the end of the day, I told my mom and dad how I felt. For their part, they told me about their project and their dreams. Together, we tried to distinguish the true from the false, the daydreams of the present reality. So I took advantage of being together for dinner to tell them my story.

On the evening of November 28, 1982, an unusual woman, in a large white dress, came up to me. She was watching me with a heavy look. At the same time, a wave of uncertainty swept over me. I didn't know who I was dealing with exactly. It was so strange, as if surrounded by a veil of clouds and countless stars. At first, I doubted what I saw in this mass of whitishfog. Was it a ghost or a real physical body? I wasn't able to give a likely explanation. But thanks to this woman, I understood that from now on, I had to travel the world to accomplish a noble mission ...

Here's what I learned. You live for the present and the future, for others and yourself. Ultimately, it's your environment that makes you who you are. You are an element of sensation and passion. If you don't feel, you don't exist. You are in the midst of all, with all and in all. You're stuck in your environment and there's nothing you can do to avoid being under the influence of everything around you.

It is the combination of all of these elements that allows you to be you and that you are trying somehow to flee. You have to face it because you cannot live hoping to benefit from the luck of others.

You are unique and since your birth, you have been surrounded by various elements whose sole objective is to help you cross barriers, take the road and go as far as possible in search of your future. You are in the midst of your fellow men, and you shine like the sun. You are perfect, you were born with abilities that you must develop to create a new, successful and fulfilling life.

You founded your own culture and you are the only one who can evolve within it. It is incomparable to that of others, even if it is related to certain family, community and social cultures. Every day, you will encounter barriers, difficulties and challenges to overcome. But no one can ever measure up to you. You are at the center of your universe and you have the power to control everything.

No one knows the way better than you and no one will be able to follow in your footsteps. No road is like the other. Every day, you have to dream even harder to climb the stairs and reach your goals. Little by little, you must understand that you have a responsibility to yourself and your neighbor. You mature and you assert yourself in your choices as time goes by. You find your place in the universe.

To understand others, you have to understand yourself. You are shaped from a certain number of elements that make you a special being, coming from cultural and social diversities. No one is better than you. Where you are, you are the miracle of the universe. The center of the world.

You are the sum of all that exists. Everything around you is part of you. We can recognize a little of you in all living beings and all human beings, a little like all these invisible particles that we find here and there ... Whether they are in the wind, in the rivers, in the sea, these particles allow us to determine the true from the false.

Everything is fusion and confusion. The others are looking in the opposite direction and you have no control over them. You hear, but you cannot know for sure if they perceive the same thing as you. The scents that you breathe all around you confirm that you are one with your environment. This is the reason why you have to return every day and make your word represent what you truly are. You should never judge an odor in your path.

As a general rule, you should always refrain from judging without foundation. Remember that the road you are on today has been traced by your ancestors and that you are walking in their footsteps. As an heir, you cannot complain about things that were not caused by you. You must continue on your way.

Of course, even if we belong to a kind of cultural hereditary chain, each one is different. You too are the product of a racial and family combination. You are a mixture of shapes and colors, and it is this mix that makes you beautiful. In reality, the appearance of your skin, hair or eyes doesn't matter.

You are the result of all these additions. Like an egg dropped from the sky and crushed on the ground, you are there to occupy space and make the planet benefit from your innate power. Soon, you will start to disappear and like dust, you will hide in everything to recreate a world in your image. We will find you everywhere ; with your ancestors, your family, your brothers and sisters, your friends, your neighbors, your community and the societies in which you have lived.

All come together and look alike and form your journey. But nothing is stronger than your power. You have the gift of directing your life in this or that way. You are an adjective that accompanies words, or even a verb that combines the actions of your dreams. Through your ability to put your ideas into practice, you will in some way influence the world and contribute.

You feel things that no one else can feel and you are the only one who can identify these sensations. You are a unique being, so you feel unique things. You live during a whole that forges you as an individual and in your relationship with others. When we talk about others, we also talk about you as part of a family, a community, society and the world as a whole. Arrange to be in the front row of this set. This is where your mission will start. At first, it may seem difficult to you, a bit like crossing a flooded river, but you have to stick to your goals.

We were in the middle of a dream. After telling my mom and dad about this dream, I was surprised to find that they had taken me seriously. My father even grabbed his old notebook to write the story of my vision. He believed so much in what I said that he decided to accompany me in my efforts. For me, there was no longer any doubt, I was going to complete my mission. According to him, after what I had lived through and the lessons I had learned from it, I had to realize that I was both a son and a human being apart and special.

I have traveled a lot to meet people from all walks of life and make friends. The goal was to open my mind to meet vulnerable kids who are victims of society. This is how I met an unknown number of children on my way, in the courtyards of the houses, in the gardens, in the public places or directly in the streets. In short, wherever the poorest lived.

Often, it was an outdoor reunion and, despite everything, they were creative and full of joy, with lots of questions and analysis of the future on both sides. First I was in the presence of two children, then soon four, ten before I ended up surrounded by an active and dedicated crowd. It was then that I started to wonder about the direction I should give to my life. What should I do to get attached to this vision?

Why couldn't I find the necessary means to carry out this mission? I spent hours asking myself the same questions: what will I do to advance in this devotion? Who am I to have this responsibility?

To my surprise, in addition to the children I was learning to find everywhere in their homes or on the streets, I had other extraordinary meetings with people who also wanted to help their neighbors.

While I was looking for people to accompany me on my mission, during the last hours before I left for Port-au-Prince, I met young people, neighbors who were doing art or farming. Although I had almost resolved the questions about my future, that still kept me from feeling a bitter taste of unfinished business. Questions were still running through my head.

I was about to abandon my community and my former life to accomplish my goal, with the impression of being guided by a superior force far more powerful than my will. I had no idea what I was creating and building with the children I met, but I didn't care. A bit like a patch of oil falling on a sheet of paper, I decided to let the halo expand.

The dream that I told my parents seemed to be premonitory, and it was with serenity that I let fate come to fruition, like a film shown on the big screen in theaters. The various events that have marked my life have always seemed to me, depending on their duration, feature films or short films ...

I did not ask myself too many questions, I rather sought answers through a deep observation of human beings ...My goal was to work to make sure that the spirit and creation were released. Why ? So that each being can be modeled according to a process of transformation and constant adaptation. I build the sketch and write the plan after ...

Often I feel like I'm hanging in the middle of two extremes, swinging around to find the core of what exists. In remaining at the center of all concerns, we are sure to end up finding the answers to the most crucial questions, despite all the unforeseeable difficulties that punctuate our journey.

One thing I have never forgotten is that there are a crowd of people who are waiting for everything to fall into their mouths, who would like to always have more than they already have. But isn't it better to educate them and give them the keys so that they can go and find the solution to their needs themselves? From the start, it was clear to me that I was going to share my knowledge with others to benefit from the network effect.

Without realizing it, that's how I started to provide support ... But I still didn't know what it would change in human development. At first, I didn't help, I participated in a community process. This community initiative has continued all my life, without my having the slightest idea of the outcome.

I couldn't take any action before I got there and got on with the people. Without realizing it, I proposed a new culture that I did not impose. This culture was based on the value of each individual, but for years I was aiming for a goal while ignoring what would be the result of such a quest.

Family integration is the only thing that works to regain strength. It's like rebuilding a new, safer path for take a safe trip. As I saw it, I felt compelled to do everything in my power to inform and convince families to accept another culture. Meeting them was the only effective strategy to make this form of culture sovereign. When I started the visits, I kept in touch with these people. And it was during my various interviews with them that I found a large part of the solutions to their problems ...

These meetings were based on trust. At first, I didn't pay attention. I felt personal satisfaction at having managed to bond with them. But years later, I realize that this fellowship was not just for me. It was not I who managed to enter into communion with all these people, it was they who entered into communion with themselves and with others and who changed their behavior.

Sometimes I want to drop everything, but when I want to make a decision that goes against the community, I can't. I feel each person in me as if they lived in me, I hear their spirit dialogue with me. Because this is what matters. It is thanks to this communion that each existence has an importance and that we can resolve conflicts.

So let's get in touch with other free cultures to find the value of each individual. I am attentive and I hold a dialogue with everyone to combine the data and seek to understand the results of each space over time. Indirectly, people get involved in the development of their community. I never try to enter their privacy, but I thank them for their presence. First, let's take the time to perceive before observing or analyzing, feeling yourself among others.

You should be able to watch yourself living in the other until you recognize yourself as equal to the one in front of you. We learn to serve with the silence of the heart, to be silent, to transform ourselves by feeling each drop of blood flowing in our veins. This is why I remain silent and take advantage of the emptiness of time, something that few people do. To better understand the sacred and unknown nature of the human being, I adopt silence.

In every space of the dialogue. I drink milk, my stomach whispers ... This milk was brought by a friend of mine, for my pleasure. This friend spends nights at playing cards at my bedside, to deceive the timing of the surveillance; he's more than a blood brother. Sometimes it's true, he even gets to wash me! We just joke to kill the wild biting weather. We are ashamed on a hospital bed, we feel insignificant, boring.

It's the hopscotch in the dark sun, I look out the window at the future. The rain tortures the time of my poor weather; until today, I live have lived as a culprit. By my name, I am king, but, moreover, I am the last of the cursed. Ashamed, on this bed, to look at the eyes which look at me like a patient. When you are a dreamer and a humanist, there is always an infinite difficulty in healing. You never have the right to live happily, the heart is always hurt by disappointment. I always feel isolated and loneliness pursues me everywhere, even in the middle of the crowd.

And every morning, I conjugate the verbs of suffering by looking at the children. They could not grow as they should. This one child who comes to see me, his eyes whitened with dreams, his red hair, screaming in silence. He does not know his true height, his true color, his initial being. He is a zombie in his lifetime, he is embodied sadness.

No one has ever imagined that if communities suffer, it is because we always have donors who arrive wanting to change everything like gods, including the culture of the inhabitants. We have always been victims of their presence in people's private lives, with this share of domination. Leaving everything to adopt a different way of life is not simple, it calls into question the very history of the family, the community and an entire people. To change your skin to only find help is to submit to some form of hidden mental slavery. We feel like we have it all, and yet we have given up on our initial dreams. We no longer exist and are still dependent on others: to think, to reflect, to create ... Trying is the only chance we have left after all. This temptation to exist must be greater than staying on the path of dependence. Even if the people we meet every day make us smile, they will never give us the strength to resist in order to develop and become independent.

We must restore confidence for the youth. It is an essential element which, when it exists in a community, allows the population to give more time to serve in a just balance. When people arrive in poor communities, they ignore that they will not be able to give as much as they want and they cannot force others to live at the same pace as them. These people come from everywhere from so-called rich countries. They have money and they arrive with a different culture, a culture of arrogance vis-à-vis the host territory. To impose on alienated populations things new and different from what they are used to. They act every day as outsiders to reduce poverty in all its forms ...

They use weak social services in place to slit or dominate people and control them culturally. We must help the youth to move in another direction, contrary to this worldly dominance which has invaded it. We can think of it as a big mouth that could lead everyone to the ocean at any time. The community is often infested with all that other countries have brought.

It's like stepping into a new classroom to relearn things about ourselves and the community. When you meet strangers, never receive them as if they were gods. You are here below to share throughout your life on this Earth the result of your creation. If you feel like you are being taken away by this bad life for others rather than yourself, you have to change spaces and stop thinking that way. Your life is like a school that you would have founded and of which you would be the teacher. If you believe in all this, you will have no desire to change schools, since you will not have to face problems ...

You have to stop waiting for help from others. No one is better placed to help you than you. In addition, your mission is to provide services to the world, your world. You should not wait for someone else to do the work for you, as they will likely be ill-informed and ill-trained for this mission. Each person has responsibilities for creating, transforming and serving. You have the power to take control of the destiny of your future and the destiny of your community. Do not let someone else take your place, go against your objective or even guide you to countries to which you do not belong.

An organized community always shocks operators more than anything else. Their first action on the people is to violate their rights because otherwise, this community will prevent them from accomplishing their purposes. Also, you can make the community work while learning good manners and protecting each other's values without letting anyone hold your hand. And if the confidence is there, the suffering disappears. We can no longer break the rules, steal from each other. We must respect people in their values and capacities.

The challenge is that people from all walks of life, from all walks of life, can meet, find together meaning in their community life around a single table and mobilize for a just and noble cause: defend fundamental values. By climbing obstacles of all kinds every day to tolerate differences, work together for a single community. During the end of community life, the first things to expect are a feeling of loneliness and a suffering to the point of forgetting your primary purpose and the fundamentals, resources.

Remember, even when you are part of a single community, you are in the presence of a form of multiple cultures. Despite the social difficulties, we have extraordinary people, wonderful people. I have never stopped being a dreamer, seeing how young people are directly involved in the development of the community.

The progressive will always be whipped by the anguish, oppression, and contempt of all those who have the power of money. This story is always the same, it repeats itself endlessly as soon as we have a community on the move. In fact, when young people are not involved in the development, the expected results always remain a dream. Getting involved in social progress is like agreeing to detach oneself from the rest of the world to be part of a whole and defend a common interest. It seems to be at stake in a fight between the exploiting world and the community, who each want to move things physically and spiritually to control all social structures.

Community life is a kind of back and forth between the real community and the rigged and manipulated community: when you doubt all these steps, you must have a priority, and make sure to turn the page towards another road while staying in the same direction. Every day we have to reinvent what the community and the youth can be. One day is not enough to take stock and to make a secure projection for the future. On the other hand, what happens on a daily basis is already one of them.

It's not about isolating yourself from the rest of the world. On the contrary, you have to stay in touch with the reality that evolves and changes every second. You have to adapt to the circumstances. Understand all the presences that are around each gesture and each look. It's not about dominating without finding an answer to every question, but rather communicating with yourself and fighting your own exclusion.

Take advantage of the defeat to take the time to grow, transform and create the being you imagine you are in your community life. Use each situation as a compass to find the solution to the problems and open up another path to success.

My name is Godfroy Boursiquot, but my friends and relatives call me Godfroy. I am the founder of a great movement for children. I have no secrets and I only consider myself a life adventurer. I am the fourth child in a family of six: four boys and two girls. I was born in Haiti with a humanist soul. I have gotten to know myself through others. I am neither imposing nor arrogant or cunning. I am just a simple, ordinary man who loves life and the difficulties that come with ...

Today, I dedicate my life to development, growth and helping others in their journey. But it hasn't always been that easy. By that I mean that I have always been a fighter; life is my greatest battleground. I live fully, even if I do not know what will happen tomorrow, there will always be time for me to rebuild one day if necessary.

I do not intend to give up my humanitarian soul and my natural conviction to serve others despite the difficulties. I am a defender of the weakest category in humanity, with no difference in nationality and religion. I was born in an agricultural and farming environment animated by community actions. In other words, I am the victim of an old province crippled by the influence of the big city.

At 16, it was with sadness that I abandoned my bearings on the farm to settle in the big city and continue my school studies. My father, Duclerc, farmed and made a living from farming. My mother, Yvonne, was always at home and took care of us while sewing as her only activity. This allowed us to have an income complementary to that of dad and to meet the needs of the family.

My parents always believed in me. They were certain that I would make a difference among the others. They had bet on me. I was their "baby" as they liked to call me. And for me to succeed in life, they did everything, to the point of sacrificing certain things to give me the means to fulfill my creative and natural ambitions.

I learned a profession that I love and that helped, thereafter, the development of my being and that of the rest of the community. Too bad no one can understand that I am the victim of those I very often defend. However, I think I have done everything to not disappoint anyone in my commitment to the community. I did my best to keep my honor I want to share my life with others, as a gift to children, in the most selfless way that makes me the man I am today.

I will never let go of what family, communities and societies have instilled in me. They allowed me to cross the doors of the professional world and to flourish. People rarely believe that they can change the world with who they are. And yet everyone can create, build, transform and share. At my age, it is inconceivable for me to take other paths. My family advocates moral values essential to them. These values, she passed them on to me and it allowed me to progress socially in the right direction. I never intended to give up and not believe in a better tomorrow.

A certain fever has gripped the peoples of the Third World, harassed by misery like a bitter herbal tea in the development of societies around the world. For years I struggled between individual life, family life, community life and the social life of the living and the dead. I have multiplied the comings and goings to adoption societies.

Until I found myself in front of my mother's deathbed. I looked at her: intubated, fed by IVs and pills like cartridges to relieve the pain. She frequently had attacks of painful contractions. She was exhausted trying to resist. She, who had always led her life with incomparable and ordinary strength, found herself unable to decide the outcome of her life, so much so that she had to rely on strangers.

Mom's illness was experienced as a merciless event that shook our entire family and friends. Even our foreign friends have been affected by this tragedy: cancer. However, mom encouraged her loved ones to stay firm and determined like real actors to live through all episodes of existence.

I watched her go and die with the hope of making her proud, and thus reviving her through me. By delicately crossing the path of life, we are all looking for a metaphor to brave the storm and thus make death flee by saving friends, relatives and work colleagues ...

Because there is only one breath of connection with the power of silence ... Yet, on the eve of any beginning, their participation is monumental. Let us consider the state of the centuries, prisoner of the judgments of uninformed men. We are always in the presence of tired memories when we leaf through the thousand chapters of tawdry history that always condemn a single category on the site that we execute in common. The limit of each is to be able to associate no dream with another, because each dream is unique in its orphan secrets. By generating everyone's silence, we come to understand that the faces we are looking at today are fleeting.

Charm and doubt, that's all that remains of these faces lured by daily stress. We are all visitors to one space. Also, there is no reason to jostle each other so that the story of reality is not abandoned by the victims of conviction.

At the bottom of us hides a child who questions the future always in its troubles. The objective? Forget the joy of the path taken by simple goals and run after collective well-being. Even if it is often the case that one is misunderstood by others, that does not mean that one has to be considered as a palliative slave to solve all the problems. Trapped in his suffering and in that brought by others, we come to have to prevent actions that others claim to have the right to do as "X in a position Y".

With a single glance, you can quickly understand that we are surrounded by goodwill, but that unfortunately most people have been tortured by difficulties and are still on the defensive! These people automatically get bad by defending themselves all the time. A weakness that differentiates them from others and makes them aggressive. They can not help but give their opinion and be superior. This is the tip of the iceberg. It is necessary to step back and contemplate the invisible side of existence to rebuild a life without anxiety.

This will provide key insights for hundreds of thousands of families who are looking for answers to their questions about raising their children. They want to give them quality knowledge that will allow them to live in a completely different way. And this is how at each break, wisely in front of this store, we spend time listening to the children, men and women, to understand their personality through sequences of new stories ...

These stories are always told in a hallway or on a bench, in front of a wobbly little table or the main entrance of the store. A rotating exhibition to mark each season. A time for pumpkins, a time for masks that represent our dead, a time for Christmas which represents birth, a time for Valentine's Day which represents love.

We tell stories as if it were a long bohemian poem. Informally, the meeting space begins to take shape via a scientific and research space where everyone connects and speaks to convey a revolutionary discourse essential to the constitution of a new world. I listened with great attention to this little boy. We had dark moments. My mother worked day and night in an assembly industry, we only saw her once a week. I was always alone and I was terrified of the company of others. I was constantly focused on myself. In my thoughts, I kept thinking about my mother, my family. I'm here, but I would have preferred to be in a large forest with plants and animals.

Here we live in a cave in a city where the errors of time are fatal. Here, every night is turned upside down by alcohol. Oblivion is destroyed by dreams and the shadow of desire that makes us slaves. Sometimes, we are too buried in the daily doldrums to penetrate reality. I just arrived in the heat of the old town. It's like a world apart, almost another planet.

In a corner, where the sun doesn't shine as usual. In a swarm of people dizzy with ghost lights. My life is like a fairytale riddle. My birth was very difficult. My father drank so much that he could spend two or three days without eating anything. I exctricated myself from this atmosphere by telling stories to everyone about my existence, as I do now. I had the sparkling desire to discover how it was elsewhere, and sometimes I found myself sitting on the bench in front of my house contemplating my house full of activities inside.

My dream was to become a great restaurateur and to conquer the world by proving myself, faithful to a philosophy of world unity. Buy a big house to create a food museum for the whole world, a place where parents can educate children and better know the composition of what we consume every day. Over time, I realized that money did not always provide happiness. In this museum, we would have the opportunity to learn to be happy and to lessen some of our suffering linked to a lack of knowledge and connections with what we consume every day.

Domination always remains an endless fight, and this since the world was world. The physical whole of this world is made up of a two-phase arsenal: one to create, study, share, train, transform and improve life. The other phase only serves to provide men with weapons of mass destruction to make communities poorer. How sad it is that we have to face these demons all the time who present us with a life of illusions!

This life comes to us in chapters or episodes to play odious scenes. We have the impression that we evolves in a good way, but in reality we are not even this carpet that wipes the feet of those who dominate us, to the point of reducing us to dust of chimerical adventures. These sufferings have no color and we drink the poison of good looks every day. It is very difficult to notice the evil that eats away at us if we are not the ones who risk being reprimanded for causes that we did not commit. Why would the poor need a donor straight down from a power parachute? Why do some people always want to extract the last drop of blood from communities by making those who are supposed to cry from suffering smile?

The crime that these donors commit is ridiculously tinged with the illusion of solidarity and the hope of real change for our communities. And nobody can see and denounce the crime until these poor people end up burying their flesh, in the shame of never having the capacity to advance with their convictions without being systematically manipulated by arrogant strangers.

I say no to this kind of help. I cry out for help to these benefactors who use my strength to cut my throat. I say no to these insults that deny my values. I say no now. Time to find a new vocabulary word that will be truly adapted to the situation we find ourselves in, since we are involved in projects with one goal: the extraction of human values.

We are faced with demons who hold us by the hand and distance us from our communities. We swim in a huge pool of insults and we are mentally drowning. The body that represents our physical presence is admired as a work in a museum of irony by so-called developed populations.

We cannot accept that someone takes advantage of our weaknesses and our abilities to bring us down. We cannot accept that someone uses our foundation to make it their battleground, a laboratory of manipulative ideas with the sole objective of reducing communities into irreparable waste.

This chemical dose of social destruction can in no way work with the philosophy of CODEHA which advocates freedom and the building of a noble people. We must have the courage to say no to the gods of the kingdoms who offer humanitarian gifts while kneeling. No ... No ... No ... I want the world to hear the voices of the weak who also say no to these gods Man is the creator of his destiny.

There should be no doubt that man is the creator of his destiny. He has the power to recreate a space where everything is possible. He does not wonder if his dream of transforming his life is still possible, he does not wonder if the creator is alive to see our actions, to question again the power of our creative determination. This power to create and transform answers an acceptable life.

It is the answer given by life when we believe in this creative power that is housed in us and all around us: riches, more opportunities than grains of sand, a life formed by people from the community and transformed by the creative force of those who have waited throughout their lives for happiness. For the first time in their lives, some will discover the solution to their common problem. They believed that they had to transform life by themselves, and that their creative ability could be the answer to this transformation. This is the answer that many people have given to their lives as men, which differentiates the rich from the poor.

This is the answer we give to our existence when we realize that we can lead a new life, to take control of our destiny to have better days. It took time, but this power, thanks to what you have accomplished, announces the expected change today. A call to success for the one who fought with strength and endurance in this life. He has been fighting for the community in which he lives for much longer. The great battle of man is to find his place in this world, and especially in his community.

The relationship he should have with his community should be genuine, frank, honest, disinterested, without attachment to the material world, and above all with a feeling of real responsibility towards his fellow men. For each problem, a precise answer should be provided by the one who lives in the community. Each inhabitant has the responsibility to answer the questions which give doubts or sow confusion among people.

One does not exist to wait and enjoy the work of others, but rather to act concerning the trends of modern times. And we are constantly looking for a unifying principle that allows all men to meet around a common denominator so that the community can develop, despite the diversity of lifestyles of the inhabitants where each has a formula of its own to achieve its goal.

And a long-sought goal: the discovery of a new path with a unifying principle can have a devastating effect if the rules do not apply according to the culture of all forms of life that coexist in a competitive atmosphere daily. We must mutually strive to respect and make ourselves understood. Never forget that each discovery has created a new life and an additional ray of light on your human path responsible for your existence.

The new ideological vision for a new path to progress is a change of mentality and behavior in the most rational sense of the term. A quest for the wisdom of voluntarism and understanding to help oneself and to help his community. The vision of a reformist conviction seeks to create modern communities in which reigns pure solidarity, a tolerance which goes beyond the physical glance and a mutual respect in a community without distrust, and without excess.

The new method offers practical solutions for oneself and is adapted to the cultural march of the community. This method imposed a rigorous research on the mentality and the creative spirit with the idea of designing effective and adapted tools that a person can use to increase his skills. The ambition is to aspire to greater freedom of thought to be autonomous. It is the elementary principles stated most often in the annals of our elders that can resolve the old moral dilemma of good and evil in the community. They bring new behavior to social life.

In the daily life of any community, everyone has the responsibility to validate a new creation every day, without accepting it, much less understanding it. In a way, creation is possible at the moment when people validate its existence. Creation is the result of an analytical balance between oneself and others in a communion of social validity.

Living better is only a question of transforming one condition into another, a question of daily creation, sometimes opposed to what is common and in total confusion with others. Nevertheless, you will be happy to bring the light to the in your world and your mission is to bring happiness. The missionary does not have a life of his own.

The existence of a community results from a permanent intervention of the different organizations which form it, starting with the family. The members of these organizations should not be content to look in the face, but rather to immerse themselves in a critical questioning of existence.

The abandonment must not exist for a responsible person. His gaze must be directed towards the future for a transformation of each moment. Anyone who is not content to recreate the official world of the great power which he enjoys does not accept his existence. A careful reading of the world shows that the misfortune of man lies as much in the interruption of his race for the pursuit of his development as in the development of his community. Community development is therefore not a challenge, as long as we have a community that is united and faithful in its conviction.

Nature never forgives the man who does not move, and man will always be guilty in front of the natural course of things, if he doesn't reinvent his path. The existence of man has been conditioned for success. One cannot hope for the fruit without having the tree, the time of maturity and the suffering of hard work, the attachment to the set goals. This method of achieving success can only work if the balance between what you are and what you want to be is balanced. It's a simple daily exercise that requires you to be very motivated and stay committed to your goals, day after day. Often this will be at the expense of what is real. The most important thing in life is personal freedom, family, community, society, friends and a sense of well-being.

It is good to communicate to propagate the humanist electrons of a tolerant fusion, to rediscover the community culture while seeking the road which will lead us together in the same direction, and this in spite of all the differences of characters and family education. The visions of each person are certainly very different from each other. And you don't see things the same way. Despite the good will that exists in each of us, the void is still felt to give us an additional chance to get together.

Together, we can fill this void which is nothing but a ravine that separates us by our culture, by our education, by our dream and our goal of achieving the certainty of taking a step towards the void of our common point. Duty belongs to all of us and there is no blame for the faults for which we are responsible. We are in a relay race; one person's delay can defeat the entire rally. Thank you for your participation in this race of discovery, tolerance, learning about individual culture. Thank you for taking the time to put the puzzle pieces together one by one.

Even if we each have our way of laying the pieces, we have only one shape, one meeting shell. The philosophy of CODEHA is built on the existence of its communities in all their differences. One of my dreams is to see everyone's well-being flourish with dignity and respect. Have the courage to transcend the pain of everyday life by fighting the self with your revenge. Do not waste this precious time by looking for a culprit or a victim, by looking for a winner or a loser.

In CODEHA, we do not try to put anyone on a list of winners or losers. Rather, we propose to everyone to come together to fill the void that we have all dug together, by jostling us in a time that is not ours, despite all the capabilities we have. The dream is to see that the cutting of the cabbage is equal to the large head of the cabbage or that each large head of cabbage recognizes that there is a bud inside. It is the evolution of the bud that gives the big head of cabbage.

Everyone must recognize their limits in the truth of the facts to build the cathedral of a vision. It is then up to everyone to stay true to their goals with a single philosophy in mind. The struggle is also to find the inner strength of each person like a lighted lamp under our feet. It's true, I don't have many means, but that doesn't prevent me from having a dream and a secret in my heart for children. I say thank you to the superior force for removing me from this hospital bed. But if I had to write a letter to my doctor to let him know about my condition, I would simply say to him: I had lost my way as in a nightmare. Faces covered with deadly scars, small hands emaciated, hung desperately on the neck of a mother …

Hungry children, prostituted children, tortured children, millions of children killed. Mirror of our absolute shame, the massacre of the innocent hidden from our eyes, and which should nevertheless prevent us from sleeping. It's like hell is holding our beautiful sky. Without too many comments, I must denounce evil. I think of the situation of children …

I remember: lying on this bed, I was listening to the news, and the saddest one monopolized my memory. Always this painted nightmare: a young woman like a hen who loses her eggs because of a single bite of a dog. One evening, in a single basket of murders, she lost her entire family: her husband and two sons killed with pistols. Even more striking, the raped girl died after three hours of agony. The anxious woman gets up from her bed with her arms tied. She looks in her mirror at her blackface in this dreary evening.

Distraught, she had left her house and the corpses behind to return to the street. A nurse, to protect me from the horror, turned off the transistor. There are certain nightmares for which sedatives have no effect. When it's the memory that eats away, no one can turn off the transistor. And we can all ask questions like me on this bed. But where did it go again? Hey! This boy. His father lowered his straw hat over his nose, but he looked around all around him. Then he raised it on his forehead and looked at the sky. In fact, he looked without seeing. Misunderstood, through his eyelids, to contemplate something as insignificant as a little boy bathed in his young blood. It was the first legacy of its first seed, the pride of its 22 years.

They had gone out to go to a store to buy shoes for the new school year. In front of the body, for a moment, he looked puzzled. In a calm tone (at the time, you couldn't complain and therefore show your anger), but in a voice strong enough for the assassin to hear him, he said: "You can be sure that if I catch you, I will do you ... For my child, his life, his broken body, his ... Tell me then, what will I do to you?" And note, I did not even to you. I'll show you... "He didn't finish his sentence, because in the meantime he had leaned to the end breath on his only son. He closed his eyes. He no longer had the courage and he needed with all his being for this operation: to close the eyes of his first and only son of seven years. He only managed to make the first obligations without being able to stand up for the rest. Leaving the child, he headed for the open door, so to speak in another direction. Without destination. He heard a slight noise behind him and he turned just in time to grab the imaginary little boy. Yes, imaginary because he was already dead. He had been shot dead by one of the assassins half an hour ago.

He heard his voice. It looked like the child was chasing him relentlessly while he was frozen. He feasted against the sky. "Imagine, heaven, I am a father and he is my child. I'm alive, he's dead. I am a loser, he is lost. I devoted all my time to him, and he did not even have time to see me cry in front of his sufferings." At least if it was on a bed, whatever the bed ... I remember my brother. My brother, who killed him? Who killed one of the fathers of our future? Who killed our defender? In him, we could see our path of glory. Who killed him? Who killed him for his beliefs? Who killed him for his dedication? Who killed him for his attachment to the poor, the poor?

Who killed him for his words? Who killed him for his work? Who killed him for his position social? Who killed this fighter? Who killed this warrior for his battles? Who killed him? Was his mission over? Is dying in a bloodbath the will of God? Why the death of a man? Who wants man to die like this in a bloodbath like the game of a contemptuous hunter? Why die like this? Die without having accomplished its mission, Lord ... Finally, everyone asks the same questions, but no one can find a single answer ... We see our parents dying, Lord. We await your intervention on all these actions. Because, Lord, we only see our parents falling into the arms of hunters who despise their prey. Ah! My child! I should have thought of this cradle ... What are you doing in there? Why were you born alive? Why were you a child? You didn't even know your mother. She died in an accident at the carnival...

Little boy, you were two years old. You listen to me, look at your hands, your mouth, your feet. Despite these bloodstains, you still look like me: you are my child, my real one, my first and only child lost as a nation.

Frankly, I tell you, you are my child. You're dead, but if you weren't reduced to a corpse, you'd probably have been my way out. Please, I'm not finished telling ... My child ... I am suffering ... For my mother ... I look around the bedroom.

I see my mother again in her sufferings, my childhood in her solitude, the hard moment of separation, and I become even sadder, more anxious.

Mum! You conceived me as a poet, that is to say, that from your sufferings, I become suffering. Of your sensitivity, I become sensitive. I wait for the sun to come back, and before the last second, I will descend from the sky of wonders, for your pleasure ... A letter to this nurse I love

Love: this used maxim, I hum it, exhausted. One morning looking for the real, I find you like the real sun. Your sweet eyes tickle the wind. You are beautiful, we often tell you! From you, my being is dressed in a nut-colored color that you would have roasted with a candle flame. You are my only swallow ...

The movement of people all around encodes the bright space of nuances and joy until the day when it is our permission to take the door of this hospital. But the memories clung to us: the nurses surrounded you and looked at you from every angle like a body lost in the morning charm of birth.

It was like a party full of music. You beat time with the rhythm. Your melodious voice in the middle seemed to open doors to the world. I remember the first day, the first second: when we cry out and hang on to time and life. Now we are missing a starting point. No idea has stopped. We are together, quite simply satisfied. The other side is waiting for us to take us to where the unpredictable has a hidden dream. You can transform this dream by changing the seeds you plant and protecting the space day after day. If you have land and you work, you sow it a little bit every day, and you develop it, it will evolve little by little. If you do nothing, then nothing will happen. However, that does not mean that space does not transform. It is, therefore, stop helping, but you should never stop looking for passion. It's what keeps you going.

Ruminate on the past to build the present, hoping to find new things and think about the future. The only reality that counts now is that of the present moment, it is the starting point and the point where we are now, no more no less. Nothing will change overnight, but over time (which is already a privilege in itself), you can give a chance to the little seed that you sowed for a serene start to change and the certainty of finding new days. The more you strengthen the way you stay in touch with yourself, the more others will take you as a benchmark for their departure. You have a great mission, that of knowing yourself. By the very force of habit, while staying true to your culture, the change will take place in you.

For example, we may very much want to see life spinning like a rocket. This desire will be transformed into energy to arrive much further thanks to the projection of the mind. It is, therefore, an excellent way to be essential to never let space evolve without showing kindness. Benevolence gives meaning to your mission, makes it possible to federate to meet people and move forward together towards a world where the result will be within everyone's reach. Just like growing the seeds by watering them increases the hope of the harvest. At first, this may seem impossible since the change is not visible immediately, but gradually. By traveling, you will understand the strong influence of nature on human life. If, for example, you like to lose yourself gazing at the sea, then your priority and your privilege will be time.

If you spend time getting lost without ever meeting anyone on your way, it will be the opposite of what you must have to overcome your uncertainties. But all of that shouldn't stop you in your quest to help others develop a passion. So life is made up of what you do with passion. You can be better control the absence of primary means and to know the path to take. Most of the time, we're lost in a universe of mind with all kinds of thoughts. While being lost in the ocean of dreams, we think of another world. We do not feel what is happening in men. We then enter a new mode of creation instead of accusing the other.

We didn't know anything at the start, we discovered everything thanks to the presence of others. We also learned things through the exile of the mind. It was from there that we began to be interested in the mechanism of creation, then to give birth again to the invisible life from a single journey. Of course, we are still very far from the desired level of achievement, but each passing day allows you to advance and learn a new lesson along the way.

Everyone has their style, their form, their culture, their way of life. What is existence? This is all that is formed to become your complement and to shape you in a very unique way. Not a portrait or a thing, but an element of fusion among everything and with everything visible or invisible, until we come to an identifiable being. No matter how far you go, the most imortant thing is to feel good. The length of your pants or the width of your shirt doesn't matter to anyone. The style of life, she's a muse for resting words, a way to find balance ... A man who exists has a name, a philosophy, a way of life, a style apart, an elementary education. Existence can bring you all of this to form a model life system. Existence is not something outside your being, but something inside you, frank and real. Whatever your character, you will find your own path and your own path, like a unique talent merged with yourself.

Of course, the building sites have already been mapped out, either by you or by someone else, in the same way, that we pray for the blessing of a beautiful feast day. Sometimes you meet the unexpected. To control your steps every day, all you need to do is spend a minute when you get up in the morning.

It sometimes happens that you forget to approach and mix with people correctly, this is why it is recommended, during mediation or when taking a new path, to think for a minute about these people from all backgrounds that you have encountered on your passage, being careful to make the connection between men and nature.

You also need to be attentive, especially in the most remote areas. Remember to get to know people intimately when you meet them one by one. Especially when barriers are erected between you to force you to stay away from them. This is how you will avoid the distance from class and family.

If you've spent the whole day looking for others, make sure that at the end of the day you take a moment to build a much deeper, clearer relationship. It will be much better than your unpredictable passages without transparency and without real agreement. Do not hesitate to talk about new projects with people to integrate them more directly. I made people meet in their own way.

There are people who never participate in meetings. We need to make sure that these people participate and that their children are part of the package. Sometimes it's embarrassing because they tell us about deep things about their family. This is how we have been integrated into each individual of each family. Once we have managed to establish a thematic connection between form and content, each person obtains a role, a speaking time which allows him to state his life plan. We knew that some people did not like it. Especially because people don't like to expose their lives in public.

But in the end, these people ended up telling us, and then they asked basic questions about their destiny. People began to meet in small groups in informal meetings, before communing more importantly in large assemblies. So people came from different backgrounds. We passed absolutely everywhere, in each small rich or poor area, in unusual places, corridors, ravines ...

Among people who live in very small houses glued to each other, but also among those who live in large houses similar to palaces. After years of fellowship, people were no longer invited to come and participate in the meetings. In an overcrowded community, it's normal for people to be frustrated, because public services cannot meet the expectations of each person, because each person has a family with a different personality and history. A way of life must adapt to everyone. One day this way of life will be expired and worn out because we will not have had time to connect and work every day. Our mission knows no rest and we are constantly going in several directions to reach the greatest number and to commune with them.

Everyone is on this big road. We are planted next to each other, victims of our traditions and left behind, waiting on an old bench that was installed a long time ago by our parents. This land is a place where informal meetings take place between the living and the dead. The old inhabitants mix their conversations with the new occupants. They tell everything without ever omitting anything, from the past to the present.

There is no one who is not totally confused in this place. Every morning that no one imagines. This way of refueling to start a day again, to get into the fray of everything that is happening. And sometimes, without anyone knowing it, we also suffer from this deep feeling of absence and abandonment. You even feel like you are living the last moment of your life. Everyone meets and tells a single story. Everyone relies on the other and relies on their next to take the right path. We are plunged into a sleep of upheaval, consumed by nightmares of wisdom like an oppressed civilization mowed down by disappointment.

Some people on this Earth enjoy life forged by another person. Some eat and drink, while others, who are weaker, ask for only a single piece of bread to be shared between them. The women, sellers of kindness and beauty, swarm in the simulacrum of a morning, an evening to find something to feed their children. Lost in the search for a corner a little more lit by the rays of a saving sun. We have too many stories of men and women to tell. It's like having a necklace around your neck, a ribbon on your face to say nothing good or bad until the old days. Like a cup of coffee on a hiking route, we drink it and leave without asking for the rest. Like saying hello to passers-by without wanting to know their name.

The biggest problem you can have is when your mind and body don't live together. Technically, they are not on the same path to make a common plan. We have become puppets in the middle of all. It is a real conflict in the face of a human phenomenon without duty, without a mission to accomplish the work of life. You have to have a mission much stronger than faith to be able to find the strength necessary to build your own existence along the way.

Originally, it was the family and education that made it happen, although there is no silver bullet that can be learned in school. In my opinion, everyone has a special place to build their own life path. We all have within us a dashboard to understand and control the natural course of organized and passionate life, from the private to the pubic area. There is no magic data. It's always the same dashboard you've had from birth. You evolve, but you don't change.

For lack of confidence, there are people who have been forced to leave. Each empty space would contribute to making his life a failure. The one who was not feeling well was the one who was looking for a different playground than his initial being. It is never easy to find a ready-made thing if it is not you who brings new things into the lives of others by forever engraving the big stone. It is by taking a test step that we will form a base to build bridges, in order to make long crossings to reach the path of success, together with indifference. Life is about adapting gradually with activities and nuances.

But what is most important is having the chance to meet others in all their basics. To dialogue with them and follow them, to exchange with others on the need to protect their talents, to begin to gather the necessary knowledge as part of a sustainable development process. First, you have to start bringing people together to reactivate them culturally. There are people of all kinds: some just heard of it and some listened. These two categories have the same affinities, the same aspirations. But before entering a culture, you always must meet people to get to know them better.

Before gathering the cultural elements, one must always see the roots. When we put them together, we did not know exactly what we were going to do. We made sure that people were interested in themselves. So, for culture, we have already made roads made up of small activities, always in connection with yourself, your family and your communities, which all form your environment. I failed once in the union of my first marriage, another time with my first and oldest employee. I panicked every time. I thought about making decisions: having a wife, hiring someone else to work with me. But I have always been lamented that I cannot keep all the seeds.

Years after failing to face the indifference of my wife and some of my friends, another adventure presented itself to me, filling my future with love, passion, and devotion. Fate already seemed to be drawn and tailored to my personality, making me the man I am today at the forefront of the crowd. Despite some devastating encounters, there are still seeds. We must sow the seed piously, despite the criticism, so that no one suffers, not even the enemies, when it comes to community. Man's ambition should always be pinned to his body.

It is the heritage of a life-centered creation lavished with all the passion of the will, authentic and ordinary mother. We are therefore pioneering an idea of development centered on human value. Leader of a movement of young people inspired and close to nature whenever a decision must be made. We were born to a loving family, a father and a mother with very modest origins and deeply affected by suffering.

Another Letter For A Friend

Well, well ... You look around, you moisten your lips, and your eyelids flutter. You make you want to look at yourself. You are young, very young, and a little crazy too.

Madness chains you and makes you lose your mind. You contemplate yourself in the mirror singing, but the solitude is still there ... Well, well ... You are beautiful and alone ... Oh! Pale, but beautiful! You know my heart is yours.

Oh! Flower of silence that does not belong to a simple bouquet. I hear the beating of your heart, like the endless music of rivers. My memory of the nights tortured by your name.

I hear the smallest sounds of silence...

For Another Nurse

Hello, this beautiful day is for you. You are leaving until another evening. This beautiful evening is for you. If you look without looking at me, I am the one who will look at you. If you speak, I am the one who's going to talk to you.

For a yes or for a no or for the rest. Finally, I am writing to you. If I write to you, it is because you are my subject, the subject of a great and true novel without words. It is because your name becomes the real prayer of my dreams.

The days of glory seem well attached to these days of suffering, these days of pain in the heart. I write and it is as if I am looking at myself, again lying on this same bed, the memory of gray and boring days when I felt misunderstood. However, in all this silence, they remain in my memory, those who have followed me in these last nights down the hallway from noon parallel to midnight ...

Another Memory

To reach a clear source, the drums of rivers, the orchestra of birds, the look of flowers, the smile of the waterfall. I walked into a dreary country and now go to bed. I'm not walking anymore, and yet it's as if I follow the shadow of this nurse in a hallway, which separates us. I write my poem with the genesis of his gaze and the madness of being a novelist. I sing the horizon of her brown color and her "pyramid" eyebrows without eloquence. I already spoke the language of silence with the last kiss on Sunday. Do you remember, this Sunday, Judith Germain? You were not on duty, you came to see me and you gave me a kiss of hope.

And ... and ... and I would love to be a writer of books without an alphabet, a poet of poems without words. If ever I was asked why my poems don't are not long, I would kindly reply that there is very little light in my life. In this room comes a friend. His gaze gives birth to a poem. Then comes the doctor, otherwise known as "the smiling one". In a plaintive tone, I hear my father talking with her about my condition.

"He was always sick, doctor. I spent a fortune on consultations and medicine for nothing, for nothing. Like I told you, I really tried everything, everything. All this with the same result: nothing."

Nodding, the doctor thinks of the other dimension of my being and says, "He is above all a poet, an artist, a dreamer. It's simple and it can't be told. He surely likes being surrounded by his friends, receiving them at his home or going to their home. He enjoys meeting new people.

He doesn't have a normal and regular life like you, he has a life full of suffering. The extraordinary life of Mr. and Mrs. Everyone is indistinguishable, it's sad. He sometimes seems uncertain, it's true, but he doesn't get discouraged. He doesn't know what the future holds. And that is both a boring doubt and a beautiful idea of freedom. In reality, what he thinks, what he is, it's all in his poems. He revolts, he revolts against how to style your hair to please society.

He doesn't like what is stupidly forced. He likes to leave like that, to go and write elsewhere. "Do you know why he's doing this, doctor?" Go for a walk instead of staying at home? "The doctor looks at me on the bed, she smiles and replies, "Sometimes you have to leave, just to get some fresh air. Perhaps you do not know the true nature of your son …

What do you mean, doctor? To be honest, he is neither exclusive nor jealous. He is open to others, to their words. He has complete confidence in his instinct. He sees existence as a great war. He likes to live with great contradictions. He needs a peaceful family unit, days to watch time go by. He likes lonely risk. It requires first that it be given the opportunity to develop its creative capacity. In the physical sense of the word, he needs a mental break. Some people think that suffering is useful. For him, suffering is included in the very pleasure of its creation, and money is yet another drama for him! First, he believes in the solidarity of generations. It is a social addition, it is an economic addition, it is a life, it is an additional influence. It is impossible to suffer without others noticing. Just a joy is Share with everyone. Then there is end-of-life solidarity which is extremely important. This generational solidarity is essential. It is sad to see the discord that continues between families and nations. He's always asking questions, doctor. He is very lonely.

From kindergarten to now, he has never felt very comfortable. He was accused of staying in his corner, of being on the moon. He is like everyone else, he likes to know how others live. He can't define himself very well, that's true.

– What sign is it?

– Capricorn, doctor.

– Capricorns are solitary beings. He finds it difficult to take advantage of the present moment. No doubt he projects himself more into the future than into the present. He doesn't want to write when he's happy. Silence is his greatest secret. "I still remember the lady's smile.

I will never forget this famous Monday. During my first meeting, in addition to the prescriptions, she gave me her moral support. She told me about the sweetness of life. "Just like building a house requires a lot of effort and investment, life on Earth also requires sacrifices to overcome the difficulties. For one, it can be poor health, for another, the lack of means. Others may find it difficult to talk to others. Sometimes the difficulty may be yourself because you are selfish. Whatever our situation, we can strive to live."

No doubt you see me outside the door. And even so! I come from a room full of nightmares, I lived a war alone. This hospital room could easily be compared to a small prison. She has a heavy share of responsibility for the psychological suffering that I suffered. She is both full of despair and hope, a sign of my loneliness. I lost the vowels of joy. Opposite, there is always a corridor, always half-open windows to look outside on moonless evenings. In front of my bedroom door, another bedroom where people talk all the time, eat and kill my word. I, my words and my words are those of silence. The music of an old bed creaking in a room without space, without decor, without perfume ...

It must be said, I was a little lost. The hospital transformed me. Lying on a hospital bed is like playing the comedy of life. I am not ashamed at all. I only regret one thing, it is the time spent not working with children. I have known many suffering, and yet I am only a quarter of a century old. The hard part remains to be done. The future of children worries me. The evil of living is the evil of our time.

I want children to want to live. I spent twelve days in the hospital and realized that there were many other values besides profit or the race for power. I myself am anxious, but I feel the need to calm people down, to advise them. Everyone leads the life that they like and that suits them. It's stronger than me, I want to share what I have with the children. I can sometimes write all night on this. This is my real relaxation. I am patient. I don't like to display my feelings. So you can't know what I suffered from. I am considered a puppet. In my country, I live in a cemetery to survive, I sell water. Sometimes I don't even have the chance to savor this water despite my thirst.

I watch my mom every morning. She is young, she is beautiful, she is pallid, she is aged by misery. Shame shackles her every day, and yet she always tells me stories of courage that our grandparents lived, the way they fought for serve their country. A country that has now become a cemetery where I live. "I don't want to name my country, and you know why. It's because you probably have this problem with you. For the first time, I travel by boat. I'm looking at the water. »

I think of my work there at the cemetery. A cemetery that does not close its doors, that does not harden its heart. He's there. He's still waiting. One day I dream of meeting my father. You know, you who read my lines, I don't know my father. My mother swims in misery like this fish in the sea which I believe to have seen in my memories, a fish which asks peace to the captains of boats, to all those which cross the sea. A transparent string is connected to my body and m animates every day like a puppet.

I live on the street with three children who I consider my family since I left my family in one of the provinces of my country. I escaped from my father's violence. Despite everything, I still love him."

I'm in a city that shines the beauty of the moon in the sky with its light bulbs. I no longer see animals, I no longer hear birds singing. I forget my name in begging. In each zone, a name is given to me, sometimes by the other children, sometimes by passers-by who call me a thug and a thief. They accuse me of everything. I'm ten years old and I'm in my country.

For the first time, I am holding a telephone to speak with my mother. I forget it, I think of my street family. We are four friends and I want to tell them about my trip. I really want to tell them that I have met other children from all over the world who are facing the same problems as we are.

The next time I have to speak on the phone, I would like to chat with a chef and beg him to tell the others to call me by my initials, who may have been drowned in misery. It's hard to imagine how I can be so skinny when I come from a rich country. If I am skinny like a puppet hanging on the wall, it is because I am malnourished. My parents are poor but live in a rich country. You've probably heard of this. I remember before, I used to eat a bun every morning thanks to my mother who worked in a restaurant. At the end of each day, the restaurant got rid of leftovers, especially bread. My mother collected them for the house. But that was when I was still living with my parents.

"My father was still there. When she died, my mother fell ill. As of this writing, she is paralyzed and cannot get out of bed. I have now become my mother's mother. I'm glad I can help him, but you know how hard it is. It was not the way I planned to help him. Despite my ten years, I had to work for the survival of my mother. On several occasions, I went to get a job, but it was difficult for me to find it because I was rarely taken seriously. If I tell today about my sufferings, it is to be able to live better. Some people understand me, others taunt me. You know, I could spend a whole day without swallowing anything and sleep on an empty stomach."

It was even worse for my mother. The drugs were coming to an end, she was going to face double suffering: hunger and pain. Despite her troubles, she used to sing old songs to me every night. Today, when I think of my mother, I imagine her sitting at a large table where everyone eats enough. I have tears in my eyes and no one knows why. Let me tell you there's too much food left in the trash. Other mothers like mine are probably starving.

Passing through an orphanage, I went down a staircase to go to the refectory where I sat at one of the small tables. A few meters from me, almost opposite, a young and pretty girl has almost finished her meal. The young lady is indeed very beautiful, slim and brunette, very elegant, looking quite like a high fashion model.

I place my order and do not miss the pleasure of admiring it. At one point, our eyes meet. Out of discretion, I pretend to be concerned and look at the building. But when I look back at her again, she is still watching me. I'm wondering how to approach it because we don't use the same jargon to communicate. She gets up and gives me a broad smile. I let her go without saying a word.

Her jasmine lips poison my eyes, impossible to control my desire. It was the candles of emotion that placed it on my way that evening, the day before my first trip to France. She is from Africa, like Haiti, the land of Africa. However, she has never been there because she is from New York. Our dreams generate the platonic spectacle of lovers. This tall brunette hides a look that thrills.

From Africa, I repeated, seeking to unravel the mysteries of our meeting through the vowels of a word. I walked to be out of reach of the captive waves of its charms. She was dressed in a white shirt, the innocent canvas of which flattered her generous forms and captivated my gaze. She turned to go to a corridor, while I, completely ecstatic, was still busy watching her slender legs like two magic wands. The smallest of his actions seemed to attract the sun's rays. She returned with a necklace which she caressed with a gentle hand. She carefully pointed her index finger at my brown straw hat, the idol of my paths. Twilight settled over the city, the sun turned towards the horizon.

She climbed the stairs with a fascinating wiggle, her long denim skirt nicely highlighting her buttocks. Her breasts were trapped in a white scarf which served as a bodice. Her natural black hair fell to her neck. She walked barefoot, her long, tanned legs illuminated in half a ray of sunshine. I was leaving the next day and didn't have time to say a word to him. However, with each passage in this orphanage, I spent time listening to the children, their history ... The stories are always told in a corridor or on the staircase leading to another corridor. Sometimes the stories were told as if they were long poems.

Financially, we knew dark moments. My mother worked day and night in an assembly plant. We only saw her once a week. I was always alone and I was terrified of the company of people. I was constantly curled up on myself. I was here, but I would have preferred to be in a large forest with animals.

Here we live in a cave where the errors of time are fatal. Here, the nights are turned upside down by alcohol, destroyed by dreams and the shadow of desire that makes us slaves. Sometimes, we are too buried in our daily doldrums to pierce this reality. I come from the heart of the old city. It's like a world apart, almost another planet. In a corner where the sun doesn't shine as usual, in a forest of ghost stones.

My life is a bit of a fairy tale story. My childhood was difficult, with a father who drank a lot. He could spend two or three days without swallow nothing. I extricate myself from this atmosphere by telling stories to tourists. This is how I ended up in this corrupt house.

My dream was to become a great storyteller and earn a lot of money so that I could buy a big house for my parents. Over time, I realized that money does not make you happy. In this house, everything has changed. I remember the first day I started dating her. It was so unexpected. The horizon was obscured by shame, disappointment and suffering. I know how many of them want to destroy me psychologically and physically when they have never met me. I find myself in my little shoes, like at the age of two, making the business grow from my beauty and my smile.

In my opinion, a house full of children is not necessarily an orphanage. I had been working in this house for four years, after having stopped my studies. When I started, it was not easy to adapt to the rhythm. I even almost stopped, because the dust mixed with the smell of the basement made me suffocate ... Every day, we had to answer the call at five in the morning. Nearby, children were forced to do forced labor.

They were exploited because they did not seem to have a benefactor. Previously, this house housed young people deprived of all social standards. What they had as rules, as standards, was creativity, talent in the depths of their souls. I was climbing the stairs at lightning speed to avoid the refectory dog. I was talking and I couldn't sleep. Another part of the house was inaccessible to us. However, this part of the house is more than important to better understand what is visible.

One morning, a middle-aged man, presumably in his late sixties, tall and white-haired, visited me while I was still in my room to escape the daily mess. I was going to meet him to chat with him, and he took advantage of the circumstances to take notes. He was from Vermont, a state in the northwest of the United States.

He said he was determined to return to Haiti for the tenth time to better understand the history of this people and wanted me to accompany him on hikes to the cemetery. I answered in the affirmative, because for me, the cemetery was the opportunity to wander around the city without ignoring daily obligations.

When I got to the cemetery. I bought a lamp to give the impression of doing my devotions. In Haiti, for twenty-five gourdes, you can buy a bottle of strong alcohol, the "Haitian Kleren". Thanks to this bottle, we can easily connect with people. During the four days preceding our visit to the cemetery, I got up every morning to go to the site and try to better understand its ecosystem.

It was ten o'clock in the morning when we arrived in front of the director of the cemetery to meet him and visit the place, without difficulty. I was wondering what I could have answered him if he had asked me about my previous visits. Every day, I took priority over other visitors.

When the director approached, I spoke, but not too loud. It was not I who came towards him, but he who came to me. Thanks to God ! He asked me to help him with the children who lived inside the cemetery because he did not know what to do with them. He then took his time to listen to me.

I spoke not only for myself, but for all the marginalized communities in the world and the whole community of the cemetery. For all the misery and poverty in which we live here, replied the director, I hope that we will be helped. I replied: "We are all victims of this misery and poverty." It was then that the director launched into a long monologue:

"At the age of five and a half, my mother placed me in foster care to work and earn money because I did not know my biological father. Much later, at the age of twelve, I met him on the street. He drank alcohol and was violent. I stayed in this family until I was eighteen. It was the happiest time of my life. Shortly after, I lost everything and ended up on the street. Like my father, I started drinking. At twenty, I was like bewitched.

I felt a presence enter my body, possess me. Since then, I have suffered from all kinds of ailments. Can you see them in my eyes, all this suffering that I have inside of me? I struggled day after day. Despite everything, I know that if I am alive today, it is because I am one of the luckiest. Confidence in human value helps me. The greatest wealth of man is his value. That's who today I am a cemetery director who seeks to understand death and comforts the pain of other living people. What I am experiencing now is inexplicable.

I don't feel like I am the strongest, but I try to always be above my pain. I had to occupy this post of director to prove that one should not only be concerned with life, but also with death. I needed to go there to understand the phenomenon of God. You know, I wasn't lucky to have a real father. I have never stopped looking for my father from other men, and I consider myself a father."

We left the director's office to begin the tour of the cemetery. Listening to it, I realized that we shared almost the same story, except that the images and illustrations were different. The account of this twelve-year-old boy who lived in the cemetery represented the same picture, but seen by another look.

I do not live today like some children who live in the same house with the two pillars of the family: dad and mom. I am not trying to understand, I am among the others. I imagine all those who judge papa. If they could understand me, I would tell them that I was born under the watchful eye of this father that everyone accuses without knowing it. You will never understand why I do not live under the same roof as him.

I don't know the origin of the story, I can only imagine and question myself over and over again. What proves that I am the loser, in this case, is that I am forced to seek an answer and to beg unknown judges to understand my suffering. The sufferings that I endure every day, no one feels them except me. A new bridge for each crossing, a new adaptation for each situation. As a new source of consolation to find forgiveness and the solution of each problem, one by one, to open another path to success. I'm my father's darling child and I'm so blessed to have someone like him with me.

It is not a question of having a common look or seeking to find a difference, an answer for everything, it is rather a communion of pure existence. I fight against myself, against my frustration. Fights that do not allow me to take advantage of the time of growth, to transform this detachment into light on my way and to become a being who can become the life support tool. It is not a question of exposing myself to disturb the reality which evolves and changes every second, but rather of inventing another world more just. I'm not sure that everyone can understand the presence that reigns over my life. This presence does not stop looking for me and looking at me everywhere and everywhere.

I feel like a forgotten inkwell on a work table half-buried under rickety piles of books and papers, lost between the physical and the spiritual world in a sort of total confusion. A back and forth of messages keeps drawing lines in my depressing life. I cannot turn my back on the vision of this physical body that my father represents. Every day I have to reinvent what

I am as a human being to have a day full of illusions. So my first daily duty is to recreate my father in my way. This story, which is immortalized in my memory, always comes back halfway, with great emotion. Even the shadow of my father's forgotten first name accompanies me. This is how I recognize myself in a dream and detach myself from everyone to follow this invisible figure ...

Every day, I have the feeling of diving into an ambitious dream, of having the chance to find joy and to live a story of love and peace with this father. I never stopped being a dreamer. Impose on everyone my desire to kiss a body, although whipped by the anxiety and contempt of others. When I broke up with my father, two things occupied my memory: separation from family and separation from real life. I suffered to the point of forgetting my first name, anxious, stressed, tortured in my soul. I felt rejected by a form of culture that I had to adopt as it was. When I met such wonderful and extraordinary people, I had to adapt to this form of multiple cultures. My inner child silently watches for any sign of hope, that hope that connects me to this eternal dream of seeing my father again one day.

Changing behavior can mean a lot. Under the human value and the desire to look elsewhere, to discover oneself always implies other people with more precise and more personal behaviors and desires. Create new things, new ideas, adults in judgment and children in simplicity. Explore the mysterious environment of children in the family, in the community, in their institution school, climb the slopes of the imagination, discoveries every second. If you take the time to explore childhood as a whole, you will discover a plant made up of a trunk, roots, branches, leaves, thorns, flowers and fruits. Sometimes a bird can land on this tiny plant. Sometimes it will be a butterfly or a large bird. Nevertheless, this plant will always keep its simplicity.

These are the things you have to understand. It is necessary to cultivate self-control because it is the basis of the child's development. The clearer the stories in the minds of adults facing the child, the more likely the child is to succeed. Judging is not the best solution and will not stimulate behavior change. For the child, the desire to go further than everything around him has nothing to do with the analysis that adults make of it. An adult judgment will be meaningless until we try to walk in the footsteps of creation, to enter the mysterious city of children.

Most often, the world of children is perceived as impenetrable, even incomprehensible, in the eyes of adults. It's like going through walls. To understand well, you must first observe well. To observe well is also to create. So you can see infant magic twice, the one that lives in you and the one that you absorb through others. More precisely, we can see the same plant at different harvests.

The first observation must be made within the family. The second, in the outside world. The two observations must serve only one objective. The child bears the mark of his environment or his models. Despite everything, the child is never guilty, even for small things. The true guide will influence the child's originality, to the point of making it the perfect extension of oneself. In real life, everything is rarely so perfect. It all depends on the imagination of the one who analyzes first. It's hard to imagine that everything is as tidy, as well as organized and so reassuring. Truth is not found by a simple glance, a simple appearance or simple prejudice.

The good life, with beautiful dreams, is not just a matter of existence like a postcard. There are rules we cannot escape, people we cannot avoid, with whom we are forced to live or work. It's all part of daily life and routine. Communication is often difficult, noisy relationships, stress, and confusion very real. However, for those who consent to live at the pace of tolerance, for those who have the capacity to evolve and communicate with others without preconceived ideas, then life can be like that of a child, as a real endless journey.

And imaginary. For humans, nothing is franker than children. Despite the difficulty of adapting, a child's life remains one of the most pleasant lives to be around. All learning desires are dreams of happiness and loyalty. It's both very easy and very difficult. Difficult, because deciding to learn and organizing to do it is never a long, quiet river. So much so that sometimes some schools are seen as courts that are there to judge or punish. A dream is always a little intimidating for the development of the child. Sometimes we want something so badly that it paralyzes us. We imagine obstacles everywhere.

We're not sure we can do it, we're not sure we can afford it, we're not sure we deserve it, we're not sure we're up to it. Sometimes we are so used to wanting something that we don't realize even more account that one could perfectly satisfy this desire to change, to transform what one is as a human being. To successfully move from dream to reality, you need to stop focusing on appearance and allow yourself some time to observe and understand behavior change in its different facets. All behavioral changes inevitably start in the same way, with a mental click that activates the present by changing desires in projection.

Until we get past our prejudices, it is difficult to know what to expect. How much can cultural differences and ways of doing things vary from one child to another? How are we going to react to these differences and how are we going to manage in any environment? With a little imagination, observation and creation, you can even, well before making a judgment, train yourself to observe and analyze your habits without denying the novelty, and thus take advantage of all the information that circulates. Get used to feeling comfortable in unusual situations.

According to his personal experiences and the results of the meetings made in connection with this change in behavior (which are the subject of great discussions between the educational institution and the family institution), three stages must be discerned: observation, absorption, and creation. After the child's creation, it only takes a week to forget everything and move on. The child's prerequisite is, therefore, to assimilate what he has already experienced elsewhere.

Three weeks to completely unhook from old habits and form new ones. Three weeks to integrate naturally into a new environment and evolve physically. Three weeks to change your lifestyle if you are well supported. It's a pretty amazing phenomenon. Once the course of these three weeks of orientation passes, one can evolve at ease, without getting tired and without feeling subject to the dictates of appearance.

As an accompanist or teacher, if you are lucky enough to overcome your prejudices, do so without hesitation. This will facilitate the child's learning and adjustment. It would be wrong to feel devalued because we are a little afraid of creating, transforming and going in search of the real being. In fact, nothing is more normal. Natural behaviors are very rare. Among human beings, those who feel at ease anywhere in the world, those who manage spontaneously in any environment despite the language barrier, naturally bending to cultural differences, are none other than children. Nothing surprises them. However, children are terribly ordinary beings, without hard feelings, naive and simple. To educate supposes the acquisition of certain know-how, know-how which develops with communication and experience.

Not everyone can claim to be humanist, charitable, or deserve to belong to the very special club of saints. Not everyone has the ability to provide peace around them and those around them. These powers attributed to the invisible world are reserved for people who are traditionally frank, with convictions. They are found among immigrants, especially those from poor or underdeveloped countries. Does that mean that even when you're poor or immigrant, you can still have that power?

Certainly! Minority races have existed since time immemorial, from natives to our contemporaries. I'm not talking about a temporary action with poor results. It is enough to transmit a vibration that revolutionizes the world, to take a fairer path so that your inner peace rubs off on the environment in which body and mind evolve. By accepting the spirit as an integral part of our existence, we receive the privilege of transforming all those who are in us and all around us, from the poorest to the richest, from the most discreet to the most eccentric.

Ah! Here, I said, I have an appointment! The young woman had planned to meet me at the orphanage at ten in the morning. I knocked on the door of her room and was greeted by her sweet smile, which had the effect of relaxing me almost instantly. "Come in, come sit down!" She said. I sat on a chair that was to the left of his bed. It looked like a small table. Suddenly, she laughed. It was like we were doing Learning to laugh.

Standing, hands-on-hips, in a posture which had been customary to him since I had known her. She had an angelic smile, a look of infinite sweetness. She told me the story of her trip, praising the exotic ... "When I discovered myself at the door, you must have thought that I had changed ... I come from a room full of nightmares, I lived a war alone.

I look at eyelids closed like windows, like forgotten days. After having devoted my time to art, to children, after having suffered several disappointments, having experienced the adventure of marriage, I return to the hospital, supported by people, like a prisoner."

Facing The Mirror

THERE ARE SO MANY THINGS AROUND us that call for critical scrutiny that we cannot be content with being confused. We are observers, and this behavior requires the use of consciousness as a motor, to allow ourselves to be absorbed in the daily evolution of the multidimensional existence of men and women all around us.

Whoever we look at becomes our image, reflecting the same aspiration, projecting the best in us. Thus, everyone becomes a source of innovation, like this young man with a creative look. After complimenting him on his presentation at a conference on the theme "How to serve customers? The first contact was made.

Humble, multifaceted character. From her eyes emanates a contagious passion. He immerses his friends in a universe of dreams. He sees them as avant-garde traveling together on the highway of joyful adventures. Being able to overcome suffering, these people fill you of affection, the expression on their faces speaks volumes about their greatness.

Altruistic person, he lives in devotion and does not exist for himself. He becomes a traveler, a traveler who knocks on each door with his magic wand to rekindle the childlike soul of the elderly. He undertakes to borrow the slope of their wisdom without ulterior motive. He forgets his being and lets himself be carried away by his silence.

While working behind the counter, we stop for just a few seconds. The silence is such that we can hear our breaths. We become admirers of the shows that Marc and his intellectuals present day after day. Their daily lives are experienced as a challenge. We are far from street clichés, journalistic reports.

This observation allows us to discover an ambivalent world. On the one hand, that of spirituality. On the other hand, that of ideas despised by society. In this latter world, books with scattered pages rub shoulders with men of all social and cultural origins, undulating amid doubt, evolving within a limitation imposed by this executioner of Alzheimer's.

That morning, the young man always arrives in the same way towards me. With his dreamy gaze, he constantly thinks of the patients. Like a troubadour, he offers a guitar serenade to customers who return home. He invents songs and communicative music whose words are sighs and the reflection of each of us. The young man in his behavior never considers people with Alzheimer's disease.

Inhabited by the wisdom transmitted through exchanges with the elderly, a remarkable intergenerational relationship is established thanks to music, a song, poetry, even a simple note. Despite the illness, the signs of weakness and physical fatigue, the latter eventually turn into great thinkers.

All these men and women become, in Marc's eyes, wise men. They are all visitors or spectators, comrades or friends, guests, fans. There are even art critics. Each of them occupies a position in spontaneity. With his spectators, he puts on a great representation every day from his imagination. Through music, he assumes both the function of creator, therapist and the status of comforter, supporter.

The practice of the visual arts allows people to overcome their suffering. It is the very assurance of taking the path of transformation of their being. A simple gesture can become an artistic work. For Marc, the goal of a day is to manage to create a space of creation and to make it known.

These places are often occupied by groups of intellectuals who act like children. Some of them are rebels who do not accept orders. Marc, in his orientations, points out to us that the ideas and the men who circulate in the great room, with their dream of living happily, can listen and obey. This does not prevent them from saying yes or no, when necessary.

Through the magic of his art, he uses everyone's movement to invent a new form of musicality. They create therefore they are. We can deduce great flexibility in the notes that are worked on every day. It is through this flexibility that we sometimes find a way for each person around us.

Behind the power of observation, in turn, faces are studied, according to the provisions of the moment. Each brings its share of mystery, past and intellectual clarity. Of a life full of prowess, these elderly people have reached a stage where society sees them as inactive. However, this is far from dampening the momentum of many of them who are combative.

The circumstances of life sometimes force us to stay behind the curtains. This place then becomes a place of observation, enrichment, where you can see how much the group helps each other. The gathering of octogenarians or centenarians makes it possible to forget loneliness (as is often the case for widowers, singles), to bring comfort or simply to belong to a social network. With Marc as a social worker, that is to say, one who, through humility or silence, received in him the power to create. He communicated his spiritual vibration to people.

Work is for him a mission or a search for himself. He is looking for his alter ego. With his companions, they become travelers who take different paths for a single objective: to live by looking in the same direction. Life is a simple gift that one receives. Our existence is built by and for others. This cannot depend on an environment limited by barriers imposed by society.

People throughout their lives strive to get others to care about them instead of caring about others themselves. Without asking questions, Marc was able to show how important and necessary it is to devote a little of our time and energy to others. By working with our seniors with Alzheimer's, he has proven that it is necessary to base relationships with others on the basis of conduct.

The main thing for him is to help others find meaning in his life, that of discovery, free will, freedom. Copying or obeying is not enough: you have to know why you exist. Above all, it is the meaning we give to life that affirms existence. As he enters the spirituality of silent intellectuals, it remains difficult to forget their complaints, the regret of having to live like this. But he clings to the result: a look or a smile that serves as a stimulus.

A Court Meeting

EVERY NIGHT, I FELT LIKE I was in court and being judged by men and women who have been scalded by my journey. As humans, I begged them to perceive me differently. It was like trying to ring the angelus and never manage to find the big bell. Only the humanity of men inspired by God. However, nothing worries me. I always wanted to be happy, to have a life that could serve as a model for others. So I worked to found a home. Alone, I dreamed. Foolishly, I entrusted my requests to my solitude. To think, you have to be calm. Spending the night is like crossing a bridge over a raging river when you can't swim. Yet another morning finally arrives. Another date with life that we are not allowed to miss. That day, I was to meet a woman.

"Hello," she said. This woman was far from being an ordinary person. Like an executioner, she greeted us by rummaging through her papers, hitting her hammer and spreading out her files. Each of his breaths looked like a sigh. She looked at us without answering, nodding just the head. One day, I took offense at not being able to express myself in front of her. In front of this table erected more than two meters from where I was, in this warehouse full of humiliated men and women.

I returned by the big door. She was there in front of me. Her cynical gaze pierced us from the main hallway. She was one of the oldest in this position. However, that day, she gave us a smile. It was a gift that she gave us, regardless of color, origin, and gender. The trick of the trade! His gesture could seem trivial to all those who had the principle of welcoming his customers.

"Come in, come in!" How can I help you? Who did you come to see? What do you need? She always asked the right questions and had all the answers. She accompanied each offer with a smile that further enhanced her kindness. "Did you come to see a particular person? Do you have an appointment? Take your time and sit down, you will find newspapers there, "she said, gesturing to the waiting room with a calm and serene gesture.

His gaze was very eloquent. She inspired confidence. By his side, nothing was impossible, even if all hope seemed vain. With her indelible smile, she handed us the palliative formula supposed to solve all our problems and mark a turning point in our lives. "In this hallway, expect to find wonderful and questionable things. You will see that our answers wander every day with calm and joy in these same corridors."

Through her words, she shared peace, good looks, good humor. It contaminated us so that we could accept the unexpected. Passing through the front door, we were received by the police who gave us permission to participate in this game of patience. Often, and despite the pressures, we managed to overcome the smallest details that could have changed our days once inside.

The experience in this hallway can be useful for anyone preparing to become a responsible person. In addition, the answer is to be efficient and to give useful principles during everyday tasks so that this can serve as a model for anyone who wants to follow it. Space is transformed into a pool of purity. Negative presence, the waste of bad thought has no place. I looked at the men and women who, like me, stood arched and were trampled on by the ghosts of the system. When I arrived, I watched around me and deep inside. I trembled with fear and thought of my daughter. My only daughter. I could hear his pious voice talking to me. I was listening to her sing.

In the meantime, everyone began to contemplate me. The looks were accusing. I was listening to him, amazed. She had her monotonous everyday voice, that mingled with regret and zeal given to her by divine hands. She called me by an imaginary name. It helped me forget my suffering. I let myself be imbued with his imagination in order to become invisible to those who did not know me.

She called me dad in a soft and affectionate voice. I savored this sweet sound that resounded in my ear. Her voice called my name to the beat of a beating heart. It helped me to forget my torments. His invention allowed me to become microscopic in the eyes of audiences who did not know me. This call sent me back to the country, in this community that had enriched me and where absolutely everyone knew me. But all that meant nothing.

Oh! I cried, cried in my blood. I looked at people as if they were enemies, wherever they came from. All those furious faces watching me ... Oh! I cried ... but rather cried in my blood. After this hellish morning, it was half-past ten when I went down the stairs, my back bent. I was coming home and the nightmares continued to haunt my nights as if I was still before the judge.

As soon as you leave the warmth of the bed which receives the water of sadness, you are confronted with everyday life. A stay in the world of the dead does not seem so bad when the pain in your bowels makes you lose physical shape and destroys your vertebrae. I bowed my back like a ghost. I heard the hammer slam on the table, I heard the prisoners' cells closing one after the other. Men and women, always furious, are in front of me. Weak and tired, I confided my wishes to loneliness. I lived this morning like it was the last day of my life. The seconds lasted for hours and the hands he clock, in my impatience, seemed chained and motionless. The day was endless. That morning was all for me. I try to remember my deep nature. Am I someone good, good, generous, loyal? I let my mind travel in order to better represent my work and my being in another dimension. What is the purpose of my trip? What path do I want to lead my life?

I often write about the disappearance of values. This time, I want to talk about the community and what is important in building a good community. More precisely, I want to explain how to treat wounds that have been kept on the heart for too long. Why do you want to wonder about a subject that many prefer to ignore on a daily basis?

An organized community is a strength. An organized community is a power that scares even the wealthiest politicians. Some have millions but do not have a mobilized and dynamic community around them. Therefore, they have problems with the power of the people. This person does not have money. Good organization can therefore quickly become a powerful weapon, very powerful. More powerful than lightning fallen from the sky, more powerful than an erupting volcano.

The communion of communities has the capacity to double the power of those who have nothing. Solidarity is one of the most powerful elements on this road. This communion is perfect for those who seek to negotiate to better develop their environment. When people are given autonomy and responsibility, they feel integrated. It is important that everyone feels involved in the decisions. The other is probably one of the best allies for sustainable development. It is by keeping everyone correctly united that we manage to mobilize around us for better development. Reduce the risks, get rid of the fear of creating and producing. No other team is as effective in supporting you. Better to have a wise enemy.

The first power is the energy of human strength. If it is so reassuring, it is because it helps to take important steps from generation to generation. It is a production machine that goes beyond the megalomania of all visual or imaginary things.

Human thought has no limits, neither in length nor in-depth. Whoever comes into the world has no limits. Everyone can make a contribution to the world. Every second, around the clock, we can work and change things endlessly. One of the most powerful, uncontrolled and inexpensive mixes in existence is the untenable air you breathe everywhere and everywhere. Unfortunately, we did not ask enough questions about the connection to produce the unit, to disregard the true functioning of the breath. Except in the case of a sanitary end, of course.

But this force remains powerful. As long as solidarity is king, no one dares to destroy it. Why? Because each person in this solidarity community is a very wise reference. Because everyone has the same decision-making rights. With very few resources, a community can achieve great things that are truly original and qualitative. Solidarity is reinforced and becomes a culture in its own right in each family, in each community.

People who organize and mobilize on their daily needs are not afraid of the unexpected. Today we must find in us a common road, where the youngest and the oldest are mobilized for a new life, a new start. Young and old, we must start now to feed on another culture, another form of thought. Families and communities are the most important strengths if you want to take the time to organize and mobilize your own resources. You are the door that opens the way to a new way of life. Get organized! The wealth you seek is within your reach. You alone are a gold and diamond mine.

Do not mobilize against an enemy who does not really exist, or rather who only exists through your weaknesses. Mobilize for a culture of solidarity, a culture of peace, a culture of fraternity, of family and community organization centered on sharing, transparency and common interest. An organized community has no enemies. The enemy is none other than a poverty merchant. It's also a way to see what we're really worth as people. Our mission is to train, create and transform things to change the face of the world. From one community body, we all live as brothers and sisters in one big family.

We are too rich to waste our time waiting for others to tarnish us with poor ideas. People who come to meet us are always attracted to something. It may simply be our intrinsic value. The wealth we seek is found in us, with us, at home, for us and for everyone. For example, a really motivated young man is worth a million to do whatever he wants to do, in terms of united authority. The other, the one who claims to be our chaplain, is, in fact, a destitute who will become our enemy if he does not find what he is looking for in us as quickly as possible. All this for what purpose? Make us dependent and poor.

It's up to us whether or not to open the doors. The other is with us only because our inner wealth has attracted him. He remains, however, an enemy. He will use all the methods at his disposal to protect himself, supposedly with the best will in the world. In reality, it brings with it violence, shame, and dependence. The enemy often takes on the appearance of a generous and compassionate friend. He is ready to do all kinds of things to dominate and destroy the community. We have already spoken of the donors who disembark and seek to reign without division as lords and masters. They are very organized, distributing smiles and bags of rice to the poor to try to submit them. Often, this only helps to divide them.

Treatment for community disease has not yet been found, but there are many easy ways to control this force that seeks to invade and influence us. The problem is that some have become friends with them and see them as big brothers. They are now living with us and have the impression that without them everything will go wrong. They were awarded all the honors by considering them as demigods.

Let us remember that these donors have sponsored abominable crimes against the poor. They encouraged the youth to confront each other. Sometimes they have openly teamed up with organized gangs to paint the face of reality in their colors. Sometimes they have pursued a policy of social assistance and collaboration with the incumbent state. The objective? To be able to control everything. They exploit us everywhere and all the time, in "all friendship".

No one can exploit an organized people who know they can make a difference, who can reap the rewards of their labor without needing to be told what to do. Get organized! Work with your neighbors! The community is also everyone who is ready to commit themselves, to remain faithful to themselves and faithful to their people.

They always come to us as if they are on vacation. They impose themselves as saviors to steal our goods. Then they call us worthless thieves. All this to destroy the communion of communities. If one day you see one of these engines of misery at home, do not consider them gods. Do not rejoice in the help they are supposed to provide. Everything they say is false. For the most part, they are just misery dealers, liars. Be ready to take charge of your community's destiny. We are all human beings, all equal. Whoever looks at you is no more valuable than you. Often, whoever looks at you cannot look at themselves ...

Today, all of us, by our presence on this Earth and by the positive acts that we carry out in different regions of the planet, we confirm that existence is a glory and that it is up to us to lead a free, hopeful and prosperous life.

Life is a series of limited experiences and adventures. It must be renovated to revive a balanced world culture that will make all of humanity proud. Our daily actions, as ordinary citizens, must create a concrete human reality which will strengthen the culture and agriculture of the community where we live. Justice will never be possible without another form of culture or amalgam. We must recognize that everyone has the right to be an innate creator. This right is acquired from generation to generation, bequeathed by the great mysterious force of the provisions of divine thought.

It is sometimes difficult to question certain things in our existence which can represent a major handicap for the smooth running and the good individual and family development of the community. Earth has always been an uncontrolled place of residence. People have always been immersed in a world full of illusions.

Accepting to live as slaves is a heritage passed down to us by our parents. They too were victims of the imposed social dependence and created by those who pretended to be missionaries. It is a conspiracy. They force us to give up our traditions and our native life. Accepting to live differently like machines, without rules, is not easy. This calls into question community interests.

Especially when you start with the means at hand and people come and go with everything we had already built. When we meet them for the first time, they make us believe that they share the same feelings and the same cultures. They pretend to be from the same family to regroup around a single objective.

The real sacrilege is to lull the youth of an entire community into illusions to corrupt them. To force a people to adapt at a rate contrary to what their aspiration dictates to them. They drop the music, the dance, the sound of the drum that rhythms their lives like a plate of fresh food. There is no more solid benchmark than this.

We have the impression of being guilty for the simple reason that we were born on a planet rich in diversity and nuances that everyone persists in manipulating and which everyone dreams of. To be the king. After all these disappointments, we end up wondering if we exist. Without speaking of power, we remember how we were when we still gave ourselves the mission to rebuild the world with strength and pride.

We are also powerful beings, with values and dignity. We can go very far, further than the crowd that is constantly jostling. When the others approach us, we leave on the other side. People tend to burn the candle at both ends and want to impose their lifestyle on others.

Man never stops consuming and looking in others for a way to improve his well-being. Here and there, people are overcome with pain and do not know how to get back on the road to success. However, it only takes a single step forward to force the rest of the body to move. Thus, one can cover a good distance reserved only for the brave.

Whether you are a man or a woman, when you have the opportunity to communicate and reach as many people as possible, then it is easy for you to progress automatically. When you're part of a community and you start to wake up the ability to recreate from elements that other people neglect, we won everything.

Without elementary fellowship among all, we are sadly doomed to failure. We are losing an element necessary for the proper functioning of the community. Communion can serve as a driver for sustainable development.

You can suffer from all the ills, run after someone dear to you, feel lost in freedom, emptied of all desire, but never forget, not even for a second, that your life is made from the greatest source of dignity. Imagine that only you can furnish and defend this world in your way. You alone can find a solution to the problems of our planet. Without you, there is no society. You have the power and the responsibility to prevent social decline.

Many people are waiting for you outside the door. Many people appreciate you, admire you and love you for the road already traveled. I would like you to remember that to be happy is not to have a full bank account, or goods all over the world. Rather, being happy is knowing that you can fight and survive all the ups and downs of life. Sure, you will sometimes face what are called life accidents, but you can face them with courage. To be happy is to succeed in finding a solution despite fatigue, it is to work tirelessly and face difficult relationships, it is to make people believe in you and your riches, it is not not be deluded.

To be happy is to find the strength to follow the path that you have drawn, despite all its paradoxes. It's about having the hope of peacefully winning battles and overcoming all obstacles. The factors that contribute to this increase in human production can usually be preserved by recognizing the value of each. Poverty has the power to impact people on several levels. This means that it is often difficult for community members to interact with each other to find common solutions.

However, according to a certain amount of research which has been carried out on this subject, these living conditions may be associated with problems of interconnection between cultures. These conditions represent a risk for certain communities, which may have difficulty understanding how to conceive of their own social and economic development. The enemy can be compared to a disease that occurs when dreams start to take shape on the way to get out of the dark. This disease leads to a lack of communion and social culture. It also leads to various community consequences.

The community enemy can be easily dealt with by the contributions of healthy communication. It must be kept in mind that there are other types of enemies, which are just as important, and hamper communication, also posing a threat to the development of community life. Today, everything becomes the subject of negotiations to find a normal balance, to decrease the number of enemies in the community. Sort of like reducing the risk to the human body of getting sick.

The lack of drinking water is considered the main source of misery. He's the enemy of life number one. But this problem can be resolved by having a well organized community. Other factors are held responsible for misery. One can cite in particular lessons badly transmitted.

We are like those who evolve in a certain way before becoming the dark image of a delicate life. Take the example of this young policeman. He was part of the national police of his country of origin. He was assigned to guard the presidency and worked at the National Palace. After being persecuted several times, he was forced to move to the United States. He was not lacking materially in his country of origin. However, he was forced to leave to save his skin and that of his family. He thanked the Lord for helping him deal with this situation, where he had to be constantly physically and psychologically prepared for possible attacks.

Physically, it has always been prepared. He had been trained to protect and serve his country and had the discipline to do so. Protecting and serving is the motto of any good police officer. He was therefore ready to defend all those who deserve it, with all his might, with his hands, his feet ... He was a fervent follower of the martial arts.

In the United States, to have a peaceful life and meet his economic needs, he found himself locked in a room with the mission of washing plates. A daily exercise performed alongside strangers. No one knew anyone and it wasn't really important to befriend each other. Adapting to the codes of his new function, was already listening to his environment. The best way to get away from everyday troubles.

124

He believed in the sustainability of the world, and that is how the ex-policeman managed to remain a stranger to everyone. In the immediate future, his two main concerns were to go to work and to have a salary. He plunged headlong into his modest work, like a passionate servant. It was his great principles of order that enabled him to carry out his work. Another example: this agricultural technician who now works in the products section, everything that has to do with fruits and vegetables. If you are not a little curious, you cannot know that he is an agricultural technician, as he is considered a stranger in the eyes of the world. Previously, he was an employee of the government of his country.

A blood brother is also in the corridors of the store. All day long, he has products on shelves. He used to do mechanics and accounting. These are his real jobs. Often, images come to mind. This allows him to realize the turn that his life has taken. To survive, he had to take a different direction and his daily life was completely turned upside down. Community development is like the body of a woman who goes through many changes throughout her life.

Here it is more a question of cultural, economic, political and structural changes. They occur while the community is looking for purity that combines community and privacy. These changes are linked to changes in power, the strength of each man and other philosophical characteristics. They are completely normal. Among the factors that contribute to development, however, are the cultural differences that characterize men and women from different areas.

There are two fundamental forms of development in the world for communities. This means that the changes that take place are unique to each lifetime. Culture always takes time to develop. The fault with a way of life that requires precise actions and where everything is done in an emergency. This affects the human environment, with problems that can be very serious and destructive. However, if you think you have various opportunities, whether political, cultural or economic, if you have already made a diagnosis of the field, then you have no reason to panic. There is hope for sustainable development.

Forget everything you've been told about how to grow your community. After many national and international experiences, we have just decide that it is the man of the community who is responsible for community development. It sounds like a joke, but it is not. Existence has shown us that real change is a structural and cultural product. If we understand correctly, the Creator's vision does not offer the same possibilities everywhere. Existence does not give us all the same chances. Working is good. But working together is better ... even essential, especially if it is with your community! It is by spending time meeting other people that you will find answers to your questions and the strength to face the ordeals of everyday life. So, even if you feel like you are different from the others and even if everyone works for their interest, you must include a moment of sharing with the community. To understand the community, here are some simple tips to follow.

Start each day by writing your priorities for today on a blank page and including new things, new encounters with these obligations. In the evening, don't go to bed without taking a moment to analyze your day. Find a way to work collaboratively and don't let yourself be torn down by possible persecution. Set yourself a clear goal that fits your vision and that will allow you to become independent and carry out your activities and your schedule.

Give a purpose to your life and climb the steps one by one. When you drink your coffee in the morning, take the opportunity to set yourself a new goal. For example, rearrange the house or garden. This moment over a cup of coffee should be the opportunity for you to build a new day. If you have nightmares during the night, start by removing the darkness that haunts your thoughts. Then make sure you have a wonderful day, sharing moments of happiness alongside people in your community. Be the most motivated person to live with joy for all the moments of happiness that come across your path. Become synonymous with hope for your friends and make them happy. Your neighbor must allow you to resume the path you had abandoned without valid reason. He must mark your steps, be a traveling companion. You have to encourage each other.

He must join your community so that you can work together and strive for a single vision, that of a better life. You don't have to work for hours and hours if you know how to commune with each person and can establish a little "routine" for yourself. You can communicate during short meetings or simply by being present until you are used to the community culture and all of its customs.

Don't hesitate to take to the streets, to go to working-class neighborhoods, to write on paper stories that people want to hear, to go out and meet people at any time during their cultural evolution. You can also behave like a member of the same family, hold hands and share the word by drawing your ideas from the foundations of a traditional life, always in a serious, respectful and loving way. These meetings, which symbolize unity and love, have a great cultural impact on the community.

Remember that to work is to commune with others. No need to use an extraordinary means. You just have to open your heart and confide in the other, the same way you could do with your destiny. There is no foolproof method for development. At least, it is not mentioned anywhere. The first inhabitants of the world must have forgotten to transmit it to us. To create something new, you have to know how to establish a connection with the old. Communing with them is the only way to maintain traditions and achieve a perfect balance for everyone's existence.

During a training session, it was mentioned that a door opens instinctively for all of us, whether we are poor or wealthy. Whoever you are, you have earned the right to exist in our world. The day started with this module "The new door is opening," and everyone was talking about it. The trainees realized that everyone had the right to their moment of glory, that we could be rich in our differences, share different visions. The road opens before us and we can all take it. Everyone, children and adults alike, should participate in this kind of training. These orientation courses are not just for business and new, inexperienced employees. They can provide very interesting know-how for each life course.

Money is fleeting while knowledge is eternal. With knowledge, we don't need money. A child who Luck has been known and used by man since the dawn of time as a unique gift given to knows can become an entrepreneur himself and take charge of his life. Each individual. The more awake you are, the more likely you are to have interactive contacts and fellowships. A bit like a sponge immersed in an oil of possibilities. You have all the assets, you are in control of your own life. If you want to function this or that way, put your being in motion and do it. Often, we prefer to stay in a corner to wait for time to pass, hoping to eventually reach perfection, without giving ourselves the means. But time flies by, and when you realize it, it's sometimes too late. Transform your being into precious gold and sit at the head table.

Man is by definition a visionary. He can visualize objectives that will allow him to evolve, whether from a material or spiritual point of view. You are the first inventor of your existence. Make your life a mystery to fuel the legend of your abilities. The goal ? To recreate your being originally, without being a slave to any copy. You have to consider yourself a missionary in the world.

To live, you must now know how to combine your projects for the future. You have the power to tune your being to your environment. In the beginning, man was built by invisible and undefined points, like a dream or a futuristic passion. This is how this project, which originally had no real destination, was born. Time then manipulated these points and directed them into unpredictable meeting channels.

They created a circle filled with elements that provide what matter needs to become a living being. Right after the formation of this circle, however, the human being was not yet born as a tactile matter. Precious in families, communities, societies and on the whole Earth, the points were untenable, without traces, without markers ... They were invisible and doubtful like the void. There were insignificant movements everywhere. A dark, chemical, dark and supple movement, with an imposed form. These dust or void spots had no solid surface to rest on.

They were untenable and damaged by time and the judgment of living things. A group of particles is fighting so that only one of them can operate without limits. It's not much to be one of those points that forms the being that you are today. The latter succeeded in crossing the veil of light and darkness.

Before these luminous and dark powers, man was born in a channel which separates day and night. So there is a life that deserves to exist without having to question everyday life. Silence is the first answer to a question of existence. There are no other truths than your silence. As you go, the point that you are takes shape and becomes consistent and conscious. The development takes place day after day, like a tiny seed which germinates in its shell to give a large tree.

Man is formed in such discretion that scientists themselves are unable to control the extent already occupied by molecules. These are scattered all over the place and form each element in a kind of language that marks its imprint and identifies each living being as a separate person, with its characteristics.

No word can concretely explain the paths of existence. They can split, sometimes even replace each other. To exist is unique, with or without others. Existence is never static. There is therefore no common or referential definition. The range of possibilities is so vast that nothing is completely independent. On the contrary, everything is connected.

Everyone must follow their path. No one is below or above another. Of course, there is self-acceptance which demonstrates a kind of physical domination. In reality, it doesn't exist since each element respects what it represents. It is not measured like distance or duration, but we are all complementary.

Everything has its place. There is a solution to overcome all the problems. This cannot be explained. The sky has its place, the Earth has its place and both are linked to form the universe. Unfortunately, you don't have enough time to fully enjoy it. That's why there is evening and there is morning. This is how the secret of time and daily scenarios are formed.

Two distances always have a common encounter. The flowing waters meet the expanse of the ocean. The sky gathers in a single movement, just like the vapors that transform into water to water the earth. The paradise secret is formed and transformed at will. This has been the case since time immemorial.

Since the appearance of the human race on the earthly face, man begins to enjoy and use whatever he finds. It exploits all the riches starting with natural harmony in all its forms ofenergy; water, fire, air and earth. All these elements give us life without asking for anything in return.

The existence of the earth makes it possible to produce vegetation, the permanent production of new products. A continuous circle of renewal of total harmony with everything, in everything, for everything and everywhere, as a complement. Everything that exists is part of this renewable seed of herbs, fruit trees. Everything is old and nothing is ever finished. The sky is always on the alert. The Earth is still under construction. Everyone has a share of responsibility in the face of the abundance of all that we imagine and admire.

Thus, ends the accomplishment of a mission. Every day is a gift that should make us want to redo the way without ever reaching the end. Rest does not exist for the creator of the day. This is the commitment of a man who realizes that life is a gift and takes control of his existence to transform the Earth. When we recognize that we have a gift for creating and transforming, no obstacle is strong enough to undermine our decisions.

We are sometimes embarrassed to talk about subjects that are nevertheless vital. I am thinking here of agriculture, nature conservation, natural medicine and leaf doctors (herbalist and shaman, NES). Society constantly has a negative reaction on everything concerning the earth's trades. Even in school, children are portrayed with a shameful image of these professions. The school appears to be training children to become enemies of agriculture. It educates against its values, against inheritances which are however authentic and natural.

However, when the scent of nature is so captivating that one would like to live there all of one's life, one realizes that research on a new way of living on the earth could change the future of the world. I assure you that a good exploitation of land could help many countries cope with the famine that is eating away at them.

Unless we have found a better way to use the cultivable space, the environment gradually releases us reluctantly. This Earth has taken the downward slope towards nothingness. Man has exhausted all available resources such as trees and mines, to the point of sabotaging himself.

My parents won an award that marked their lives forever. With this book, I renew this pride they have experienced. By reminding everyone how good it is to commune with you and with others, how we can all play an important role on this planet, this book serves as a bulwark for all those who believe that a better life is impossible. We need everyone's talent to build a New World. Nothing in life makes sense if our lives, both rich and complementary, cannot be distinguished.

You, who is reading this book and look up thinking of your ideas for renovating and revolutionizing the modern world, know that you are the most beautiful wonder in the world. Many people expect everything to fall into their mouths. **They Send feedback History Saved Community** expects life to renew itself, miraculously, without having to make any effort. They focus on trivialities without taking part in their construction. In the end, the first phase of their life was never passed. It is up to them to decide to cross the line to achieve a perfect existence through hard work and ambition.

I try to accept myself, not as a simple worthless individual, incapable of creating a new world, but as a slightly dusty seed, better than anyone to share values, like a perfume that perfumes its passage. It's not just me on this path. To move forward, however, I am the only one who knows where to go. Luck accompanies me and I am the antidote that will cure all my ills. No one can do it better than me.

Take a second to listen to the palpitations of the muscles in your body, their musicality. The pump that circulates your blood is the sound instrument that justifies your being alive. This is what makes you feel great. It is you in another dimension. What you were in the past was just a glimpse of who you are now. Never do anything for something, rather do it with others. You can also do with yourself. You do not exist if you can't find people to complement you. The world does not belong to anyone other than you. You must live every moment as if you were the master of the world. All lives are made up of a set of diverse elements that are unique to each. Every life is a flower. Learn to smell the differences, the qualities that each person has in them.

Among all these flowers scattered to the four winds and all these differences, sometimes we can manage to identify the person we are. Give your best and you will know who you are. If you want to be happy, don't wait another second. Now you have to start walking the path, this is the sine qua non-condition to reach the goals of your long journey. Everything you can do in life is conditioned by the attitudes you adopt to motivate yourself and others around you. If you don't do what you have to do, know that no one will do it for you.

It's what you put in place right now that can determine your future and all its virtues. If you think that the road is too long or that you do not know it well enough, look around you and you will see that many will ask you for advice and the best strategies to put in place according to you. They will want to take the same route as you, even though you were scared of all the challenges it involved ... After a while, you will realize that you know the route better than anyone.

You don't necessarily need another person, race, or territory to make a difference. The change is in you. You are the result of this change. You are a special species that survives after all. Strength is useless if you are not passionate about life. The strongest are the most passionate. These adapt better to the terrain. Failure does not exist as long as time continues to run. The days go by and are not alike. People seek perfection, but sometimes forget to do something great centered on their value of beauty and kindness. You don't have to move mountains to be useful to the community. It's those who start doing little things that make a difference. It is what can be done today that is difficult.

But with a little time, nothing is impossible. It's the wait that can be a little more difficult. Remember, the door that opens the way to success is yourself! Be open to everything that you do and you will fearlessly enter the big leagues. There is no limit when you have a real mission. It is not about gaining visibility. It's just about becoming more humble, more discreet. The light we need to see the way is thought and good fellowship with ourselves and with others. Some tips for integrating a foreign culture. After that, you will have to face everyday. You will learn a little more about your existence every day. You would so love to have a successful life, to take a new path, but you don't know where to go or how to take the first step.

The next time you feel like taking the first step, think about starting where you were born. There is no better place than where you are now. Start a new phase of your new life today by simply listening to your heart. Triumph will come when you have this confidence. Hearing someone mispronounce your name will know you are you and you will always be yourself despite all the storms. Of course there will always be doubts, but taking a new path means learning a little more about yourself, about your daily obligations. The idea is to get natural benefits without much effort. One might wonder if in the end, we are not wasting a lot of time following others. But in reality, you can just organize yourself a little better and take initiatives to recreate your life.

To recreate a new life, you can always learn from others. It is necessary to acquire new social habits and to shake up the ones that are already established, that is obvious. But when it comes to creation, putting into practice, it is often enough to organize and seize the opportunities that accompany each experience. Here are some tips to make your trip to a new life and new habits a success. This new culture will accompany you throughout your crossing. First, accept the day in its temporary dimension. It is a sharing of energies and vibrations of all kinds. As for you, accept to feel things. Agree to absorb everything around you, everything that shapes your existence and the person you are as a whole. Accept all the facets which make your personality and adopt a behavior by your capacities. Each day is a new day for you. Become a stranger to rediscover this new time in the midst of which you find yourself.

Your passage on Earth is fleeting and you have a lot to understand and learn in order to lead a simple but rich life. You spend whole days doubting the decisions you make. Most of the time, you work a lot to ensure an attractive monthly salary to have a balanced and socially stable life. To get to this first step, you can decide to commit daily to a community. For example, you can start in a family and enjoy all the benefits that this built environment brings. You start from scratch using an improved everyday method to exist. If your goals seem impossible on certain mornings, don't be discouraged. Rather, try to accept the situation, because in any case, you do not have the power to control the context. You may also be subject to unexpected events that you did not expect. Walk the wrong way or be different of the person you aspire to be.

It is part of your metaphysical and spiritual dimension. This is what allows you to build a new canvas to take the lonely path you are in, whether you are popular or not. Whatever happens, every morning a new day dawns. You weren't born knowing everything, but you can learn new things every second that goes by. Second, merge your body and your mind!

This fusion is the combination of sensation and observation. This observation step is essential in the existence of man. It is doubly useful, because it combines the body and the soul with the dimension of the mind and sensations. It allows you to contemplate a set of reactions to give a new creation adapted to the immediate environment of man. Take an example: if you exercise regularly, you naturally feel ready to deal with fatigue and stay in top shape. And if you also pay attention to the signals from your body, you will also make significant progress in learning the human skeleton, not to mention metaphysical. The invisible and chemical side of man. How do we create?

To create yourself is to find yourself in a vile dimension. So much so that imagining how you transform yourself remains a real mystery. The fact remains that you can face everything with your head held high and that you never bow. But to achieve such a result, you must be able to relearn simple things without ever judging.

You have nothing to fix, everything is perfect. Faults are the things that you refused to commit to. But you did it for yourself and for all humility. Creating is very simple. You leave aside all the confusions that disturb your ego to focus only on your integration into the culture of sharing. The idea is to take advantage of the present moment. To transform yourself, you only have to start with your trick by choosing to become the person you want to be.

Then, as if you used a magic wand, you will become master of your transformation and you will feel all the changes taking place in you. We don't put an end to the creation and the finish line is never indicated. Also, you can't know when the transition is coming. Nothing is static. Everything can be completed or changed at any time. The creative and semantic functions that form the language of argument bathe in the light of a new day.

So whatever you want ends up happening and transforming. It is always what men and women need most today. We find ourselves in a circle of rehearsals and learning on a daily basis as well as in a new creation which will aim to reproduce a new world in the image of our expectations. To repeat the same movements is not a sin. Relearning to walk to take a new route is not a defeat. It is commendable to relearn the lesson, with submission and hindsight, to follow up on a disappointment. Fearing the rules is also not cowardice. Rather, it is cultivating respect for others and for yourself.

It's an acceptance of oneself in the ultimate and foreign dimensions of our authentic capacities. We have in our hearts the key that opens the door to a necessary passage for a new start and new creations. Culture imposes habits on us, but in reality, we don't have to have rituals. Every day everything is new. One morning can be very different from another. This is how two great elements of existence converge to give birth to a creation system for each individual.

Fit Me or Not

I SAW MANY CONFUSED PEOPLE AROUND the illusion that life Reconstructed since the day I saw the first tangent of my native culture arrive. Slowly I polish that moment like I had to clean the instrument of wood that I had been set on a path, relaxing my life. It was an improvised moment. One fellow traded the passes with quick-thinking, professional acts. I survived. Sorry, who knows the way I can find a job ? I said. I asked anyone. Excuse me, guys. Do you know where my English can be better how I can learn to speak well, I asked… One of the people volunteered, helping me to find a house only a few miles it was a way my first job. It is where I had my first experience in the kitchen it is where those elderly people lives.

The receptionist said expansively in rapid, Italian-accented jovial, "I am *so* very glad to see you." She had heard from mutual friends that I would be interested in his place to work. These same friends told me that place is the most meditative place. I know is not only the place to work it is also the place to educate your-self. It is nice a beautiful day, I had my first step of the dream I had: find a job. Now I love to know is fit me or not. I had a feeling my roll to that place will fit to the moment. I know any one who starts a Workday…wish to be a happy day… That lady is middle of the age older, shot, caring. She smiles easily. She looks like a real leader or an artist, one who is likeable and engaging. She took me around to the assistance leaving. There a place was construct mores then twenty years with compassion.

I remember a poster that showed three birds apparently well-fed, visibly multicolored, presumably forest birds, coming every day to eat in front the door. The message below it read: "What are you going to do for the world, the ecosystem of the world?" She opened the door and with a gesture offered a peace. "This is my reference place for now but my best it is the nature: outside the door," she said.

Those moments remind me a friend of mine. One day we sat close to each other in what was not more than a closet of a small garden like a room inside the nature. Overflowing plants from each side of the four natural walls. There were plants of all sorts from the world a perfume combination in roses, lavender, cactus and lemon grass. "This is also our natural medicine garden," the lady explained. "We encourage people to coming any time to visit the plants and test anything they wish.

Sometimes the visitors return over and over and sometimes they don't. We get new plants by season or having parties and dances. The price of admission is a plant." She explained his program. She spoke passionately and at length, occasionally pausing for breath. Although my hold on the English language is reasonably secure, I could not always follow here. Here is what I understood: She also works with people of the very poor community. She has generated many projects throughout Africa.

She began his work when he himself was a very young lady, twenty years old. This was in his small country in Africa. That first program continues with the help of women volunteer local staff. She does not believe in school at least as represented by those one sees in poor countries. Instead she creates clubs, situations in which women can come together work on projects particularly in agriculture and the arts, play non competitive games, and engage in active, convivial learning.

Above all, he believes in freedom. He sees learning as a process of transcending one's current situation. "It is a matter of opening door and windows," she said. She therefore places travel at the center of the curriculum of his non-school. His various interactions with each other and women visit back and forth. Travel is a central component. Last time some of the women from Africa spent three days with in USA to see the curiosities. These included the National Museum and a visit with my children from Africa with whom she also works. Some African women's had never been to USA before. They were overjoyed. She believes in transcending all conceivable barriers and frontiers, whether geographic or psychological.

Independent Thinker

FROM THE LITTLE VILLAGE OF La Vallée Jacmel, as Gody I reach is international. Currently I had a project in the Dominican Republic and hoped soon to generate a regular Haïtian-Dominican exchange. I love language. I am fluent in French and Spanish and writes poetry in both. He had just begun to learn English. I was born in Tuff, Haiti, in beautiful La Vallée de Jacmel, the fourth of six children. My loving parents taught me that a good education was important.

The first time we went to Port-au-Prince, I was 12 years old. Where I saw families too poor to send their children to school. Many kids lived in the streets and cemeteries. I wouldn't really want to go to Port-au-Prince. I have more chance to accomplish my goal of future in La Vallée. We do not have any freedom in the city. Most people in Port-au-Prince come from other places. So that's very different. It was a big confusion in my choice living in Port-au-Prince, it was a big challenge for me…any words can describe that jumping: from rural area to the city, we need courage to struggle every day…

I lived all my friends behind me in the land; feeding animals go far away to find water, playing in the garden: I really miss that atmosphere of my land. Only your hearth knows. No body can understand how deep that distance with your lovely land is painful. Even your feet have to be adapted with the concrete road. It's just extremely hard for me to adapted.

I remember the first time I went to Port-au-Prince it was with my dad to make a vest for me. It was before a marriage ceremony of a brother to my godfather; at the time I was ten years. When I arrived in Port-au-Prince my first act was to observe. Imagine the first time we went to a place where you hear any music of birds, any drop of water in the morning even above of the leaves.

I just thinking the basic of things, so the music of birds. All-natural things are made life better; some simple thing no more than a single food, music and flower perfume. All consist mainly of human connection. Every one has a connection with the nature or some things coming to the nature.

I had formed an organization to contain his programs. I call it "Rope of Haitian children". "A rope is composed of many tiny strands,". "Imagine that each of these is a child. By itself it is weak. It comes apart easily when I pull on it. Now imagine a hundred, a thousand such filaments woven together. It is no longer a thread. It is now a powerful rope. It can lift heavy weights. It is almost indestructible."

"Children, are the most oppressed group in the world. But they are separate like the strands." I described children who are pressed into backbreaking labor on sugar cane plantations in the Dominican Republic. "They are slaves." "They work long hours under terrible conditions for virtually no pay."

"Do you know about the 'restavec-yo'?" "These are Haitian children who are simply given away as domestic servants by parents too poor to care for them. The receiving families agree to feed, clothe and educate them in return for their labor but in reality often abuse them." "My goal is to unite children on the basis of their common interest in being treated properly. "Some day, they will all be liberated."

"CODEHA sponsored a kite making contest this year." "In the weeks before Easter, Haïtian boys and sometimes girls, too, make kites." Gestured toward the expanse of the city beyond the library door. There, hundreds of kites could be seen soaring and diving. By example last day two little boys interrupted the course of the time. "We need tissue paper, they said. And then, gave each of them two large sheets, one red and the other, white. "These guys are making kites."

140

"We make lots of things here. Things made by the children." "They are excited to learn whatever we teach them. This is a learning place but not a school. But we do not want to become a traditional Haïtian school. Schools in this country train obedience. They create a slave mentality. Here at CODEHA in everything we do, the children take initiative and come to appreciate their own abilities and intelligence."

"How do you manage all this?" someone asked me. "Surely you must have others who work with you."

"Yes. People volunteer. I cannot pay a salary. Wherever possible, older kids work with the younger ones. But frankly I like to do as much as I can myself. I have my own ways of operating." "How are you funded?" someone asked me.

"We aren't. We are too busy to wait for funding," I said. "I don't have time to write grant proposals or to approach people for money. We do what we must and manage on whatever contributions happen to come our way. UNICEF gave me a tarp for our workshop in the yard. Most important is that the children themselves make things that we can sell."

"We meet here in my family's house now. Eventually we hope to get a place of our own. We will need money for that. It will come. But meanwhile we work with children." "What was your own childhood like?" Someone asked me. "We were poor but not desperately so. But there were times when there was not enough to eat. We worked the land. I have two sisters and three brothers."

"My mother died when I was thirty-eight and then during adolescence, I became very ill. I am still not sure what it was. But it turned out to be a good thing because I was forced to stay in bed where I had nothing to do but read, I was eight. I remember that was excellent for my development. It saved me from having to go to a rigid Haitian school. For some reason I have always been an independent thinker. I could never tolerate arbitrary authority."

At five AM the next morning I picked my friend BOB up at the Hotel. We drove to the bus boarding area that was full of people, shouting, selling things. Gradually, almost imperceptibly, the busses filled. We got into one. I seemed to know half the passengers. I shook hands extravagantly with the men while clapping them on the shoulder and he kissed the women on the cheek or was kissed by them, not seductively but with joy. It was a family scene.

At sometime past eight, the bus coughed, groaned, and lumbered along its precarious way. We were stuffed tightly in. Some people sat in the aisles and others sat by threes in seats that designed for two. It was a long, slow, painful trip. Our vehicle crawled relentlessly up steep hills, leaned out over precarious valleys, and crept across unlikely roads carved from sharp, limestone rocks. BOB legs and backside numbed. BOB and I barely conversed. We arrived at three thirty in the afternoon. It was a voyage of no more than fifty miles.

La Vallée De Jacmel is paradise. The air is fresh, the land is green and abundant with animals—donkeys, horses, goats, and pigs and crops of corn, papaya, oranges, millet and countless other of life's necessities. Nature and centuries of farming elegantly sculpt the hills. The people are gentle and approachable. "Do people go hungry in La Vallée?" BOB asked.

"Only at certain times of the year when we get little or no rain." That may happen in late April or May. But, although all of here are poor, usually we eat." I have always observed others a child's walking around. Naturally, the environment we use to lives was good culturally with the family. Cultivators, plants from vegetables and animals. When I was in elementary school, I remember we had in the neighborhood agriculture center; the director of that center was an agronomist who loved to motivate people to become responsible leaders. I used those examples to transform my existence in the field of leadership and agriculture motivator.

I used any opportunity around me to help people. Help people to discover them selves as a key to change the community to become a big house where we living a harmony. I started to visit different family to understand their culture. I was founded a way to sit-down with them. Raised long-time friends and transform that friendship as a culture to work, to play, to shear ideas and tolerate each other. Try to understand they dreams, how those dreams can be a reality and then used in diary history to built life.

That's why when I started to meet those families. I was observed and catch different situation to understand and create a new opportunity to help. Unfortunately, most of those communities I was involved don't had a leader, who decided their interests. Doing things with them was difficult; we had to create a new concept. I was born poet. My family came from a passion traditional haitian farmer of hold fashon agriculture. My mother was a talor.

We're very happy that you made a wonderful trip and the project went well. Your report is detailed and helpful in all our expectations moving forward. Communication has once more proved to be a very powerful tool when used appropriately.

We've been faced with very difficult times but this not the end of it, we may have to overcome other rocky situations in the future. We're getting to know each other better and the ride will eventually get smoother, if we accept to respect and invest trust in each other. There's nowhere we can go and nothing we can do if we do not trust each other.

We all have very good intentions and I'm convinced of the goods we can bring to the wolrd. Our cultural differences can be understood but deep inside we are who we are. Thinking of changing cultural habbits is a lost war before we even get on the battle field; we instead need to understand them.

I realize that the best way to help a community to succeed is with connection of people to their environment. Encourage people to connect with the nature, keep hem wear of that nature also help hem to believe that nature is their pharmacy, the first available food market, incomparable source of energy we need. Since that time, I have dreamed of becoming a Herbalist to understand myself and those around me, to understand the raison that cause certain disorders and find the solution.

My house is about a mile from the main road straight down a steep hillside and then along an uncertain yellow dirt path. It is a small, whitewashed cement building with a tin roof and French doors that were painted bright green. These were opened wide during the day and shut at night. The house has only one tiny window set in a side room. It remained shuttered throughout my visit. In total there are four small rooms and an outhouse.

Surrounding the house are carefully tended fields of corn. Rabbit hutches are set behind it but only one is being used right now because my parents are visiting relatives in the United States—Boston—and are unable to take care of them. This house is the center of CODEHA's activities. Children from settlements throughout the area come. They learn to garden and participate in arts and crafts, music, writing and other activities. After some time, the children took a trip to Port-au-Prince.

I showed my friend a new coffee plants the children are growing. I explained that currently one hundred and twenty-seven local children are involved. There are others who participate in a second center further down the valley and a great many, an increasing number, in Port-au-Prince. His dream is to have cultural centers of this sort everywhere in Haïti.

"It is essential that children have a place where they are accepted fully and where their creative expressions are valued." I am a poet and an artist as well as an educator in the progressive mode. I believe in dialog. Rather than punish a child, I talk with him or her, usually in a small group where the issues impinging on the misbehavior are clarified and the motivations of the child are explored. "I try to create a group that is strong, supportive and positive; a group a child can trust. Such a group expands conceptually as it develops and takes on more functions."

I work internationally crossing all conventional frontiers including class, race and nationality. I had generated exchange programs with children from the Dominican Republic. "The group with which I am ultimately concerned is all of mankind," I continued. "We are all on this earth together.

We need each other. We are part of each other, part of every human being in the world and they are part of us."

Nature, too, is central to my philosophy. I believe that all children, particularly those who live in big cities need to be brought close to nature. "They need, "to have the sense of being at one with all of life. When they live in accordance with that realization, there will be peace.

"How can there be violence in a person who plants corn and avocados and raises animals?" "It is a contradiction. It is impossible."

"Where did you grow up, Gody?" BoB asked me.

"Right here," I said, "in La Vallée De Jacmel."

La Vallée De Jacmel

WHAT DOES LA VALLÉE MEAN?

The origin of the word "Valley" is not officially known to designate this mountainous area. La Vallée is an old vacation spot for French settlers, and it was a word used by French priests of the time who, when they crossed the great Saint-Antoine river which is now called Dumez, located at Leaving Jacmel, said: "Let us cross the valley. "This space exists since it corresponds to the place that separates the city from this mountain called Valley by chance, but whose name has remained firmly rooted in language habits.

Jacmel is a commune in Haiti, the capital of the Sud-Est department and the capital of the Jacmel arrondissement. The commune of La Vallée is located between the towns of Jacmel and detained. As a capital, La Vallée is 27 km from Jacmel. Despite its name, it is a set of small valleys and plateaus and it culminates at an altitude of 800 meters above the level of the Caribbean Sea, dominating the bay of Bainet to the confines of the peninsula of the Dominican Republic of Bahoruco. Due to the altitude, it enjoys a relatively temperate climate, although sometimes wet, which vacationers love. To get to La Vallée, you must, from Jacmel, take the national road 4 in the direction of Port-au-Prince, and branch off shortly after on the left. The road winds up and it takes a good hour by car to reach this mountain village with pretty houses. In the Caribbean southeast of Haiti, colonization has left behind an organized people, a diverse culture thanks to its population of different origins that has far exceeded its borders. This territory is still divided into several areas of habitation which were called tribes in Indian times and which have been marked by various community actions.

146

The people of the Valley have a very efficient system of organization based essentially on the value of the inhabitants of the area. Each area or neighborhood in the village has its laws and customs that have endured for years. With the Valléens, each house in the area constitutes an independent element and is managed by a council of elders and by people who have social influence, elected by the population.

However, the inhabitants of La Vallée disregard the presence of the central power and continue to keep the territory of the Valley under their control through organizations corresponding to different dwellings, placing them under the ideological powers of the living force of the area. The valley community has gradually become autonomous with a system of generalized cooperation under the responsibility of each individual in the community. The Valléens were able to resist with the infrastructure they built themselves thanks to the financial contributions. La Vallée has a model of collective education, centered on the community and which allows the population to grow and solve their problems alone, to have a better knowledge of reality and to be able to share it with the community. Schools, therefore, become a learning guide for improving the lives of people, and schools are seen as a space where the community can share each other's ideas, and where all are equal.

Of all the municipalities in Haiti, La Vallée is the strongest municipality in terms of organizational structure. It is one of the very few areas in the country to have preserved its autonomy for more than a century. The Jacmel Valley is the perfect destination for the first trip to Haiti. Besides, there is a good chance that this first trip will not be the last. It is easy to immerse yourself in the cultural bath of the City of Jacmel and catch the virus of conviviality! The look of artistic works is contagious, Jacmelian art is a plate filled with the many cultural tendencies of the southeast of Haiti.

The region has everything to please. From exotic art to spirituality, passing by a charming and smiling population, beaches and rivers suspended on the sides of mountains like music clocks, mountains, hills, valleys or still a plateau … Anyway! A canvas decor for this mountain village called La Vallée.

You can discover magnificent stone monuments, natural musical routes, foliage tickled by the gentle wind of the Caribbean Sea, and enjoy a comfortable environment for tourist adventures, or even transport to 'extraordinary quality with its winding roads. Everyone takes a look at it with ecstasy, and it's a real pleasure!

At first glance, the huge mountain picture can cause a great shock. However, with use, one quickly falls in love with this simple nature. On a horseback ride or a tap-tap, a van lost in a setting of a traveling muse, to visit the blue basin and the ravine that separate the town of Jacmel and La Vallée, you can stop to taste a good dish of fried food by the roadside the (fritaille) is a traditional Haitian dish composed of green bananas, sliced and then fried, also called weighed bananas, NES), accompanied by a pikliz (spicy cabbage and carrot salad, NES) in a itinerant restaurant. This, naturally at your own risk, but to avoid catching a virus, just avoids raw vegetables and drinks any water! If you respect these instructions, we are convinced that this adventure will please you. The rest of the trip will take place in the mountains of La Vallée, offering itself as a dish on a furnished table.

In La Vallée, it is easy to communicate with the farmers and settle the formalities necessary to access the surroundings of the area without taking the slightest risk. Most people end up in La Vallée to escape the heaviness of the city heat, and we cannot blame them! For them, the valley community has developed a form of proverbial communication suitable for everyone, and families are ready to receive people regardless of their origin, region or country even if until the end of the 20th century, the valley tourist market was not yet very developed. There are still areas to explore in terms of social structures, but it is an organized community in almost every neighborhood with groups of people who inhabit the area.

The Valley perched on a mountain overlooking the Caribbean Sea near Jacmel and Bainet offers all-inclusive packages to other coastal areas of Haiti including hospitality, sand, and sun. As the beaches of Jacmel are among the most beautiful in Haiti, the decision seems completely justified. It is, therefore, possible to spend a week or two in Jacmel in complete isolation, seeing the country only around his home, its end of the beach, the quiet town, and the surrounding areas. However, the region has a lot to offer. La Vallée, a cooperative stronghold in Haiti is said to be one of the most beautiful villages in the country. Despite the absence of major infrastructure, many neighborhoods are organizing. Where efforts to energize are evident, in the districts of La Vallée, there is always an old man to tell you stories under the fragile gaze of the moon and the millions of stars.

The Valley has no beaches, but rivers orchestrated with a musicality of stones that spin under the pressure of the water. On the course of the rivers, one can easily imagine the gleams of a diamond and when the rays of the holy sun open their eyes, The Valley is superb! Besides, there is so much to observe that to satisfy all your desires, you have no other choice than to want to stop the time that shakes you and that makes the task titanic, even impossible. What we can say is that La Vallée has an incomparable charm. There is a very pleasant atmosphere, like everywhere in the country, which is due in large part to the open and warm character of the Haitian population. It is possible to visit La Vallée from the excursions offered by all the community organizations in the districts of the valley area. It is also easy to get there on your own, as the area has a good traffic network.

In the center of the community as in the whole area, several neighborhoods, rivers, mountains, waterfalls, caves, and other remarkable things are worth a visit. These include, among others, Bassin Bleu, Séjourné. The caves, rivers, and waterfalls, in addition to the freshness of the trails, are included in the list of tourist sites in the area.

At noon, the cave of good health is also worth a detour. To visit La Vallée is also to be confronted with the results of an organizational revolution that strongly influenced the contemporary valley era. On the one hand, it is clear that the region has an excellent system of organization and education.

The Valléens will tell you however that if they have an exemplary organization throughout the country and benefit from a sufficient number of motivated and competent people, they are in dire need of financial means to develop and keep up with technology. For the rest, the Valléens must organize themselves daily despite their needs to advance towards development in almost all areas.

Little little-known locality and still far from the big development machine, Le Morne à Brûler is not without interest, even if it does not have particularly attractive infrastructures and its rivers and waterfalls are not as large of these regions much more open to visitors. The region, like many of its neighbors, has experienced its share of social exclusion. And even if Le Morne à Brûler remains rather poor, it seems, however, to fare better than its neighbors in terms of cultural conservation with its popular music, the Rara. In the shadow of its musical event, the neighborhoods mobilized as if to build a cathedral and took the opportunity to express their joys and their everyday sorrows. This music is of historical inspiration and has a very advanced spiritual dimension.

The activity is feverish around outdoor markets, colorful and very crowded, but, on the outskirts, the urban density is lighter and the population seems rather proud of its musical activities more focused on their lifestyle since they reflect their story through songs hummed on kilometers of roads cluttered with stones and sometimes mud.

If the districts of Morne à Brûler are not particularly remarkable, on the other hand, the countryside is incredibly beautiful. In the country festivals of this church, Mont Camelle is particularly interesting in July. On a crowd of pilgrims from everywhere, the beauty of the landscape blossoms, the road winds gently through a mountainous landscape and we come across several natural and pleasant pictures. All superlatives are allowed when it comes to Ridoré, a fascinating region if there is one.

More than a century ago, this hitherto very closed region barely opened to other regions in the area, and the presence of public services and that of congregational schools made heads turn. The rider has changed since then, much changed. At the time of the creation of the parish, people were already pointing their index finger in the walls of Rider. From the police station to Timari, at the high school founded by the inhabitants of the community and built on this summit, one can easily overlook the Caribbean Sea and look at Jacmel in front of you. The eyes have taken the place of telescopic observation machines on this plateau, which can be presented as a large house with several bedrooms and different public services. Narrow alleys where a good part of the population lived surround this plateau and give the city a strange silhouette.

We realize that the former inhabitants of this plateau were not among those travelers like the nostalgic gypsies who move around daily and who constantly complain about time or space. There were no markets for tourists so that the people who lived in this area could hold on to a financial return. The city and its center appear poor in the eyes of foreigners who would often be ready to invest their money to live a healthy adventure, deprived of all reception facilities, but happy, far from the consumer society.

Paternalistic comments are very frequent among travelers. Those present in the city would like the weather and the normal evolution of things to also bring rays of sunshine to this population. People keep arguing to change the face of the area. However, in the so-called developed countries, they are not lucky enough to have an advanced organizational structure like that of La Vallée de Jacmel.

Ridore therefore changes at a sick turtle pace and remains hell for all those who want to see progress sing in all areas and, let us face it, some changes are not all happy. But many aspects of Ridore come from a civilization of macabre centenarians. Time evolves, but people do not change their mentality, they refuse to progress. The built-in city, the great walls, the temple of 1910 remain immutable with their remarkable architecture, and under a plaintive sky, thousands of pilgrims come each year from everywhere to celebrate Saint John the Baptist.

Ridoré has always fascinated and rightly arouses curiosity. It is a complex universe, of an unknown cultural richness, and which will probably always remain surrounded by mysteries for the visitors of this small plate which one finds at the top of The Valley. At first glance, one would be tempted to think that these walls dating back over a century trap the Ridoré area. We must not be afraid of getting lost in the panoramic vision that it offers to its visitors, and on the human relations side, we should not hesitate to forge links with this open, warm and always ready to contact population. And, as we already knew, the reception of Haitians is one of the best in the country and the area.

Even if sometimes they are closed, the doors are always open to the world, to tell a story, drink a coffee, share a glass of wine made from local fruits. The best cocktail in the world! It is no coincidence that the plateau is one of the most visited places in the area, it is just because the center of public activities and the large market built by the people are in Ridoré.

From Ridoré and particularly from its mountain slopes, it is easy to observe the whole area and to see more easily how one can organize a hike to other tourist and mountainous destinations up to the waterfalls. One can, for example, easily organize a trip to the Blue Basin or Brazilian Bainet. Visiting Blue Basin is a dream. It is a mystical and magical place. It is one of the basins of the country that, in strong sensory experiences, is of great richness and all the senses are used to contemplate the space. The Blue Basin is an extremely curious space in its design. The different spaces are like containers constructed expressly by human hands so that in certain places, water spills out like in a swimming pool without anyone knowing where it comes from. There are three pools in single file of a depth that have not yet been determined today. Voodoo ceremonies often took place at the edge of this legendary pool.

But let us go back to the plateau to admire the infinite beauty of this area called Nanmari. On the north side, one can observe the valleys and hills of Laviale de Kalacou. There are no large rivers here, rather small streams that cling to the mountain railings. Women, early, enter the trade and travel on trucks decorated like Christmas trees. On their stalls, the goods punctuate countless spots of color, an already vivid landscape background. Laviale has a very sunny landscape and offers a nuanced decor of mango, banana and coffee leaves. Raising animals is difficult and this population still faces the greatest risks in obtaining certain animals such as oxen, goats and donkeys in order to transport their goods. Driving in this area is also dangerous given the terrain.

On the other hand, we still have the chance to observe rare birds like guinea fowl. We can hear the bursts of voices rising from the mountains trodden by travelers, including that of women who travel every day9 at 10 kilometers round trip, and who sigh when they are tired; also hear the trumpets sounding in the hollow stomachs of the children on the hunger corridors or the barking of the dogs which do not give a chance to the silence of a morning since these women must wake up very early to go to the markets in different places, each day of the week. Laviale is an arid area that is not as fortunate as to produce certain vegetables that require too much water for their development.

Ridoré is a very fragrant village: the scent of jasmine and the aroma of spices fight against the smell of the flames of skyrocketing animal skins at the slaughterhouse still unfinished to this day. The population is proud to spare their children this pollution from the city of Port-au-Prince where the peasants usually send their children.

The central village of The Jacmel Valley is a very tasty landscape: in addition to the free, there is the pork griot which, cooked with a little chili, warms the mouth from the first bite. A small fire that quickly spreads throughout the digestive system! You should also know that the food served in the traveling boats of the merchants of free has nothing to do with the food served in the Haitian restaurants where the flavors are much sweeter. A glance at the past and the recent history of the valley region shows that La Vallée gave birth there and trained great men in various fields of human activity.

When we focus our attention on education, we can say that among these great men were born a cardinal, generals, ministers, directors and finally creators, thinkers, and founders ... Let us stop there, a book would not be enough. The movement of time that forms the years and the centuries separates the history and the life of these visionary men. They already belong to legend thanks to their sense of community organization.

"What did your parents do for a living?"

"They were *cultivateurs,* farmers, like everyone else here. Peasants."

"I don't understand," I said. "You talk and think like a university intellectual, yet you come from this remote peasant village where probably most people are illiterate. How did that happen?"

"I think credit may be given to my illness. For much of my childhood, I had to remain in bed. To this day it's not clear what was wrong with me. I saw many doctors. Maybe it was psychological. But I had little energy; my stomach was upset. Often my eyes became watery and I couldn't see. So, I lay there quietly, thinking. I read a lot whenever I could find a book. I read everything that came my way. Maybe that's what made me different. But, you know, I am not so different. I am really a peasant like everyone else here. The only thing unusual about me is that I am a peasant accustomed to expressing my thoughts. I love words. I love language. I love poetic expression.

"I spent two months in the Dominican Republic where I learned Spanish. I am now learning English. I write poems. I wrote a book of poems in Spanish and many poems in my native Créole and French, my second language. I communicate in every way I can with people and with nature."

We toured the community. We hiked a mile or more back up the steep mountain to the main, dirt road and then along it and down again in another direction until we reached the town center. We visited the large, active market that was clean and obviously prosperous compared with other markets I've seen in this country.

Then I took BOB to see the hospital and medical dispensary. It was a simple, dignified cement building, constructed by community labor and administered by Catholic nuns. Many people sat waiting to be served. The staff consisted only of two doctors, three nurses and three social workers. Basic medical equipment was minimal. If a person requires an operation, he or she must be brought to Jacmel fifteen miles away on dreadful roads. But compared to what exists in most Haïtian communities, this center was adequate. I again shook hands, slapped shoulders, and kissed cheeks everywhere we went. One might think I'm a politician, but I claim to have no interest. It was rather as if he were everyone's son, brother or father. His high spirits were infectious.

I was happy to be home and people were happy to have me back. The reunion takes place weekly. I live in Port-au-Prince, but I visits La Vallée every Saturday to conduct the CODEHA program.

Next, we dropped in at the town hall and met with the mayor and two of his assistant mayors. And then we visited a home for retired teachers where a fine old gentleman who had a central role in developing the town greeted us. He was a member on the committee that built the school, constructed the public marketplace, created the hospital, improved the road and organized the credit union. He was the most progressive and appreciated leader of the town, elected or otherwise.

It was dark as we stumbled along the paths back to my house. I carried a flashlight for my benefit and used it from time to time. An elaborate dinner was waiting for us. It was prepared by Daniel, a adopted brother, a man taken in by the family when he was having a hard time. He served us breadfruit, potatoes, beef and various vegetables. It was delicious but BOB was too tired for serious eating. At nine o'clock BOB was a sleep.

Morning. BOB took a Haïtian shower. Water is a valuable resource here in La Vallée De Jacmel. There is a cement cistern behind the house that catches the flow from the roof during the rainy season through a simple but efficient network of gutters. Most families cannot afford this system. For them water must be hauled in buckets from springs far away on the heads of little girls. When there is no rain, every family must use the springs.

I handed BOB a dishpan and a plastic cup. I opened the cistern's spigot and poured a half bucket of sun warmed water into the pan which BOB then carried along with a piece of soap and the cup to a roofless stone cubicle a few feet away. A green lizard crept along the wet back wall. A tiny yellow bird flitted overhead. BOB poured three cups of that water over my body while soaping myself thoroughly. BOB then used what remained in the pan, cup by cup, to wash the soap away. BOB emerged, refreshed and reasonably clean, pleased that BOB had consumed but a fraction of the precious liquid that BOB would have at home while dumbly unconscious of its value.

As BOB sit typing in my tiny dining room. BOB look out the open French doors at the bright mountain morning and then see a peasant hoeing in a nearby cornfield. A boy is cutting weeds with a sickle. A rooster crows here and there and then there again. A horse tethered between the house and the outhouse, called a *"watay"* in Créole. Sounds to BOB like "water."

Popcorn Words

LAST NIGHT BEFORE GOING TO BED, BOB thought I had said, "Use the water for a toilet." When BOB looked puzzled, I showed him the outhouse. Two donkeys are tethered in a neighboring field, as are a goat and a black and brown cow with long horns that lows piteously. Birds soar, dive and sing.

There are thousands of red hibiscus blossoms between the cornfield and the path to the house. Peas are planted among the corn stalks. There are numerous banana and mango trees, and pineapple and avocado plants. Everything seems to be growing well. A great artist has been painted the landscape a delightful shade of green. Unlike much of the rest of Haïti, life is well sustained here.

The morning began slowly. BOB sat in the sun and wrote. We got around to breakfast at ten. BOB and I chatted. BOB has trouble following me. I speak quickly especially when I get worked up. BOB French is okay but not that great.

I see myself as offering a framework, an *"encadrement,"* around the lives of the children. I think it is necessary to build a group with which the children can come to feel a sense of belonging and commitment. Such a group should resemble a democratic family, a community that is both a reflection of and a stimulus to the cohesion of the larger, natural community in which the children and ultimately all of us are immersed.

I believe that the arts are vital for children. But to be educated properly, they must become immersed in all of nature as well. I think that children should learn to create for the sake of realizing the beauty that is within them. And, not unimportantly, to learn skills by which they might earn a living.

"I am," Gody continued, "opposed to all coercion and violence. If a child transgresses, we engage him or her in a dialog involving the entire group. All those affected by the incident--including the offending child--would be encouraged to understand what happened in all of its dimensions, both from the point of view of the child him or her self and from that of those in the larger community."

As I speak, I gestures excitedly with my hands, sometimes spreading my arms wide apart, palms up, raising them toward the sky. A beatific expression comes over my face like a man who has found his god. But I'm not motivated by religion. Although raised a Catholic, I insists that I work with kids simply because the work is interesting. "I like kids," I explained to BOB. "All kids. Who is to say why? It is also a matter of justice.

There is no reason why poor children, *les défavorisées*, should not have the same opportunities in life as everyone else. Therefore, one might see my work not as a religious calling, but rather a humanistic one."

"How did you begin?" BOB asked to me.

"My first involvement with kids was when I myself was twelve years old. I made friends with *"restavek yo,"* children who are given to families to rise in exchange for their labor. Sometimes the arrangement works out well but often the children are exploited badly. I met with them, got to know them and learned their stories." We talked for almost two hours and then, because BOB got so little sleep yesterday, BOB eyelids began to flicker. "Do you need to rest?" I asked BOB.

"BOB need to catch their breath a bit and catch up on their notes. What you said was interesting and important. BOB want to write down everything so he wont forget." BOB computer battery was getting low and, since there is no electricity in this town, he decided to record with pen and paper as all people once did. As he began they're writing, three children drifted by one after the other. First to arrive was graceful, age thirteen, and shortly afterward her sisters showed up, bright-eyed, seven, and finally, pensive, nine. They stared at BOB and smiled.

Welcome to Codeha
CODEHA (Corde Enfant Haitien)

Hello,

I am writing on behalf of my daughter, who is already at La Vallée. She came to Haiti to work as a volunteer with children, but she also wanted tointerview Haitian teenagers about their hopes and dreams. For her project she wants to spend two weeks in La Vallée instead.

She is an experienced volunteer (Soweto, South Africa, one month in 2009 at age 15), an assistant kindergarten teacher for her job in the USA and an excellent dancer. She will of course perform any work the community needs, but she is very skillful at getting children and teenagers to find creative ways to have fun with games, music, art. She can teach English or dance or help in any other way the community might need.

The difficulty I see for her in La Vallée is she does not speak any Creole and only a little French. For her project, the interview questions are not too difficult, but the answers may be harder to understand. She intends to videotape each interview. If CADEHA accepts her proposal, perhaps if she could get some translation help asking the questions and someone to hold her video camera, then she can translate the answers from the video back in the USA.

This is very unusual and bad timing, but she is hoping since she is already there and willing to work, CODEHA can help her work it out. The results of her study could be beneficial for CODEHA. She is scheduled to fly out of PAP Haïti. I can be reached by phone or email any time of day or night to answer any questions. Thank you, CODEHA is a old grass root Organization founded by Godfroy Boursiquot (Gody) who's alwas in Haiti preparing for a week long celebration of the Summer Camps that are sponsored and organized with the collaboration of our community. When CODEHA was founded in 1992, the main focus was to work with street children. Gody, a journalist by trade has dedicated most of his life providing assistance and literacy to street children in Port au Prince and all-around Haiti and the Dominican Republic. He has traveled around the world in a quest for a better life for youth.

Political and social instability, and natural disaster have forced him off his path. Over the years, CODEHA has established its actions and focus primarily in La Vallee). The population of La Vallée used to be very engaged in the development of their community, but politics and poverty have created a certain laisser-aller. CODEHA has become more oriented toward rebuilding the community with the participation of all the active sectors.

Children continue to be our focus because we believe they are the leaders of tomorrow. We invest a lot in building trust and values in the children we work with. We're convinced that empowering the people is key in their development and success. CODEHA has been engaged in Agriculture, Education and Social Development. Our children raised livestocks and grew vegetables that are sold at the market to pay for their education.

After the earthquake, we were touched by the image of Valléen peasants on the side of the main road with bags under their arms waiting for food delivery. This is not the community that we grew up in. Something unfortunately has been taking away from these people, their pride. At CODEHA, we feel obligated to address and start a solution to the problems.

Our first action was to analyze our situation, our community, and compare it to the rest of the world affected by famine. We remember the food crisis of 2008 and realized it may just be an alert to what is to come. Most of the countries that have been receiving humanitarian help in the form of food have become completely dependent and famine has found its way to settle within these populations.

They have adapted to the situation, encouraged by political corruption. Hand-outs have become a way of life for millions. If a meal can be given to every member of a family every day for 365 days, there is no need for that family to cultivate their land. We realized once more that the future of our community is our responsibility. Our moto became: "We need to build where we are with our own values". To this day most of our activities rotate around this idea.

We decided to engage in developing agriculture in La Vallée at a larger scale. But the landscape of La Vallée does not offer much of a choice, it's very mountainous. Nevertheless, Valléens used to produce enough food to feed their families and sell the surplus. Drought and deforestation have changed all the parameters. The farmers who continue to practice farming with pride do not have the manpower any more. Most of the able youth have chosen to immigrate to the Dominican Republic to work on sugar cane plantation. The remaining are driving motorcycle taxi in Port au Prince, Jacmel or La Vallee. Today most of our land are not cultivated and food have become a very luxurious item in a lot of regions.

It will take time to really make a change in the practice of agriculture in La Vallée. We have elected to start with the children of today. A new concept of agriculture is being presented to them in this new format "The School Garden" developed by CODEHA. It will add some prestige to the practice of agriculture in the region. Agronomists will visit ourSchool Gardens and present training on how to raise livestock and cultivate the land. Local farmers will come to present their own way of doing things. The children who are going to become farmers will benefit from the two concepts. Food production will no longer be our problem but....

In order to develop agriculture, we need a key element, "Water". Water is rare in La Vallée, this is the reason why we'd like to make it our entry point.

Where You Are?

CODEHA SUMMER CAMP, TAKES PLACE IN 5 locations in LaVallee. The residents of the community help organize these summer camp serving 1,000 Haitian children. CODEHA volunteers from the community and volunteers from several countries come together with a commitment to build themselves along with the youth of LaVallee that they serve during the summer months.

The importance of knowing where you are. The local CODEHA organizers want to be sure that volunteers are not only serving the people of LaVallee but are also serving and growing within themselves. Everyone has a reason why they are here and a goal for each action they take. In acknowledging this together they can shape the outcome and open themselves up to assist in achieving the goals of others. In the days spent at CODEHA with the Haitian volunteers, volunteers from other countries, the children, and teachers are given the opportunity to grow mentally, physically, spiritually, and emotionally.

'Build who you are, where you are'," are the words of Gody Boursiquot founder of CODEHA. "Our children and community have such spirit, talent and determination. We want to help them find that beauty inside and encourage them to share it with the international volunteers. We know learning and growth is going to happen on both sides."

Plans and organizing of the Summer Camp is ongoing and lead by CODEHA founder Gody with the help of local school principals, teachers, and parents in LaVallee. They have already set up committees and are preparing the logistics of feeding, organizing activities for, and creating a fun learning environment where their children can explore nature, language, art, sports and much more with the international volunteers. There is a strong commitment from the community toward the success of the camp.

Community members are currently meeting to plan for the international volunteers who will be staying at the homes of residents within the community where they are serving this way the volunteer will actively participate in a cultural exchange. The hope is that the volunteer will experience the culture, traditions and challenges of living in Haiti, and that the community members will also benefit from this living arrangement by learning about the volunteer's country and culture.

The message Gody preaches is, it is not about bringing anything, it's about the gift-less exchange, sharing in the experience together. Always while traveling, we must embrace and cherish the raw, heart to heart, cross-cultural connections; we all have something to share.

In What I Believe

I DO NOT BELIEVE IN SCHOOL at least as represented by those one sees in the world of discrimination. Instead I create clubs, situations in which children can come together work on projects particularly in agriculture and the arts, play non competitive games, and engage in active, convivial learning.

Spent time in the days with the children to see the space he lives. These included the nature and a visit with children from place to place with hem it's also works. The country kids had never been to the city before. Take the time to visit. I believe in transcending all conceivable barriers and frontiers, whether geographic or psychological.

Above all, I believe in freedom. I believe learning as a process of transcending one's current situation. I believe as a connection of culture. It is a matter of opening door and windows. Life is movement learning is traveling. His various interact with each other and children visit back and forth. Travel is a central component.

Currently I have a project with people to different country's and hopes to generate permanently a regular exchange to the people. I love languages and communicate. I am fluent in different languages and write poetry in those mediums. Every day it is like I just begun to learn any thing around me. I am founder a organization to contain his programs. I call it, "CODEHA," an acronym for *"Corde Enfant Haïtien," Rope* of Haitian children.

A rope is composed of many tiny strands. Imagine that each of these is a child. By itself it is weak. It comes apart easily when I pull on it. Now imagine a hundred, a thousand such filaments woven together. It is no longer a thread. It is now a powerful rope. It can lift heavy weights. It is almost indestructible. Children are the most oppressed group in the world. But they are separate like the strands. I can explain children who are pressed into backbreaking labor on sugar cane plantations in the Dominican Republic. They are slaves. They work long hours under terrible conditions for virtually no pay. Like I know about "the *restavec-yo*".

These are Haitian children who are simply given away as domestic servants by parents too poor to care for them. The receiving families agree to feed, clothe and educate them in return for their labor but in reality, often abuse them. My goal is to unite children based on their common interest in being treated properly. Some day, with a flourish, they will all be liberated. We make lots of things. They are excited to learn whatever we teach them. This is a learning place but not a school.

They learn to garden and participate in arts and crafts, music, writing and other activities. But we don't want to become a traditional Haïtian school. Schools in this country train obedience. They create a slave, dependent mentality. At CODEHA in everything we do, the children take initiative and come to appreciate their own abilities and intelligence. To manage all this I have others who work with me. People volunteer. I cannot pay a salary. Wherever possible, older kids work with the younger ones. But frankly I like to do as much as I can myself. I have my own ways of operating.

From the little village of La Vallee Jacmel, i reach is international. La Vallée Jacmel is paradise. The air is fresh, the land is green and abundant with animals, donkeys, horses, goats, and pigs--and crops of corn, papaya, oranges, millet and countless other of life's necessities. Nature and centuries of farming elegantly sculpt the hills. The people are gentle and approachable.

We are too busy to wait for funding. I do not have time to write grant proposals or to approach people for money and receive deception or humiliation. We do what we have to and manage on whatever contributions happen to come our way. Most important is that the children themselves make things that we can sell. We meet here in my family's house now. Eventually we hope to get a place of our own. We will need money for that. It will come. But meanwhile we work with children. My own childhood like a poor but not desperately so. But there were times when there was not enough to eat. We worked the land. I have two sisters; three brothers and two adopt brothers.

My mother died when I was thirty-eight and my Dad died when I was forty-eight then during adolescence I became very ill. I am still not sure what it was. But it turned out to be a good thing because I was forced to stay in bed where I had nothing to do but read. That was excellent for my development. It saved me from having to go to a rigid Haitian school. For some reason I have always been an independent thinker. I could never tolerate arbitrary authority. I saw life in everything around me. My work it was an improvised action. And starting likes a game of cards with any situation to create a new approach to adapt my self. I asked my self many time: Do you know where and who you are Gody? I need all the time that question to create my strategies.

In 2004 I worked in Haïti Port-Au-Prince making prevention disease for the kids leaving in the street, inform and educate. I worked my way into a big position of social work manager for that organization medical...I traveled and spoke all over the place where the kids are in the street and talk to them in Theys culture of the moment. In 2008 my mother was dying quickly of lung cancer and at the same time, a woman I loved deeply told me he found another man and that our marriage and relationship living together; was over, it was then, that my daughter left me literally with here mom: I was devastated.

To some people on the outside they say my life has been difficult, even my kids are confused that my life can be so challenging while theirs now is not so difficult. I wanted them to have an easier time and so alone their whole life. I made it happen for their future, I pushed them; at the times to their age; but now they understand, and I am so proud and grateful for them. Everything I have: I must give to the people...

For many years all my family, live traditionally as if in another world, another community on the conservations where the people placed them so many decades ago: I have done powerful times with my people...I was told years ago that I would have to leave everything I know and everyone I love and go far away to be with the people that need my help...so many years later 2004 I applied and was accepted into the organization (ATDK Monde) invited me to go to Peru. I knew ATDK Monde was the "way" the reason I was going. I was placed in a most challenging community young people in Cusco. I was soon with the Community....as you can imagine after with many challenging situations some dangerous, some heartbreaking. All beautiful and enriching for my life. With ATDK Monde I was happy in spite of all the development and successes I can't stay longer.

I was Peruvian I became one with the people I was serving. Peace people like that! my name Gody sound more than any seasonal bird on the farm. I was respected by the chief's family of the village I am still part of this community learn how to speak 'Quechua' and more!!!...when I returned to Haïti in January of 2005 my life has changed completely, my perspective of life.

I did not know what I am to do now. I applied and interviewed to do many jobs and nothing. I do not know why, except when I came to (Plan De Parrainage). When I read how some people do jobs that they are happy to work to support her family.

I have done this too, and still will being grateful for the work, but I could not understand if all the jobs I applied for it, like some people I am overqualified yet I'm happy to work. My wish is to work with the underserved, the homeless, the refugee population, children, and families. Those who have HIV/AIDS positive, children live in the cemetery. I want to continue to serve. I have nothing yet I have everything in my mind.

My nickname is Gody it means big piece...the story was the times I was borne an old lady gave me that name. She was a friend of my Dad's, she lived in Jacmel at the time my mom was sick, she was at the hospital and that lady was open the house door for us and she always staid next to the people who need her help". I am moved to tearful there is so much to say, is good tears. I am Happy Grateful to see people engage and learn about others. My pleasure so far, I have learned that my Dad and mom are wise and give me a very Bright Light about myself and people around me. I have an endearing Spirit that draws Beauty to my life. I have learned that I have met people for a reason. Many reasons I suppose.

For each time we speak or visit people so that I can learn more about myself and the reasons we exist and met others. It is not an easy life yet. I am grateful and yes there is a reason I lost my Dad my mom: everything that has happened in my life has brought me to now. All these moments taught me to see with my entire being not only with my eyes to speak with my entire being not only my voice to listen with my entire being, not only my ears by this.

I have learned that we are all in this life together and we all have a story. I have learned to walk my talk to walk with truth honor integrity and humility. There are so many twists and turns and mountains and valleys on the road of life. I know you to hwo read me now know all these things I say and sometimes I get very afraid, but I keep moving forward anyway. I can feel it in you hwo read me now: Yes. I know this… Did you look at inside of you yet? I'm also beginning to understand: why. One of the reasons I wrote that book…is: I needed to meet you as reader: that is why I saw the light in you as I told you coming back from your source.

I am a sort of bridge, I also connect people to some people on the outside they say my life has been very difficult; even my children are confused that my life can be so challenging while theirs now is not so difficult. I wanted them to have an easier time and so alone their whole life. I made it happen for their future. I pushed them at the times to their age but now; they understand, and I am so proud and grateful for them.

Is okay I knew people like you were tired to read me but: could have you in my reader! Sometimes to. I would like to show you my writing from my day to day and night to night experience. I do not see any pages from my observations from the people around me like that on my counter of life. I have so much to say for now; I watch, I observe thinking and Look up the way I can go to move pieces of my life. My first memory Dad told to me that's inevitable when you are from to the island that is part of world history a long time ago, we must go from different places by boat. There sometimes you take a scary boat over and over: that is how people get from one country to another and back in forth by boat. You would also love the adventure. It is all worked by volunteers and movement All people with special needs!!!

I love it there and it is also a part of everybody's history. **Volunteer went to Haïti.** I love this. After a volunteer went to Haïti. So many memories in this repport. And help me every day to remember Haïti. I can't wait to publish this book and explain this adventure and all the ideas I can bring to the new generation.

As the plane dipped down lower and created that euphoric falling sensation in stomach pits, the entire plane erupted into loud, hearty laughter and then subsequent, jubilant conversations. And this is where the old man next to me, who had no teeth, and could not read or write, smiled at me and handed me his passport and customs documents so that I could fill them out for him. From just these few moments, I knew that Haitians were young at heart, and while they possessed a quiet poise, they were *never* too proud to ask for help.

Haitians are the most genuinely friendly people I have ever met, and I love that the bonds immediately transcended language abilities. In fact, language itself broke the language barrier. Waiting at the airport in Port Au Prince, I discovered this in less than ten minutes. With my trusty Haitian Creole phrasebook and our new Haitian friend Jameson, I tested out my broken creole, and he would respond back in broken English. We lightheartedly laughed at each other's silly sentence bits but praised each other's efforts and abilities (or lack thereof).

Late that night, we arrived at CODEHA's home base, the site from which over the next month we would span out into 5 schools across the region of 'La Vallee.' It served as the site to which all volunteers return on the weekends to reflect, build fences, create gardens, and work on other projects.

CODEHA is a grassroots organization of Haiti, which grounds volunteer and community efforts in educating the children of Haiti. CODEHA stands for Corde Enfants Haitian, which literally means 'a rope of Haitian children'. In a larger sense, when we all work together to educate our children, we climb the rope that pulls communities, and the country, to higher places.

The home base of CODEHA completely reflected this vision. It was a miniature, thriving community with energy of electrifying proportions, complete with guitars and slacklines. This oasis hosted a rainbow of international volunteers and Haitian leaders, children and families who came together to play, work, love, teach, learn, and to share.

Gody, a middle-aged Haitian man and the passionate leader of CODEHA, immediately and vehemently shared with us that we are not here to 'help,' but *share* in the experience. CODEHA was well known and highly respected because of Gody's relationships with the community. Although his candor and childlike attitude pushed my buttons *so* many times, his ever-radiant energy and poignant enthusiasm proved him to be the *epitome* of young at heart.

He shared with us CODEHA's motto: **(Konstwi ak sa nou ye kote nou ye). In Haitian Creole, this means (build who you are, where you are)**, and I made this my mission while in Haiti: to build solid connections with those around me, and to relish every experience. Gody, in part, inspired me to do this. He was (is) a role model for being fully dedicated and present to those around him, and he lives for the relationships he so easily creates with people.

He always said, "You are not my friend." I was taken aback the first time he said this to me, but he continued, "you are not my sister, either, or my brother... ...you are my existence."

And he said this with such extraordinary authenticity that it took my breath away every time. This is a true testimony to his character, and it completely embodies the spirit of the Haitians.

They let you in, swiftly.

This held true when we helped the older Haitian women cook. It is amazing how the little things here can be a great bonding experience. We sorted through bags of grains and corn and picked out bad pieces for hours on end. Very quickly, I learned that this was a delightful afternoon bonding experience rather than a mundane chore.

Haitians can joyously engage in seemingly tedious tasking while *completely* enjoying life.

While doing this, we became fast best friends with the young Haitian girls by singing Bieber's hits together. Eager to break the cultural bonds and transcend language barriers, we came up with cool handshakes, braided each others hair, painted nails, and they taught us 'peche,' a game similar to jacks, except it's played with rocks- the Haitian twist. And when we ran out of international pop hits to sing together, it was never awkward to just be silent and bask in each other's peaceful presence.

It was about being who you are, where you are. It was about sharing in the experience with each other.

Church further exemplified these cross-cultural capabilities. As the Haitians sang, their voices carried a mellow sadness but an even more powerful undertone of hope and optimism, which seemed to cleanse the air of the surrounding rubble and turmoil. Their dark eyes penetrated our souls as the priest openly thanked us for our help and support. His attitude was neither a plea for more help nor an insincere thank-you-but-we-can take-it-from-here. There were no underlying power struggles, no arguments of authority, no 'us versus them' mentality. It was an honest moment of the community appreciating that we were willing to share in the experience with them.

I am so grateful that they were willing to let us share in their frustrations, efforts, and struggles. Although I may not have carried a heavy as a burden as they do, not a day goes by that I don't think about these vivaciously happy, enduring people with indestructible spirits.

I miss walking in town and continually uttering a friendly "bonswa" to everyone I see. It was always said in return with a genuine, large smile and an excited wave. In Haiti, greetings were always reciprocated with an unparalleled openness, optimism and excitement. (I fear that here in the states, the process of saying 'hi' to everyone you saw would be a very daunting and discouraging task.)

At one point, us volunteers and fellow Haitians even shared a bumpy 3-hour ride packed in the back of a cattle truck. The young American volunteers mixed with the older Haitian generation made for a youthful combination of never-ending sing-alongs consisting of nonsense creole phrases. I laughed as the oldest mama sang her heart out to these "joy" songs. Her voice, though wildly off key and hoarse, radiated her lively, youthful spirit. My heart felt so full as I belted out call and repeat songs in Creole, and to think that this is an everyday occurrence in Haiti…

Many people have an erroneous notion that you would have to pay money and attend a fancy spiritual yoga retreat in order to have these insta-connections, but there are some places in the world where duets of fast connections and ever-friendly exchanges are an everyday, ordinary dance.

Haiti is one of these few places.

As Gody would preach, it is not about "bringing" anything; it's about the gift-less exchange, sharing in the experience *a junto*, together.

Always while traveling, we must embrace and cherish the raw, heart to heart, cross-cultural connections; we all have something to share with each other.

Americans came to Haiti expecting to change lives and to supply the students with material goods, which they are 'deprived' of. Silly, because people here are deprived of absolutely nothing, in fact, they are teeming with enthusiasm, gratitude and youth. Embarrassingly enough, we came with bags of pencils, paper, string, markers, and every possible medium of coloring and crafting.

We had beads and parachutes, and yes, it was beyond exciting to partake in crafts with these kids, but in all honesty, the most practical and repeatedly used item I had brought was my Leatherman pocketknife.

We came into this experience expecting to make a difference, and maybe we did. But we learned more from the Haitians than we could ever expect to teach them.

Hey Americans, jokes on us; no Haitian needs a lesson about life, love, goods or work. Even if I made a difference in my children's lives, they taught me a better way to live mine, and for that, I am eternally grateful.

People come to Haiti with deficit modes of thought. However, it would be so disrespectful, degrading, and pointless to pity these people. Sure, compared to our standards, we can feel bad, but our perceptions, tainted with un-necessary and extravagant material things prove to be a poor judge of fulfillment.

Every day I remember that my children in Haiti are choosing today whether they want to use their ration of water for bathing or for drinking. Then I must ask the age-old question, why do Americans, who have so much, seem so deprived, when societies like Haiti who have 'nothing' are so happy and fulfilled?

Does it take nothing to truly appreciate?

If this is the case, America is surely going about fulfillment in the wrong way.

Their pencils and paper will eventually run out, but they will still walk barefoot over the rocky terrain for 2 hours just to be able to sit in a broken school desk for a little while. The bracelets that we all made together will eventually fall off and disintegrate into the dirt, but that will not fade their shining smiles, energy, and zeal.

I miss, most of all, the rolling velvety green hills, which span the entire Vallée de Jacmel, and wrap people into Haiti like a hug. America practically steam rolls down our hills and any other imperfections to have a completely flat land on which we build cookie-cutter houses, with fences to keep the neighbors out.

And I wonder, when the land is flattened out like this, does it teach our kids not to climb mountains?

Where kids learn on the rocky terrain in the rolling hills in Haiti, they are not afraid of climbing, or falling; their caution is thrown into the wind, and they boundlessly chase soccer balls across drops and rocky areas.

I can only imagine that ones imagination, inspiration, and willpower for life is embedded in the land they grew up in. And our children in America who walk on sidewalks and who can only play on manicured lawns without so much as a rock out of place may never be able to learn how to climb over obstacles or push themselves to higher places.

As I lay in my comfy bed I think about how I would give anything to be back on the concrete floors with our dusty, lumpy thin mats listening to Haitian and American voices combining in a sweet symphony with the strumming of guitar chords and the string of nearby cockroaches coming through the windowless windows.

It's the ripple affect; I don't know how far our impact will go, but I *do* know that it starts with educating our children. And our children recognized the love and passion we came with, which makes my volunteer work a success.

But our passion is minuscule compared to the passion and perseverance of these kids, better yet, the whole country, which is destined for great things despite the physical environment.

I believe that the ways we gauge success are skewed. America likes to measure success by the amount of resources we consume; with our consumption of materials, resources, and unnecessary things, yes, we are number one. But, as Haiti taught me, what if a country was defined as successful when everyone felt belonging in a community?

When everyone you cross paths with lets you in with a smile and a wave, which raises up every soul in the country with unconditional love ... What if we measured countries in terms of the love they share and their ability to support each other despite life-shattering conditions.

Often, I associate the term 'Globalization' with grand, sweeping gestures of domination and upstaging, and rightly so; the deprivation and disposal of culture that can accompany globalization are devastating, but benefits are reaped as well.

Globalization makes it easier for us to travel, to experience an array of cultures and colors, and because of this convenience, we should be striving to share in this experience together. However, to think big, we must think small. Simple things like rocks & pipe cleaners...

Who knew that one bag of pipe cleaners could generate a creative, inspiration-filled afternoon? This summer, at children's camps nudged in the hillsides of Haiti, little Haitian hands molded pipe cleaners for hours on end crafting bracelets, glasses, and endless inventive designs; they twisted gorgeous fake bouquets until their hands were sore.

The older Haitian male teachers were just as enthralled with pipe cleaners, and it was heart warming to see the teacher's enthusiasm and curiosity equaling that of the children. I loved seeing one of the Haitian teachers, Maurice, wear a pair of lime-green pipe cleaner glasses *all* day, and I couldn't help but laugh as he started to have a serious conversation with me about our lesson plans for tomorrow, still wearing them.

About a week later, we passed by a town meeting being held by some of the women, and I noted that an old, Haitian woman was wearing a fancy pair of blue pipe cleaner earrings.

To this day, pipe cleaners never cease to amaze me. What universal, useful items!

Outside the aura of the children's creative spirits, the Morne a Brule schoolhouse was a devastating wreck, still in bad shape from the earthquake. Had this school been in the U.S., caution tape would have sealed off the premises, and kids would have been scolded for going near the dangerous mounds of dirt and rubble. The main concrete schoolhouse on top of the hill was falling apart, and chunks of concrete and rocks were scattered all over the uneven landscape.

On the last day of the children's camp in Haiti, we used this to our advantage. We had the kids collect their favorite rocks and falling-apart-school-bits from the piles. The students then wrote words and painted pictures on the rocks, and all of them ended up going to get second pieces of rock to decorate.

The energy when doing this project was explosive; it was so moving to see these children personalize and be able to take part in renewing something that had been so devastating in their lives. I realized that they were not just painting, but they were reclaiming their land, their school, and their hearts.

After the rocks had dried, the children were able to go set them in their own special place outside. This was such a simple, yet inspiring activity, and this can be done almost anywhere in the world. A small, universal activity, *which leaves a big impact on the souls involved.*

An old, happy, Haitian man, Gerard, who had always looked out for the children during the day, gestured for me to paint him a rock. I took my time and made it very sparkly, and his face lit up when I gave it to him. Every time we crossed paths for the rest of the day, he would give me a bright smile and an enthusiastic thumbs up.

It's the little things like this that count. He got a present, a rock. But I got a flame ignited in the pit of my stomach that urges me to do more, to see more, to meet more people like this man.

It was lively pushes to keep exchanging with people, to partake in the little experiences, like this, which make the world a little smaller, and a little friendlier. Maybe globalization does not have to mean showy Coca-Cola advertisements… it can mean painting a rock for a new friend whose smile will be dearly missed. Globalization is funny, fickle thing.

And just when I thought globalization couldn't get any fickler, up in the rolling hills of Haiti in La Vallée, four hours outside Port Au Prince, I saw a kid eating a starburst, and I sang Akon songs with my Haitian friends. How is it that Haiti is so far behind in infrastructure and common sanitation practices, yet I can still hear the infamous, irritating Nokia ring tone wherever I walk? If you're cooking over a fire, while texting are you new wave, or old school?

Because of globalization, Haiti is an inexplicable, explosive combination of old and new; it's fashionable and acceptable for everyone to wear second hand clothes that have been shipped from U.S. thrift stores in large quantities. I have never laughed harder than when I saw a scrawny Haitian man wearing a shirt that said, "Don't let my big tits scare you, I'm really a nice lady." Globalization can also make things hilarious.

Some of the most dazzlingly hilarious moments of my life included participating with the Haitian children in the insanely intense, enthusiastic game of duck-duck-goose and other nonsense American games. And I will never, EVER forget the whole group belting out the call and repeat joy song A TOOTIE TOT; its repeated motions had all of us sticking out our tongues, and butts, spinning around in circles, and simply acting silly together… everyday. For me, these moments make globalization worth it.

Globalization: it's happening, & the fight against it is not worth it. However, we can preserve the integrity and character of every location by cherishing our connections with those around us, and of course, savoring the little things. Vote pipe cleaners and rocks for globalization.

A Volunteer Report

My two weeks volunteer experience in La Vallée de Jacmel in July of 2010 was invigorating, inspirational, and rewarding. I was the oldest person (57) in my group of 13 volunteers, but my age in no way limited my ability to contribute to the work projects being done.

Everyone in my group embraced a level of work that suited her/his physical abilities and was supported by a communal bond that encouraged participation at every level. The emotional impact of our presence, and the hope it expressed, was also palpably felt.

La Vallée de Jacmel is situated in the remote mountains of southern Haiti. Most of the inhabitants in this region live an agrarian life devoid of "modern amenities." Many live without electricity and running water, which means no lights, refrigerators, televisions, showers, toilets, or stoves (gas or electric). The rocky, rutted roads are best suited for "tough truck" commercials.

The local diet, of which we partook for our entire stay, consists mainly of starch-foods such as corn, plantains, potatoes, rice, and beans supplemented with fresh avocadoes, mangoes, carrots, and papayas. The midday weather was intensely hot and humid; the nights sometimes cooled to chilly. It probably showered or rained half the nights I was there. Lodging with a local family was offered, but I opted to camp on the Codeha grounds, in my small tent, because my ability to communicate in French or Creole is nil.

My group accomplished quite a bit in our limited time. Most of our work involved taxing, manual labor in the heat of the day. Our first project was to clear concrete, earthquake rubble from the second story of the Codeha Community Center. Next, we built a barbwire fence to protect a recently planted bamboo grove on the Codeha grounds.

This job involved hand cutting and digging both fence posts and postholes. The soil in Haiti is laden with lava rock and limestone, so digging was always difficult. The procurement of barbwire and baling wire was a daylong task that involved a store-to-store quest in the city of Jacmel (a forty-mile drive that takes two hours) that finally resulted in success. Nothing in Haiti is readily available; nothing in Haiti is easy. The fence materials were purchased with volunteer provided funds.

Still at the Codeha property, we dug a small landfill (litter is ubiquitous throughout the country) and grey-water drainage ditches, weeded the overgrown community garden and replanted half of it, and organized the community center's library onto volunteer-built bookcases. One day was devoted to a volunteer-hosted party for 100 local, school-aged children.

The activities included drawing, dancing, music, juggling, crafts, soccer, and improvisational games. Alongside the local Codeha volunteers (who were wonderful), we served the children lunch and frantically washed dishes and utensils to keep up with demand.

Three days of our time in La Vallée were devoted to a trip to the town of Mon Abrulée. Our journey began with an arduous, five-hour hike through the breathtaking (figuratively and literally!) mountains. Our mission was to plant a bamboo grove, community garden, and host an activity-party for local children, all on the property of the community school. The ground in Mon Abrulée was even rockier than Codeha's, but both the garden and bamboo got planted along with the building of another hand-cut, hand-dug, barbwire fence.

The work on these two projects was accomplished by Codeha volunteers (local and international) and a dedicated group of residents. We camped at the mayor's house and were fed by his gracious wife and extended family. Before hiking back on the third day, we hosted our party for the local children. What it lacked in organization was more than compensated for in the smiles, laughter, and human interaction shared by all. When we were asked to introduce ourselves, to all assembled, I happily declared: "In the U. S., I am a teacher; in Haiti, I'm a worker. In the U. S., I'm 57 years old; in Haiti I'm 17 . . . Haiti makes me young!"

Our last project was to plant a third bamboo grove on the side of a mountain a couple of miles from Codeha. Terraces had to be dug into the hillside and, in addition to the daunting steepness, the ground was as rocky as we had experienced. Local men and women, who were more comfortable on the terrain than we thankfully, joined us.

They worked with a diligence and joy that was truly inspiring. I must also credit the incredible effort, in all these projects, of Codeha's co-founder. He was a quiet man, but his actions constantly spoke volumes about his commitment and resolve to improve the lives of those around him. Our third grove and fence were completed with three days of sweat-drenched exertion but with no injuries, save sunburn and blisters. I hope I have conveyed some of the intensity and depth of my volunteer experience in Haiti. I have not dwelled on the beauty of the country, nor the ample fellowship among the volunteers, nor the excursions to the waterfall and the beach because my personal commitment was to work for the good of the people there as much as possible.

Codeha's dedicated staff, made us feel more than welcome, they made us members of a family. At first, some of us were upset by organizational lapses, but, in retrospect, I understand that to truly help in Haiti, one must be prepared to be patient, determined, and undaunted by delays and poor planning. To reiterate, "Nothing in Haiti is readily available; nothing in Haiti is easy." I recommend this project to anyone who is up to the physical challenges described. La Vallée de Jacmel is not the epicenter of misery in Haiti, but, perhaps, it is the epicenter of hope. The work to improve people's lives there is vital, meaningful, and heartwarmingly appreciated.

Changing Lives

FINDING A WAY TO CHANGE YOUR life is simply making the firm decision to get back on the road. It is important to have a project. It identifies that you have a mission with specific goals that give meaning to your life. This responsibility grows in harmony with the people you meet on your way and the naive friendships that ensue.

All the missionaries who bring us peace today have been at war for a long time to defeat the adversary. They have gone through trials of all kinds. We must overcome the fear that sometimes makes us back off and prevents us from advancing towards the goal we have set for ourselves. Whoever has a mission never gets lost on the way. Either he gives what he does not have, or he shares what he is or what he has earned.

A mission begins with an idea, an identity, and a person like you who carries it day after day. Life is a journey and each day represents a new beginning. The big challenge in life is to train as if to win a competition. It is a continuous training which finds its balance without judgment of value. It, therefore, makes sense to commune with everyone to learn continuously. By attaching to each other, we take responsibility for ourselves. This allows us to offer the best elements in our possession to maintain the proper functioning of the community, but also of ourselves.

Needless to say, the very idea of taking a trip is already classified. You are a special being with a unique adventure. Do not seek a path or follow fashion, rather accept that you cannot control the passage of time. There are many things in life that are unachievable until you realize that you exist. Sometimes people even have a fictional existence of which they are unaware. Finding your place is already a visa, an open door to face all the difficulties that one encounters, whether physical or spiritual. You have no less power than any other. We are all capable, fairly, of finding what we seek in our thoughts or in reality. So, you can choose to be whoever you want and nothing and no one can ever match you. It is time to turn your poverty into wealth so that you can share the joy that everyone expects. Change the way you see yourself so that others look at you and see in you the positive image they are looking for.

Changing your mentality and environment is not a bad thing as it allows you to give less importance to your weaknesses. A person who wishes to take another path to change their personality must be able to accept themselves. She must also accept to find on her way, during her journey and her adventures, people who will give her the opportunity to live new experiences and to surpass herself. While remaining, of course, in the real world of differences. At first, we don't really have a fixed idea of the trip we want to take with this or that person. But whoever wants to climb the ladder must be able to rely on his own vision and on his inner strength. Taking a new route requires a lot of preparations, whether spiritually or materially. It's a whole organization of life. In all of this, the only thing you should never forget is that you are and will remain the mentor and leader of your own life.

No one could take your place. It is a privileged position that only you can occupy. A passionate traveler risks nothing as long as his goal is set, and he knows how to leave and where to arrive. Everything is written as soon as he takes the first step towards his goal. You must be sure that no one can stop you from crossing the barriers. Perhaps the path you are taking has already been followed by another person, but no matter what happens, if it is the path you have chosen to achieve success, then you can consider that you have no rival. It should never be forgotten that the goal and the objective are always confused, but that it is about a common competition where there is only one trophy for only one winner: you! Before embarking on a journey, do not hesitate to ask for advice.

On the other hand, never stop on the way to ask for directions from someone who is even more lost than you. Finally, you are in the best position to know the route. Often, only appearances count. You never take the time to move towards the goal you have set for yourself to succeed. Also, it is important to prepare for a good trip. You must really understand yourself, have fair and achievable goals, and keep in mind that all the paths come together and that we should all end up in the same place. Tolerance is a challenge that everyone should face, as it is one of the greatest practical exercises in human existence.

You are the Product of your Experiences

YOU ARE AT THE ORIGIN OF everything that makes up your life: your successes, your defeats, your glory, your misfortunes, those of your friends and your enemies. That means your number one enemy is yourself. You are often the source of your own misfortunes. The main failure is to forget your values. You value others, but never yourself. However, you are a treasure trove of time and space. You can count on you to build your own destination and take steps like a borderless traveler. When you are on Earth, only you can create your own path. Confidence in you is, therefore, the engine of your decision system. This decision system will never be obsolete if you work to find a real existence.

Whenever you decide to live and share in-depth this magic that is existence with your own source, it is an innate compromise that you make. It is important to remember that all the sources around you are worth nothing without you, especially when you are not passionate enough about life. Life is the beginning of everything. This life, you must find it on your way. It is naturally present in the fruit of your work, of your daily creations. The environment in which you live is beneficial for the development of your being, if you are integrated into community culture with modesty.

To stay fully awake and be consistent with everything, you need to improve your appearance. It is a job that takes place second after second. The simple fact of not being attentive enough to be able to adapt to daily life can disrupt the entire functioning of what you have in place to exist and create. If you don't create, you are certainly present, but you don't really exist.

In this case, we can say that your values are rather rare, not to say totally non-existent.

You are the product of your own experiences and your self-confidence. Good deeds hindered the necessary development, which would make it possible to split the wealth of an entire community for the growth of each entity. Someone who does not create, solidify nothing, fractionate, multiply and never share cannot consider that he truly exists. We cannot exist without sharing its creative potential. This is what allows us to transform what we are: living beings with an unrivaled power that allows us to dominate the other species that inhabit Earth.

Each living being is a treasure to transform and share to improve the life of our neighbors in all circumstances, out of solidarity. It's about reconnecting with the nature of who we really are. In truth, our ideas and thoughts to transform all that is material into eternal purity make us rich. Existence is not a chance; it is a succession of commitments. If today, we have the hope of being able to find a solution to the problems, it is thanks to you. The world is saturated with negativity and you are the only light that shines amid darkness. All memories should be as positive as your journey. You have a strength that everyone would like to have. Charity is currently very expensive. The living is transformed as if they were goods known to all. People who get into development get very wealthy in very little time. Anyone can do it anytime.

The forces everyone is talking about in the community are we, the people of that same community. Community means communion. Without this fellowship, we cannot be strong. The gold mine of a community is its ability to communicate daily. This force is so real that all those who want to reign seek to destroy it. But it's part of the culture. Difficult to understand them because they manifest in light. A light that blinds, a light that closes the original path. They arrive in the form of heat. This heat is not used to heat, but to burn. They come in the form of water. Water that is not used to quench thirst, but to drown the whole body.

Life is an Eternal Beginning

THE WAY WE LIVE OR THE way we evolve as an integrated person to militate directly in the community is a fundamental asset for the safe and sustainable development of humanity. While men and women fight more and more bitterly on the strategy to follow to live better, there are however everywhere on Earth wars based on differences of values. The combination of machines is beginning to replace human intelligence.

Usually, we have an indefinite or indirect role to determine as a human being, on a bridge that we have rebuilt differently to go in another direction. Either the reception of what one gives is badly perceived, or the exchange that one has to make is at the beginning badly imagined. The messages we seek to disseminate can be perceived as outrageous when they should allow the complete liberation of the human spirit. It may seem ridiculous to have to stick to an ancestral culture, to dress and eat in the same way, to carry the same messages, to opt for the protection of the planet. Want to go the furthest possible to defend a just cause is not a sin, but rather an act of responsibility to change. Appearance plays a major role in this change we are talking about.

There is also a tendency to give more credibility and to associate qualities with people who seem well or better placed. This is how our appearance is completely banished. We open a door for others, but at the same time, we hide behind this door. The longer we wait behind the door, the more time passes, and nobody talks about you. One thing is certain: the longer we wait, the more valuable this thing is to us. The social causes, which are the most seen, and the most heard are also those, which are the most valued. Even if objectively, they are not the most important.

Everyone sees the world in his or her own way, even if we share the same daily life. Time passes and when the end of the day comes, we no longer wonder. However, there is always an answer to blame the climate: the sun or the rain, the cloudy or clear sky... It is always quite simple. So simple that you cannot even notice the uncertainty of the time that always goes by with precision and leaves us in the waiting list of events.

A man never has a specific place to celebrate events and create circumstances. Only time has this power, but it only passes without ever lingering when we experience precious moments of joy. Everything has a specific time. Even when the first and the last, by definition, are in the same space, they never look alike. They will never have the same place at the same time and in the same position. It is always difficult to understand the distance from a loved one. For us, to be deprived of our fundamental right, it is any situation that we all live for each other...

I don't even have to tell you, but every pain is unique. We have all taken risks for a loved one. Making sacrifices is a fact of life for someone who knows nothing. Just as it is always difficult to lose a loved one. But even if they are gone physically, it still feels like they're keeping us company.

Here's something that gives hope and proves that an absent loved one can continue to occupy our memory. One of the best drugs in the world is love, according to different research. I recommend it to everyone. Even to start a new path, love is always recommended. It's a phenomenon that goes beyond scientific fame. We do not need science to prove our love, but we need love to demonstrate the ability of science.

People simply refuse to receive this love. They frequently attend their funerals gradually. They run the risk of not even appreciating themselves. Without this personal love that we have for ourselves, we cannot understand that another can suffer while trying to get closer to us. We can no longer comfort and give courage, to ourselves and our loved ones. We can no longer give hope that everything will be fine. We are so deep in the pain of absence that we often forget our injuries. Like all these people who suffer because they are just parents.

They are so gnawed that they seem to have been abandoned on the side of the road. They then forget that they are part of society and that they are active members who contribute to the well-being of all. You become a sponge that absorbs pain. We experience these pains, but we do not see them. You make your enemies yourself. When you are ready to accept everything, when you do not make enough efforts to perfect your life and strengthen your qualities, then you become guilty of your sufferings.

You should not be ashamed to take the way back. Life attached to nature is neither imminent nor static. It is ensured by simple laws specific to nature itself and without avalanches... After experiencing a bleak life on the way of others, an ethical angle even ridicules my skin color. Honestly, communing closely with this nature has not been a bad thing. If I had to relive this experience, sleeping in the woods, eating green leaves, I would not hesitate to seek in the depths of my being the charitable love necessary to cultivate humility daily.

My brothers and sisters, make life a journey of restarting. Make sure that we can live in communion, a communion made of back and forth and small simple gestures ... By being the actors of our scenarios. From a nearby environment, the acquisition of each security is confirmed by behavior from the start, until reaching a safe destination. There is no better start than leaving empty-handed. After becoming aware of the existence and taking possession of a real human being, taking a new direction is a bit like being born a second time.

When you exist, the journey is neither too long nor too complicated. Much of the journey has already been taken by parents in their good manners. The contemporary will, therefore, must return while respecting mores and customs. Powers are fleeting. Nostalgia will therefore not allow you to slow down the passage of time. Therefore, there is no point in indulging in bitterness. The biggest difficulty in life is to see the days go by without being able to create or produce anything. We could compare this feeling to that of being in a devastated environment where nature itself seems dead as if it were a pile of rubbish among the others.

It reminds me of the millions of men and women locked in their loneliness. They may be children deprived of their loved ones and who must prostitute themselves for an unfortunate piece of bread. It is with shame that we see children starving or being tortured and raped every day. These images should keep us from sleeping. I remember dreaming of hearing babies born into the world singing for a hopeless life. The anger of these sad children monopolizes my memory. I always have in mind this image of a museum for tomorrow. Children haunt my thoughts like weird visitors. They would already like to play the script for their film.

There are many barriers to a single injury: shame. We leave this dream to the dogs. You can hear them howling under the full moon of an ordinary evening. However, the idea is also to offer children a chance to discover a new world. Finally, when we think that nothing is possible, we can always say to ourselves in a low voice: "This arbitrary space is the museum of the soul."

We often feel insignificant, as if we are not weighing heavily in the balance. We are too flexible concerning the weights that are imposed on us. We are still on the same path. We go back and forth, thousands of kilometers a day. The route always follows the same pattern. I close my eyes and let myself be enlightened by the popularity of my banal and ephemeral memory.

The goal is to further protect my schedule. It is like climbing the steps of a grand staircase. The days pass. The silence is extremely heavy and omnipresent. Day after day, my path splits and I find myself at the crossroads of several roads. For the first time in my life, I find myself around a table full of food. My soul comes, eats, and drinks. This energy gives life to the lucky ones. To come to work, you always must enter through the big door. The life of tomorrow is still here. The roots of this life come from everywhere. She is among us and with us. Holding this book in your hands, you must imagine that this story is a balance sheet of your life.

How would you react if one day you saw your name written on the walls of your city? Have you ever wanted to find yourself in front of a crowd of strangers and to have the happiness of being considered a leader, a reference for the community? Have you never wanted to be recognized by everyone for your lights? Have you ever dreamed of sharing your wealth, your potential and putting your talents at the service of others? Have you ever wished you could shape the future to steer the world towards sustainable development? A world that would be built like a big house, with materials of excellence, a guarantee of tolerance and unity. Have you never wanted to make life triumph by listening to all these committed hearts beating in unison so that living beings survive?

Never ask time to take stock of your life. Do not waste your strength asking life what you should have done to reap the rewards of your labor. Since existence was built in a scramble of germs, there is no reason to accuse the time of finding nothing. We are all jostled by the lack of responsibility, but the speed with which time passes has nothing to do with it. I carefully select the paths I take to reach my goals.

Regaining Confidence

YOU ARRIVE IN MY LIFE LIKE the rumors of the city, upsetting everything in your path. It seems to me that I am like a window that gives way in the face of the storm's onslaught. In front of this window scrolls my crazy dream to cross your path one day, like a stranger on the highway. You drink at the source of my desires. Watching you is like watching a sunrise...

In the blink of an eye, you cross the threshold of my door and enter the room. Don't ask me to imagine because I don't know anything... Neither your body nor your mind bores me. Everything connects me. Sometimes it's hard to be penalized by the time... We hit the road together. The urge to leave tempted us. It is an experience to remember. There are steps that you better climb alongside someone in your imagination. Too bad. The time is now over. It does not matter, even if you sometimes want to be at happy again together. We wanted to show that we have things in common. Our blood is the same color.

Fortunately, there is something positive in our relationship. You are mine. We never really felt at odds over the words. The two of us are good, as if we are one. It must be said: having things in common has allowed us to meet on the path of life. We had a lot of emotions the whole time that our union lasted.

I know that soon we will get closer. So, I try to take advantage of every moment, even stubbornness. That's silly to say, but it's also fun to be far from each other. Without a gesture, you take my head ...

You are like cloud dust. You float and your breath accompanies me. You are my shadow. Your habits follow me, a bit like the referees follow the players on the field. You are in my last straight line.

No one has ever imagined that the world could change so much the day this donor father arrived in the community under the pretext of doing lift people out of poverty. He exposed everything on a back-up tray. This donor father is always present in their lives. It makes them forget the people they were before it came into existence. Because of him, community members think only of suffering. They do not remember that they can live without the one who forced them to forge a new culture. Renouncing one's former life to prepare for the most urgent calls into question enormous and incurable wounds.

Especially when you do not have the power to decide for yourself. The other becomes our father, our boss. He is at the forefront of community life. If, however, the community dared to decide without asking for the patron's endorsement, then it would risk receiving a penalty commensurate with the affront.

I remember when I first met this father on the street, it was like a dark painting that no one else could understand. I felt like I was living in another body with another person inside, another thought. I had the feeling of taking another path, of adapting to the present time, of throwing the ball differently and in another direction. Towards mysterious roads on which are men and women in love with life.

It was as if I had left the mainland, the one where I have lived and worked since forever. I had been separated from the others. We had destroyed the road I had decided to take to overcome myself and I had been forced to take a new one, supposedly guaranteeing me better living conditions. On each side of the shore, we had to fight for a new alternative without controversy. There is always the temptation to turn back after each defeat in life. But the people around us daily have encouraged us to stay stronger than ever to regain confidence and move forward, to allow each of us to be effective and find our balance. Here on this complex Earth, living things have arrived unaware that they could not live at the same pace as before. They come from everywhere. They have vastly different visions and goals, but also the ambition to conquer the world day after day. As an antagonistic image of each presence, we act daily to reduce extreme poverty in all its forms: social, economic, and cultural.

I always thought that the world was a great road that we had to travel at all costs to find this father. The school I go to does not give me the real esteem I'm looking for. The classroom is a place where teachers still tell strange stories, especially when you have in mind to find and create this father. No one can behave well except this floating image of the father. If you were in my place and you perceived the evils that I feel, you would see how much we suffer when we stay in a school where the teachers increase our problems. In other words, the time spent in school is hell. Each person has their difficulties. You can hear how hard it is for me to talk about a family relationship when I have no real family. All of this makes me think that life is a hopeless ravine. Instead of pampering my being, it violates my rights and prevents me from finding the strength to run after the one I am looking for. Also, I'm thinking of everyone who's not fortunate enough to learn what I'm learning in school. Everyone who would like to be in my place and hold my hand every day. If they knew that, I just needed confidence ... That is enough to destroy the suffering and to make disappear the bad images which I have in the head. There is nothing worse than breaking the basic rules of life. I feel like I was raped by others. If people are to be respected for their values and abilities, then I ask that my dignity also be respected. The fact that people from all walks of life can meet and find meaning in their lives together is not a challenge. Rather, it is a duty to be fulfilled: to motivate oneself around a cause just and noble, respect his right to live with this father.

It is by climbing mountains of difference every day to stay in the classroom and work with others that I begin to understand the presence of a father in the life of a child. This father is more important than a glass of milk for strengthening bones. I have three requests to make to God. First, I would like God to give me the chance to give birth to a source of brandy to dedicate it to my daughter, my very dear daughter. A great road that no one would have ever taken. I've already gone through it: it circulates in my daughter's pious blood like that big pink foot decorated with thorns. It's the best friendly choice I can make to save the world from my world. Secondly, I would like to ask Him to play musical notes to awaken the love of the people around me. These musical notes can transmit everything. They have the power to make difficult sites easy, and even to change invincibles.

Finally, thirdly, I would like to become a postman and distribute to my beloved princess large love letters to prove to her that no one can love her more than I do. I want to inhabit the city in her mind until she becomes a woman. She will be proud to have a dad like me. If all these requests are not answered, I will reinvent the world and I will dedicate it to it alone. The child she was will be a source of hope. All the great visions that she will have come from the ethical codes that I gave her during her childhood. In a truly short time, it will rejoin my life path. I am sure my daughter has a gift.

When I was ten years old, my mother knelt before me one day to sing me a wonderful song. As if I were a god, his god. In life, she has often faced uncertain tomorrows. She encountered many difficulties in her way. Her only wish was to support her children. It comforted me that whatever happened, everything would be fine. These various experiences mean that thanks to her and the example that she has given me throughout her life, I too want to accompany others. Mom once said to me, "Give yourself up like a lamb and the savages will protect you between their teeth without ever swallowing."

You must let those who need to destroy the other for their survival believe that you are their prey. We must never forget that time is running at full speed. The older we get, the more time weighs heavily on our heads like a burden. Everything has its own time and everything has meaning for its time. I thought a lot about what my mom told me when she talked about the nature of things. I in my turn succeeded, with a belief in a fighter without limits, to tolerate, accept and chart every day a new plan according to a destiny already set out.

My first plan of life was this: going up my stairs day after day, walking after walking, being open to other plans while staying upright in my sneakers, stop waiting for the approval of my peers. No one knows who you are except you. And again ... You can also ignore who you are if you never manage to shut up and understand the emptiness that scares you so much. She taught me that a gesture repeated in everyday life is more frightening than an actual accident from which we would have escaped unharmed. My desire to wear only a simple hat was something mysterious to some. It made them want to question me.

A secret can shake up the manager unless the manager is only running an elementary daily newspaper. So, I decided to live inside the secret of doubts. My goal is for people to gradually look down to understand that there are oppressed people on the first steps of the social staircase. These people always need to understand why and how when it is enough to listen to the explanations. But so goes life: the great richness of silence! No one can advise you on things they do not understand themselves. You will never be left behind when people are in the middle of their lives where they're listening, where they give keys to close windows that are secretly opened on other paths. I am thinking of geography, history, arithmetic, and grammar. So, when I was sixteen, I left a magnificent nature behind to go to the big city to continue my studies, a student career I had was discouraged by insecurity and uncertainty of all kinds.

The people who accompanied me did not understand anything. I was the only one to conjugate in the present the verb of solitude. It was tiring for me to have to give up my exploits again and again. So, I had to choose my path, another metaphor to link reality to everything around me. I learned to observe friends and family members. I have traveled all over the country and around the world. Without having real notions of geography, without knowing in advance the place where I was going to stop or even where I was likely to arrive. It's exactly like taking a trip to emptiness to face life's challenges in away. These trips taught me a lot.

Briefly, I knew how to differentiate and know the suffering of a poor child. It's useful when you dedicate your life to helping and defending children. In this way, in my servant life, I have had lots of contact with poor families. I have lived for a long time in poor countries, but also in large rich countries where we still find the poor...

I have seen them everywhere. Their case is not too different compared to the poor in underdeveloped countries. When I met new people in a rich country, it seemed a little strange to relive the same experiences. I have always wanted to fight poverty. There's only one world for the poor and one race for the rich ... That's what makes the difference.

If the world were understanding and supportive from a political and social point of view, we would know why we behave in one way rather than another. This simple question would naturally find its answer. This would allow us to solve all the evils that poison this gift of life. We always want to change this life, but never lose it.

So I lived in solitude, with no one to understand me. Who could I have spoken to? At some point in my life, I decided to abandon everyone, without hatred. I stopped performing the same formalities as usual. A few years ago, a memory came to my mind. Since I had no one with me in my words the means to explain this slight vacuum, I preferred to isolate myself, try to hit the road, all alone. A rational, but difficult journey.

It was a matter of life and death for me. I was barely twenty years old. Hell ... I wanted to enjoy all the benefits of existence. The first power I detected in me surprised me. I had a sense of responsibility, especially vis-à-vis the thousands of people who lived around me. My life was like an island inhabited by remorse of all kinds. I was much more isolated than an orphan victim of abuse when this orphan misses an opportunity to get out of it. Let you imagine how I survived with neighbors who were strangers to me ...

One evening, a strange vision came to disturb my sleep. Little by little, this vision took place in my life. She woke me up and drew my life. The color is sound, the passionate sketch, without monotony. I jumped on my creations as if suddenly I had entered the right door. Life has shaped my steps to exhibit my talent. I observed well and saw a completely extraordinary landscape. Here is the best portrait I can do of this nature, later. I managed to make this environment my prayer corner.

But my destiny, of course, is linked to my body and my mind. I am ready to climb lovely mountains. I am ready for the world to reveal to me the reason why nature is angry. It is not the fault of a nation or a race. In my career, I have accompanied many families. At the age of twelve, I had not learned anything at university. It was the contacts I made every day around me that was the most instructive. I was open about the opportunities the world had to offer me. I never got discouraged. I, therefore, consider that this learning of life constitutes participation in my evolution. Evolution as a human being who must keep his eyes open to his space.

Amazing things happen every day. It is part of our creation and our human evolution. Remember that we exist by observing and absorbing everything next to us. There are thousands and thousands of ways to take action to improve our lives and the lives of others. When we are passionate, death, fatigue, hunger, thirst, fear of death has no control over us. I manage to propagate my mission as a child. I always imagined that I was evolving in a big desert where it was necessary to start from scratch to build a new appearance.

I lost everything by being afraid of failure. I did not take any initiative. I looked like a man who got lost in the middle of a human jungle. One day I finally managed to speak to my daughter. It was then that she said to me in an unbelievably soft voice: "Please, write me a book so that everyone will know."

When the lie is too demeaning, we dare not speak. This is how I got out of my torpor. I wanted to know a life full of truths, to share, to adapt my language, but the shame reminded me all the time that to achieve it, I had to carry out a new mission. Until then, I had mainly observed and studied the organized approach of nature to relearn the history of life.

It does not matter if fate hit me in mid-flight. During this fight, I never felt fear. I just felt like I was murdered like a sheep that is slaughtered. What I wanted most was to lead a simple life. It was one of my main goals. I wanted to live under the same roof as my two children. Also, I was amazed when my ex-partner informed me of the judge's decision: a total ban on the means to explain this slight vacuum, I preferred to isolate myself, try to hit the road, all alone. A rational, but difficult journey.

It was a matter of life and death for me. I was barely twenty years old. Hell ... I wanted to enjoy all the benefits of existence. The first power I detected in me surprised me. I had a sense of responsibility, especially vis-à-vis the thousands of people who lived around me. My life was like an island inhabited by remorse of all kinds. I was much more isolated than an orphan victim of abuse when this orphan misses an opportunity to get out of it. Let you imagine how I survived with neighbors who were strangers to me ...

One evening, a strange vision came to disturb my sleep. Little by little, this vision took place in my life. She woke me up and drew my life. The color is sound, the passionate sketch, without monotony. I jumped on my creations as if suddenly I had entered the right door. Life has shaped my steps to exhibit my talent. I observed well and saw a completely extraordinary landscape. Here is the best portrait I can do of this nature, later. I managed to make this environment my prayer corner.

But my destiny, of course, is linked to my body and my mind. I am ready to climb lovely mountains. I am ready for the world to reveal to me the reason why nature is angry. It is not the fault of a nation or a race. In my career, I have accompanied many families. At the age of twelve, I hadn't learned anything at university. It was the contacts I made every day around me that was the most instructive. I was open about the opportunities the world had to offer me. I never got discouraged. I, therefore, consider that this learning of life constitutes participation in my evolution. Evolution as a human being who must keep his eyes open to his space.

Amazing things happen every day. It is part of our creation and our human evolution. Remember that we exist by observing and absorbing everything next to us. There are thousands and thousands of ways to take action to improve our lives and the lives of others. When we are passionate, death, fatigue, hunger, thirst, fear of death has no control over us. I manage to propagate my mission as a child. I always imagined that I was evolving in a big desert where it was necessary to start from scratch to build a new appearance.

I lost everything by being afraid of failure. I did not take any initiative. I looked like a man who got lost in the middle of a human jungle. One day I finally managed to speak to my daughter. It was then that she said to me in an unbelievably soft voice: "Please, write me a book so that everyone will know." "When the lie is too demeaning, we dare not speak. This is how I got out of my torpor. I wanted to know a life full of truths, to share, to adapt my language, but the shame reminded me all the time that to achieve it, I had to carry out a new mission. Until then, I had mainly observed and studied the organized approach of nature to relearn the history of life. It doesn't matter if fate hit me in mid-flight.

During this fight, I never felt fear. I just felt like I was murdered like a sheep that is slaughtered. What I wanted most was to lead a simple life. It was one of my main goals. I wanted to live under the same roof as my two children. Also, I was amazed when my ex-partner informed me of the judge's decision: a total ban on for the third time, I cannot understand why the old man left again without saying anything, without apologizing. He does not want to talk more. I will see him soon, maybe tomorrow. I spend all my days observing him trying to guess if he looks like me.

The sun is terrible. The sun is terrible but not brighter than the memory of my daughter running through my memory. The waitresses look at me curiously. "Don't think I'm crazy ... I'm not crazy! I've never been mad, even in the worst case. This is the first time I have dared to express such a feeling. I need to talk to someone, "said the girl. He left. I love our looks, his hands, his intelligence, his charm. Everything makes him want to communicate. In a way, you can develop a relationship with him. "But he travels continuously, my daughter. He's not used to staying put, "says the waitress. "I too cannot bring myself to stay in one place for too long. This is how I see life. Besides, I don't even wonder.

— You must restructure your life, create a new way of orienting yourself and focusing on human values. Use the power of your thought, the wealth of your heart.

— For me, a traveler is above all a human person, in touch with nature and Man to weave bonds of human solidarity and promote a deeper understanding between adults and children in their environment."

During his travels, one has the feeling of reality, of space that changes, of time that moves and of society that changes every day. There is the song of birds, the music of water, the growing plants, the transforming flowers, the clouds dancing in the sky. There are hikes that are done. When you travel, you have everything you need to be happy.

The beauties of nature, the music of the birds, the simple things: this is what drives me to travel. At home, the need to find my father arises especially in front of nature shows. I feel that my life, my mission since I was twenty, is to simply throw myself into the world of adventures. I learned to travel alone, no doubt thanks to my thirst for discovering nature, listening to birds, watching flowers, serving others, and finding my father.

The need to travel often manifests suddenly when sometimes we had something else in mind; I'm here and suddenly, I want to leave, without preparing anything I seek to live in depth the mystery of my existence, that of others too, as well as the full reality of things. Looking back at the story of my childhood and my painful life, I realize that for a very long time, the Supreme Being has staked my life with experiences that prepared me to face different trials, such as the fact of to be separated from my father. After several years of trouble, I find that many other children like me are suffering. Personally, I make a commitment to free myself. I don't necessarily have the words to explain myself. Let us just say that the need to travel often manifests suddenly.

I remember the first risk I took was when I started traveling to uncertain places. I slept with people I didn't even know. I took risks to be able to understand the inner life of other children, those who looked so much like me. It is something I can't explain, it's too sensitive. At the age of twenty, I realized that others could do nothing for me if I did not take charge of my destiny. I remember that Chapter 12 Using the Wealth of the Heart Who among us knows right away when a new idea comes to mind? Who manages to defend their rights?

No one is better placed than you to see your dad as he is. I know you cannot answer me, but I am present, and I follow you daily. Ah yes! I am indivisible just like the blood which runs through your veins and animates your body day after day. Like an atmospheric canvas that wraps its invisible veil around you, in the places where you live, where you live and where you evolve.

Power is a verb that you must conjugate in the present tense. It is not a matter of believing, but of knowing that the solution is possible. You can't see me, and you can't talk to me even if I know you love your father. But it is not with the word or the look that you will be able to communicate with me. Thanks to a technique invented by love, you will not see your father's physical body.

"But isn't he afraid of being mistaken for a wizard? Asks Yvonne. Good question... We encountered all kinds of situations, from the simplest to the most complicated ... "Oh yes! I too thought about all of this in detail. Some people choose to live in a very uniform way, avoiding getting mixed up in anyone's torment. "The girl smiles and asks another question: "But what do these people have?"

— It's not about owning something special, daughter. Rather, it is about trying to juggle the inequalities of the world. "Then, silently, they isolate themselves in a universe of their own and it is then that they start to become invisible. Of course, the speech becomes crystal clear! "It is by keeping your style that you will feel stronger. Each person has a reason to live. She must choose her basic principles herself to found her style and lead her life as she sees fit. This is an ongoing search to find out why we exist and what meaning we should give to our life. How do we see the world? Do the people you meet all have the same goal: to make a success of your life? Does it change if we take different paths?

You can take as references all those who have succeeded from scratch. What makes a traveler unhappy is not the length of its path, but rather the multiplicity of paths that can disrupt the orientation of its objective. For a life to be good, you must focus your goal on one path. You will then can assess and reorient yourself if necessary. It is the desire to be great that gives life to the person you are. Each person is enlightened by their experiences. When you have a dream, you must meditate on it every day. You have to think about the future and believe that you will succeed in imposing what you want to do, in your life as in that of others. Despite the nature of society's prejudices, despite the risk posed by this way of life. Some people put it into practice in a book to share their experience. These books were not written without difficulty."

The trick came to me one morning when I was thinking of a loved one. The spiritual power that binds the two beings served as my guide. I felt it manifest every time I thought of the other as if it were an extension of myself. Is it difficult to live in such a way? This gift of gently enduring pain like a memorable cross is extraordinary. It is a communication that the Divine transmits to everyone, a plan of first-class social and spiritual transformation, worthy of the name. Since the time of the Crusades, logic has never been dominated, although it often presents a good theory. No one has ever dared to go to the end of the imagination. If it exists, it is only very rarely found on this planet. People with such a gift are sadly slaughtered by the unpredictability of time, time and space. They are sent as a letter to the post. The enhancement of all moral and professional ethics leaves something to be desired.

The desires that we feel to draw closer to one another and completely forget ourselves are the consequence of the Divine. It was He who gave us our humanity and made us inherit the planet.

On the other hand, we must affirm our good faith when we have to make a difficult decision intended to improve the lives of all, to raise our consciousness, to seek a newer world. Whatever we choose. God will not condemn us. If it is our choice, He will even agree to show us the way. However, He will never force us to accept his suggestions. Neither now nor ever. Life would probably be much easier without these incessant movements and if we were not to keep everything in us, without ever exposing our weaknesses.

This is not why the power of invisibility manifested itself. Despite the inconvenience, this way of living could cause, it is impossible to stop this journey once it has started. This it would not be a good idea to stop it anyway. Leaving an old life is not easy. You question your commitment, especially when you leave your place of origin for the first time and join people from a different culture. Sometimes the distance and the change make you nostalgic. We want to take the road back, but the people we meet every day give us the strength to resist.

I know people who have had the opportunity to get away from all this fragile power many times. They wanted to see something else, to take a different route to find someone. But taking a new easier route risks destroying the richness of the adventure represented by this great power. There are people who have decided to stick with what existence has concocted for them. Sometimes it's a loved one who dictates their lifestyle. The important thing is to always have a path to follow because it is the central point of existence. This is how people manage to experience adventure as fully as possible.

What matters is to protect yourself behind this invisible world to save its values. Instead of using violence or committing suicide, we choose to live differently. No one can penetrate and understand the path that you have decided to follow because it belongs only to you. A person exasperated by social imbalances and humiliations develops a technique to become invisible while retaining the moral concepts of normal life. This form of escape is a way of dealing with the serious consequences of separation.

Is the invisibility of a man in the physical world perceived as a dangerous phenomenon? Absolutely! All of this creates distrust and fear. We must lock ourselves up, barricade ourselves and veil ourselves. Just like a father who has lost faith in injustice. A father who feels attacked by the eyes of others, those who despise his value. To protect yourself, the safest way is to become invisible. It is about valuing existence starting from values and ethics. But where is physical freedom?

We must certainly regret the reduction in the areas of freedom recognized by human nature. But one does not have to remain in total ignorance of oneself. We can go in several directions. Going in several directions is an interesting idea ... But how can we do it? What we are today depends on the voluntary missions we carry out with others, but also on lived and courageously supported experiences. Each of the faces you meet and each space you tread under your feet increases your knowledge and your strength to transform everything. Each physical place and each person who is part of it. Men were, first of all, a mysterious source of inventions to complete our creation.

Life is shaped by adventures. Everything you do is subject to the magic of existing or not existing, to a situation of success or failure. There is never a failure in life. The adventure belongs to those who decide to advance in this school of life. It is a school without a rival. The path is clear, and it is on this that adventures are formed with men and women who want to meet the nature of the invisible world. You have to be frank and honest. Power belongs to those who run daily after the time of simplicity. I cannot let my dreams die, I nourish and protect them by internal and external journeys. I feed them in my sufferings and my rejoicings. I always have a positive image of my travels: trips often to unknown places and without a road map. I always cherish the madness of reaching the goal ... I do not believe in chance, but in the fulfillment of a commitment. Everyone has a gift from somewhere, you just must guide and feed it with the madness of being happy and natural.

I never drop a commitment; I have a vision of things that I do not give up easily; I don't let anyone make decisions for me like I never take someone else's place. I do not pretend to say that the ideas of others cannot complement mine and that what they think is not right. On the contrary, it is important to take into account the opinions of others.

When I was younger, I always wanted to have my own space, it was one of my first goals: to be lonely and free. I always had the spirit of a traveler, always had an image to discover in my head. I believe it is out of love for life that I chose to take this meditative journey. Indeed, I have seen images of hell several times on television. In the world of spirituality, we make relationships that open opportunities. It can help in life.

A spiritual lover must be able to adapt to the lifestyle of others. What is important is the relationship between you and others in the community. The lack of communication with the community has made some people fail. Man must be able to adapt to the community in which he evolves. Regarding leisure, take your free time to read, take a walk, look at others and listen to nature, the song of the forests. The impression one gives often determines the relationships one can have with people.

I believe the real man comes from inside. You must be careful not to be resentful, to try to always have positive thoughts, to be as natural as possible, to feel good about yourself. If you are lucky enough to live in the countryside, take the time to practice walking. You can play with people, go deep into nature, eat fruits, vegetables, and fish, meditate. Never ask yourself too many questions about the future.

Use the wealth of the heart. This wealth will allow you to produce fruits that will nourish your spirituality inherited from your parents. You'll see that in the meantime, many people will come to you and ask you what is the secret of your well-being. At first, if you don't know what to answer, stay calm. Calm is a natural and innate power in man. It is magic power.

In reality, I understood one thing: you cannot be a spiritual actor if you have not found a harmony, a balance with yourself. If I am a spiritual actor, it is above all because I love life, I joke with others and myself and I am simply always true. Many people think that I am a rich man. In fact, yes, they are right, because having a heart awakened to everything around you is not understandable to everyone. I believe in the richness of the heart, in the power of thought, in human value. For me, the most important wealth is in the one in front of you.

I never understood these people who say: "I want money to live", without ever saying: "I want love, attention, human value, spirituality and I won't keep this spirit of sharing to exist". Here is a rather dark and unattractive landscape. There is danger everywhere. If the boat capsizes, the concern is for everyone. Despite everything, whoever is part of this invisible world is happy. One can wonder about the reason for this happiness. For my part, I would say that it is thanks to a homecoming. The purpose of this homecoming is to seek adequate solutions that will lead to a situation that generates justice, stability, peace, and security.

Be careful to grab onto the boat drifting on the ocean. Live your life as you see fit, not according to someone else's wishes. The best way to move forward is to focus on your own life, to set an example and a role model for people and then help create new forms of existence and a new strategy. It is an incomparable dedication that accumulates day after day. An uncompromising, multidimensional, and renowned exercise that inspires thousands of people from different cultures daily. The Divine, by transmitting wisdom to us, has made it possible to turn on a spotlight that lights up a social renewal according to your choice.

Instead of ignoring and distrusting each other, one should promote trust and develop a sense of friendship. To establish a dialogue with the invisible, we must start by valuing what we are and believe in the virtues of spirituality. How do we do it? It is not very hard! "I am here to inform you that your father's soul is intimately linked to yours. He is by your side and never rests, whatever happens, despite fatigue, exhaustion, humiliation, in the rain as in the daylight.

The main concern of your dad is to support his daughter and value her beauty as a flower hiding its fragrance. Make you evolve through what he is, not through what he has. Besides, we do not build with what we have, but with what we are. The child that you are represents the silence of a power that he possesses. This power is the future of his life.

As a silent being, you have all the keys in hand to become invisible too and save this world from false judgments. You are for him a basin filled with love which propagates real life without mixing. The world is unable to separate you. In his invisibility, he is there to see you smile and see you grow like the flower of this invisible garden, like a river pouring into the ocean. You are the title of my book, the name of my doctor, the words of my conversations, the speech of my conferences, the music of the turtledove that sings in my cornfield and the sigh of my last day, it's still you. As in a playground, I watch you walk, swing in my memory. No one has this divine power to inhabit my life! You jump in my heart and you keep jumping, you trot in my head and you keep trotting.

Like a reciting prayer, like a stone thrown into a bowl filled with water, you dance in my blood and shake it. The liquid in my veins irrigates a body that makes you grow a love like no other, transparent flowers and jasmine galore. All the kilometers that blood - my blood - travels through my veins are dedicated to you and it will never stop, stop. Unlimited sharing, you are my blood and my life. A rope connects us and the middle separates us at equal distance. Everything else is ours and no one will ever have the power to set boundaries and erect barriers. You are the lighthouse at the bottom of the ocean which indicates the direction to the boat. We are not separated by the waves of this azure blue sea; the same wind takes us to the same place.

Big as the ocean, my love is the boat that carries you. I only have a rowboat, there is no room for hatred. The space is yours; I govern the boat while observing the water that supports us. I scrutinize the transparency of the waters that take us, I enjoy the beauty of the canvas that invades us. I row and at the same time scoop to make the canoe and our trip more luxurious. Our eyes open on the turbulent caps of the great vault. Our memory grows in a perpetual back and forth of untenable points. Almost invisible water droplet dust veils the space occupied by the confession of a whitish cloud.

For back and forth, we are two witnesses, or better yet, two friends, who delicately oscillate on the thread of life: a little good forward and a little good back, once to the left and once to the right, we cross the vital alley. We enjoy this natural gift together, amid aquatic species whose agility serves us as a spectacle during their dive, establishing a brotherly game with the boat and the spiral movement of the waves. The relentless divers escort us: special service throughout our trip. The currents cross each other as our eyes meet on the highway. The reef barriers cannot trap us on the waterways thanks to the saving bounces of these small animals which serve as our guide.

They are looking for nothing else than to create a close bond with us by escorting our undulating caterpillar race: it is a duty of bravery that they want to accomplish by following us. You are my companion and you are in the foreground in the boat. In this adventure, life for you is just a card game. The least protected have no right to speak to each other while the power of the oppressors directs them.

And consider each image of this journey as a message that can bring you closer to the goal. You are immersed in a hopscotch game for a life of pure utopia. Thanks to the smallest details, you reinvent your goals, you animate each object in your image and you can even challenge the power of metaphor.

The right to rest is trivialized. You are always in a deep search for the truth. Many other children suffer because they do not have this divine power that you have to dare to have the audacity to have an invisible dad and that the end of suffering is often the result of a transcendence that forces time to stop. But meanwhile, nothing has changed, we are in the vision of new birth. Today, still on the boat, I see another syllable floating in time.

A pendulum that oscillates in your existence and turns the needles of the watch. I'm looking for you in the shadows and in the city. You walk as if to cordate life. It's like celebrating a birthday that is repeated day after day. Let me share with you, once again, the secret associated with time and life! You have had it since the day you were born. You have the power to fly as high as you want. Nothing will prevent you from succeeding in your life or going in search of your real father. If you close your eyes, you can feel your dad's hand on your head.

Receive the luminous wisdom of your father, the inherent source of your inheritance. I remember when you cried when you left your mother's womb. I remember the very first moments we spent together when you first heard my voice. You didn't leave me a second. Trust me when I tell you that you are as essential as the air I breathe. Nothing is more important to me than you and the gift you have. You are the beginning and the end of my days, my daily miracle.

I remember when I stood in front of your bed and contemplated your tiny anatomy. The movement of your hands made the sunshine, its rays came to illuminate your smile. A smile that alone could spread peace. You appeased me. The purity of your indivisible breath of mine paralyzed my words. The nakedness of your innocence mingled with the light of your sparkling gaze.

I can still imagine your smile. You are a girl, my daughter. You are not a stone or an inert piece of wood. We could compare you to a flower that opens its petals, revealing its fragrance every morning.

I hear your voice! I hear your heartbeat ticking. Like a clock, you predict the future in a succession of monotonous music. Your voice crosses the silence of space, the obedience of fate. Your voice manipulates the blood harvest.

As I accompany you on the way, I watch your shadow move. I hear your voice! Thanks to this voice, I have the impression that you will live to serve others and turn their lives into leisure. Like a drum, I hear the beating of a heart, a voice like that of a bird singing in my head. Sometimes the rhythm is light, sometimes it is gentle. The doors always open with a soft voice. This voice is not unknown to me. God's will always take on an air of music. That melody He hears is your voice.

Your voice could be compared to a symphony of flutes. Each sigh is short of breath. This voice is there in everything; it is like a relentless presence that welcomes me every morning. It is hot, powerful and even fun. I am tired, stressed. All that means nothing. I am always immersed in my imagination. You look at me tenderly and invite me to smile, to take the road by your side, a path, an avenue. With you, huddled in memory, it feels like we are living just to find a physical body, to feel a breath. There is a time to look in the face, watch sleep, watch food, watch it grow, watch it run, watch it sing, watch it dance, and finally watch everything and magically feel everything to transform a life together.

Although I have been silently lured, I am relieved to have evidence that my blood is flowing through your veins. The irony is that the only person who can alleviate my distress is you. You fill me with joy. This fragile absence is just an empty passage that I must endure, as a father. I dream of seeing your name written all over the city walls. I dream of seeing you sing for all the other children who have suffered from the absence of a father or a mother for several years. This tired and rejected father turns to smoke to kiss his daughter's shadow. Nothing but an illusion ... Again, and again imaginary hikes ...

These mind hikes allow me to dream of the day when I will see you again, my daughter. You are a miracle, that of the confidence that I instilled on the road that composes your existence. On the at a single glance, you can see the dust of your steps for hundreds of millions of kilometers thanks to the receivers that the Divine has placed in your eyes. You will then be invaded by the magic of unparalleled love. Like a seed patiently waiting to become a huge flowering tree whose pollen-filled flowers would produce a multitude of different fruits.

The harmony of your voice with mine composes the words of a song whose power comes from the words "I love you". I can hear your laughter and your tears. I can talk to you like no one else can. No other girl your age has as much power as you do to communicate with their father as you do now. I want you to know that when I started, I was frightened. I was afraid of appearing to be someone bad. I had become a silent and lonely madman ravaged by illusions, always in search of happiness. I was afraid that people would think I was guilty. Little by little, I felt my being disappear. Tortured by a feeling of shame, I let myself be crushed like a child. I knew everything I heard about me in court was wrong. But that was another reason to justify the anxiety I felt. It was then that I learned to use the spiritual side of my being to exist. I am deeply grateful to the world for allowing me to engage in this process. A process that makes me invisible and reminds me of some of the great truths in the history of life. Thus, I realize that thousands of people trust me.

Your father's wisdom has been matured at length during his journey. I am someone who has always wanted to bring new things where there are none. For me, becoming invisible was a question of commitment. Gradually, it became my design. The existence of everything is no coincidence. One is the complement of the other. You get nothing from life. On the other hand, you give him something. Anyone who knows and accepts his value is free. It is this freedom that will give you the chance to move from one state to another to achieve this transformation.

The days pass and the silence is still there. We work, we hear, we watch, we listen, we meditate, we observe, we absorb. Everything becomes a time in one friendly space. The invisible man is someone open with a soft voice and a tender gaze. Her smile is an invitation to have a coffee or a glass of water. The one who becomes invisible is an original person, like your father. One of the best and oldest traditions for this practice is to use it the right way while keeping it as simple as possible. Deep down, I knew right away. So much the better, because that was exactly what my being needed in these troubled times: to remain invisible! Of course, if it worked, it was because I used this unique experience for a specific purpose: to reinvent my being.

What I mean is that this experience occurred to me when a storm came to devastate a large part of my life and delay the realization of my dreams. It is gently that the Divine has performed miracles in me so that I understand everything, one after the other ... This experiment was to protect my worth in your eyes, my daughter. It transformed my life and my vision of things. Through these words, I will above all try to explain how each man has the power to become invisible and what must be the most important for him in matters of existence. Because to exist is not only to be there physically. To accomplish the great mission of existence, one must recognize the different dimensions that makeup man. The spirit behind this book is much larger than the book itself if we consider individually the historical evolution of each life in its time and space. And I wish you to understand that I could never have written a single word if I had not been guided by the spirit of the heart that the Divine has sown in me to faithfully fulfill his will without going further than myself. Now I am going to start a real conversation with you, my daughter, through the invisible force ...

I would not have made this trip a few years ago. I am doing it now because I want you to understand and to see in more detail the steps to take on the path of life. Not only is it possible to remain invisible, but this world also represents continual luck. This invisible world is both a door open to the universe and a boat that takes us with it on the path of existence. When we allow ourselves to be overwhelmed by the force of ocean waves, our dreams are shattered by a feeling of injustice, like butterflies tormented by the wind. It gives us the chance to discover our capacities. To develop by ourselves the will to act so that we can organize a divine revolt, according to our lived experiences, without trying to satisfy anyone.

Just like this morning, the sun is coming right here right now. No one can stop it, even when it breaks the beauty of the drops of water running down the leaves. No one can stop this divine power. The latter helps us to understand and act prudently without getting angry. Anger often torments life as water torments a small space. Even if you are not with your dad today, I want you to know that I still feel the urge to hug you. Do not give up hope of seeing me again one day, because we are on the same lonely path and we are looking for each other. The glances crossed encourage us to take a step further. I give you my word, now and forever: you will never disappear from my life. I am in a perpetual quest for beauty in the hope of finding the sacred power that will serve as our connection. Only the Divine can stop our race and prevent us from forever clinging to each other to create and recreate what we are. Like a frame of love and happiness.

No one can understand what you are. We could compare you to an opaque liquid enclosed in a vase sculpted by divine hands. This trip that you decide to take together can put you in an uncomfortable position compared to those who refuse to understand you. But you are miraculous dust of holy creation. Sharing is the very basis of existentialist philosophy. Everything in life is subject to sharing. Sharing is more important than speaking. Sharing is offering what we have in our hearts.

It is not a gesture of mercy or a request for a favor. In sharing, favor does not exist. The very instinct of sharing demands that it be manifested by real facts. Human thought always gives this possibility of creating new things to adapt to the present moment. Sharing is the great dimension of the human being who testifies of daily existence. Accepting the other for what he has does not mean accepting him for what he is. You must go beyond your physical appearance and accept the other for your positive or negative acts. This dimension of sharing must come from deep within to tickle the human heart during each beat. Sharing is the biggest abusive connection in human memory to justify existence. The desire to exploit the other always upsets the patience that one must have to tolerate the passage of time.

If sharing goes beyond any culture, any nationality, any color, and any language, then our vision must go to the simplest: the unhappy, those who suffer the most in the world. Sharing must awaken and fulfill human dignity. Sharing friendship inspires family and community life. The one who can understand and listen has the mission of helping individual tenants on Earth to rise above their uncertainty and become confident in their worth. Indeed, trust is the most powerful force to produce and transform. All communions must inspire confidence in us. Man is only alive if he is animated by a particular mission. It is sharing that gives our family life its authenticity, its value, and its dignity. When you give and share what you have with the one who accompanies you, you deliver you are being to the other. It is opening the door to sustainable progress in family and community life.

Sharing opens the way to happiness. So, this is the fulfillment of your mission, Sometimes, we need this appearance to meet social demands that don't always give the expected results. Appearance is the mirror of our social condition. It projects the image of our daily lives. You can make it a cathedral or less than nothing on the contradictory paths of life. We are often manipulated by the power of others or those who use their weakness to put obstacles in the way of community progress. Pain often reveals the ability to find a great source. Wade between power and weakness ... It is an instrument of social transformation which uses tolerance to make others accept their being. Always keep in mind that the obstacle is for the helper.

Fatigue is not for the recipient. The donor is the unfortunate who cares to analyze the problem and the social condition of the requester. The big contradiction is that the person who has the capacity to ask is not the one in distress. This person confronted with a difficult situation is rather always exploited by another. Very often, this other has no relation to the person who suffers. They are men who have no state of mind when faced with the suffering of others. Unfortunately, the man who has this gift never appears under his identity.

The need to live makes us impatient. We do not want to wait to know the result of our experiments. Acting with the innocence of your being is one of many ways to spread the truth from your heart.

214

The thing that gives life a taste is not always visible. The sage takes a thousand detours to accept all those who exist in his universe. Given... Give a look, a smile, a little of your time, a consideration, a financial gesture according to your possibilities. Give to change, transform, improve, help and not to hide your shame at not pleasing the needy.

Give meaning to your life, invest your time creating new ideas, ideas based on commitment. Be ready to serve your neighbor wherever you go. Become a servant for yourself and for others. Become the king of fruit trees, the source that hydrates, the light that illuminates space. The one who lives is the one who gives. The crop belongs to the sower. Let's open together with the doors that, through different paths, lead to the same goal: success ...

Never give anyone your power. Harvesting requires patience and perseverance in multiple and worthy works. We must not refuse time for growth. What makes an individual what he is are his thoughts.

Man can easily destroy himself, but also be reborn by his thoughts. We recognize the tree by its fruits and the man by his works. The tree produces by giving its strength to its fruits and the man by giving his life to others. Whoever does not give does not receive it.

Man is the most powerful heir on earth if he can control his ego to put his being at the service of the common good. The real man is in his thoughts, his gaze, his way of life. To live better is to give and to know how to give. People are not there to receive; they are there to give. They receive what they give, but not what they expect from others. Always learn and relearn how to give, and how to give. Giving is the answer to existence. The limit of what is called the space between one who receives and one who gives. Time is a universal gift that you get without asking questions or seeking answers. Time allows us to act and never judges us, we who enjoy this harmony every day.

If you do not know how to take advantage of this time, do not judge the arrogance of human beings. You might find yourself on the path of stupidity, reckless daily harm. Never give out of pity or to receive something in return. Never give anything to make yourself visible to others. Never do it in half measures. Do not give to blame, to take revenge or to gain power.

Take inspiration from the breath of the wind that wakes you up in the morning, from the spring flowing in your garden. Give, but always refuse to sing your praises. The glory you receive by giving is never a good sign. If you really want to achieve good results by giving, you must learn to breathe deeply to get the puffs of your own breath. Think of the purity of your heart, of simplicity with which it works. Consider it with respect, because it is the one that circulates the blood in your veins and protects your appearance.

The only thing that goes beyond is to give existence to other beings. Our look at things already reveals in part what our living conditions are going to be. Our desire to move forward explains the perilous stages of engagement. The body is a simple envelope which should not be representative of our qualities. This does not mean that this body must be despised by its host. How do we live without our physical appearance? to face our ego's refusal to make detours. You must want to do things by yourself ...

Without a qualitative orientation, one can find oneself clinging to the post of blind power. If you never know how to open the doors of each corridor, you risk being trapped in an uninteresting mission without help, although you have the keys. Never give what you have, but rather what you are. We will never get to the end of the road without the first steps. First, light up your life to share your light with everyone in your community, starting with you. Every second, this good deed will justify your presence. Getting involved in a community is a good deed. You will not have to regret a single day of this experience.

At all times, we must obey the rules of philosophy with detachment so that our life does not depend on the services rendered to the community. It is time to join hands with one another to ignite the fire of community engagement to the human being. Let us open our eyes and face changes in behavior and habits. Let us listen with an attentive ear to the powerful voice of human worth. Every day, it presents us with new perspectives by distributing new responsibilities. As of today, if you hear the silent voice of your creative ability, do not harden your heart.

Anyone who has gifts for inventing, creating, listening to what intuition dictates to him at the present time is free from difficulties. Travel, meet, listen, share, and teach creation as a reinvention of the human being and continuity of divine power. Create if you have within you this light of confidence. Humanly, it will take you away from the uncertainty of the darkness of doubt and death.

By warming the earth, the intention of the sun is not to take, but rather to render service to the plant by meeting a daily need. When the sun gives its heat, the rain automatically soothes the dryness of our rest and enlivens us. The source is always the end of another source which goes in another direction, with another flow and another dimension. This makes it possible to combine the maturity of a long path which is certainly invisible.

However, the space of land occupied by the perimeter of the water wisely gives its dust to transform itself into a terrace of traveling mud. It is giving, again and again giving ... Water gives the earth its inexhaustible source. It is by trusting the people around us that we can confirm to the thirsty the existence of this inexhaustible source.

One life always expands another, a bit like the life I present to you. You have to forget everything to live another life. It is the only way to remain invisible to the person you are. Go to the end of his commitment, remain invisible to everyone, never show the rhetorical face, never exceed the limit of his mission ...

The barriers we see are neither barriers nor obstacles. You always must force yourself to take one more step to pass the tests. You must also resist the idea of repeating the road in the same direction and having the conviction to advance until the end of your path. Don't forget that this path is incomparable. This is where your strengths lie.

They will serve you to chastise all common bad intentions. Take the time to reinvent your being. Escape unconsciously is already a work of invention. You should be aware that there are natural laws and that it is, therefore, essential to remain true to oneself throughout one's life. The best you can do is try to be more receptive to natural powers. Always organize a new action to capture the passing of time while finding a new spark in your own life. Your parents, your friends will always have a variable and surprising place in your life, with different feelings. You will have to manifest holy emotions and a holy character. In an environment overwhelmed by the abuse of men, you may not be used to recognizing a positive transformation when it appears before you.

At least that's what the madness of humanity teaches in its bitterness. For the balance to be struck, some of us must undergo a transformation. Do not be surprised if the transformation you imagined is nominative. Your being will seek to stifle any reading whose the heart needs to get out of this tunnel. If it's not you, it will be someone else. The main reason that keeps us from landing in the invisible world is our ego. It holds us and swallows us gently like plasticine instead of participating in an inherent transformation of the human being. Everything has turned to derision. Wanting to live in harmony with ourselves and others can put us on the road to real transformation.

What we are is found in experiences and books. Even the characters in these books tell us about the future. I did not know anything at first, I discovered everything thanks to the sea. I also learned things thanks to the exile of my mind. It was from there that I began to be interested in the mechanism of creation, then that I sought to find my invisible daughter through this unique journey. Of course, I'm still far from finished, but with each passing day, I can move on and learn new things. For example, I may really want to see my daughter. This desire will turn into energy to reach further in the realization of the mind. So, it's a great way to better control my daughter's absence and know which way to go.

Most of the time, I am lost in my universe and I am overcome by all kinds of thoughts. While being lost in the ocean, we think of another world. I do not feel what is happening in men. I then enter a new mode of creation instead of accusing the other. There is no starting point and I have no idea where to stop. The simple fact of being with you fills me with joy.

The other side is waiting for us to take us where our dream lodges. It is important to know what you are looking for, otherwise, it is impossible to set goals. The conditions for obtaining the result are therefore in the clarity of mind. Otherwise, it will be quite easy to disperse.

I was separated from my daughter when she was a month old and I still find it hard to believe. His presence is always real in my daily life. Sometimes I let my mind wander to understand this phenomenon while retaining the human being that I am. I was trying to hold my breath hoping that someone would come to my rescue.

Therefore I started at the detach from the world to go after my daughter in another way. From her side, she also began to look for me in her imagination. I feel like I'm at stake in a fight between the physical world and the spiritual world, a back and forth. When I am depressed, I turn my back on this physical body.

Reinventing the conception of the day becomes my first duty every day. I accept the existence of everything around me. I am not trying to isolate myself from the reality that evolves and changes every second, I rather try to adapt, to my presence in everything. I am not trying to find a reply to everything, I'm trying to commune with myself and destroy my inner frustration. The takes advantage of the time that passes to grow, transform, and detach my being from all that is visible and representative of any form. I use my appearance as a basis for finding my way, but never stop in a fixed place to judge where I am and where others are. I never miss a moment in the course of time. Each situation is my compass to find the direction of the crossing.

The attachment to material wealth does not stop you. However, I am deceived socially and spiritually. Time serves as a mount for irrigation in advance, but not to comment on the past. Each experience that comes to me opens the door to another path to success. If you do not want to spend your time, no one will do it for you. This is how I contemplate the world. My gaze does not trap me in doubt. I always try to trust others, without ulterior motives and without questioning time.

In short, the human being is full of qualities that he shares with his fellows and other living beings. Adversity is the awakening of human consciousness. The priority interest of every element of the planet is to ignite the fires of altruism, from starting to collect the confessions of the physical and material world.

It is often the art of merging with others that leads us to make a conscious decision about who we are. Among living things, we are privileged people who have the power to build and assign responsibilities

To find what we are looking for, we must have the desire and the courage to disappear. This is the only way to lose the desire for revenge, that desire that eats away at the bright side of life. Never believe that you are a victim. Stay away from any sense of suffering from hope. Continue to help others. This is a unique opportunity for several reasons. This singularity is first due to a way of life. Forgiveness is unconditional.

That is why he invites people who are experiencing separation to move from body to mind. In this case, suffering has become a necessary mystery to travel until returning to the sacred world.

This perpetual preparation for success must be done now. It is not tomorrow that the day of much-desired innovation will come.

To prepare for the change, refer to the current demonstration. Take a step forward and you will see that by then you know how to get started. The credibility is also a denominational channel. In most cases, it is an asset that is acquired through success!

We slowly failed and then withdrew throughout life. We did not want to engage in community activities and have our own experience. It's a kind of agony. We are completely unable to understand ourselves because we are manipulated like puppets. The system controls us. It is as if this system was built to pamper us and reduce us to less than nothing. We can do nothing but obey established laws.

In life, all those who recognize themselves as being alive and who are fully aware of existing among their fellow men inspire the hope of coming out of a coma and having better living conditions. Those who trust their spiritual power to flourish have found a first answer to the question they asked.

Under certain conditions, it is not so easy to understand the role of each resident on this Earth. What is the participation of invisible forces? The answer is not entirely clear to men. There is nothing you can do but trust spiritual power. It is trust in this power that can help us accomplish the work of our journey vital.

We have a mission much stronger than faith. Mission, work, duty, and power are very different things, which are often contradictory. We are puppets in the middle of everything. These are two different aspects of the human phenomenon because the mind and the physical are not on the same planet and do not have the same problems. This angelic call sends me back to the country, to the community that has cherished me and where the whole cosmos knows me. Now that doesn't mean anything.

Separated from Dad

BORN IN 2008 OF LOVE WITHOUT energy, my mother broke the foundations of my future. How poignant it was to see my father taken to court one morning, without knowing the reasons!

Today I want to tell you about this mishap which I find shameful and which marked my whole childhood. I was a month old and I already recognized my father's calm voice when he hummed songs in my ear. It is a good souvenir. However, my life has been very tormented since I quickly found myself distant from this father. My existence was then disturbed by an unprecedented storm. What will you think of my family situation? It was at the age of five that I first met Dad. I ran into him on the street by chance, and it shocked me a lot because I was not given time to look at him and touch him. I often have this question that comes to my mind: why was I separated from my father at birth?

What is the real story of my existence? Is it the fruit of love or has it been chosen to harm my father's reputation? The only thing I know is that I come from an ambitious immigrant father and mother ...

It deeply marked my childhood. I spent years in the lie. It's like I'm locked in a golden cage to keep me from asking questions about my father's absence. Mom will still make the decision to make me meet dad on the street. It has revealed part of the truth to me, but much of the story remains in the shadows.

Today, at the age of puberty, I want to break my chains. But if one day I am asked the circumstances of my birth and where my father is, I would be unable to answer. In 2004, papa was in Port-Au-Prince in Haiti. He worked there and it was also where he met my mother. My grandmother was a cleaning lady in the company where he worked. My father was the head of the social service for this organization. He mainly worked with children without home.

He was the head of a mobile clinic on the streets of Port-Au-Prince. My mother eventually returned to the United States with my father, but it was mainly because she had found another man. She circulated gossip about dad so that he would not be accused of his infidelity and betrayal. She forced me to call papa this lover I did not know. It was then that my life became hell and my days became black. No one can imagine how my father changed people's lives. When he arrived in the community, he offered help to those who wanted to get out of poverty. He is always present in the lives of those he saved. It allowed them to forget who they were before to focus on what they are now.

All my childhood, I was separated from my father. The story lasted a long time since I am still tirelessly looking for it. I was lost socially and died psychologically. Little by little, I learned how I had been left out of my father's life without my feelings being considered. However, living with your father is a sacred right. Especially when it comes to a father like mine. I was separated from him to run the system, a system I could not understand.

The first challenge I faced was in 2012 during my first year of school. I was exposed to everything. I felt like a fly on a bench, completely isolated. The adult who accompanied me to class did not care about me and he left me there. Mom couldn't be there that day, she had to go to work to support us. So, I was isolated, sitting behind the management door, completely upset. I felt hunted. Everyone looked at me like I was less than nothing.

A teacher asked me to enter the classroom, but I knew I was going to have a bad day. I was waiting for someone to call me. The flight is better than abandonment and loneliness. In my mind, I have nothing left of my father's image. I only know her face from the photos. Why would you want me to learn to live in a society when I have always had an absent father? Why am I introduced to teachers when the only person I want to meet is my father?

Even today, I still think about it. I would have preferred to go after him rather than face this school. I was told that school was a gift, but I was insulted. In my case, the school turned out to be a miracle ... It allowed me to fill this void inside me that was eating my lungs. Despite everything, the school now allows me to testify on behalf of all those who are not fortunate enough to be able to tell their story through writing. All those whose lives are like mine and who die in silence.

Children die these days for the same reason that makes me write today: the lack of a father and/or mother. I had to learn the right to live with my father by listening to the teachers to speak. I suffered when I saw other children leaving school with their father. I always asked the same question, but nobody wanted to answer me: why doesn't mine come to get me? Why doesn't my hero attend school meetings?

I always wanted to share my daily life with my father. I sought the answer to my question from my mother, but she never deigned to answer me. She just sighed and looked at me severely so I could get this topic out of my mind for good. But I wanted to understand the absence of dad. Later, by doing my own research, I learned a little more about my story. At some point, I became old enough to understand for myself what hell I was in. It was there that I made the decision to go looking for my father and go to the meeting children who have gone through the same thing as me. I call them: the victims of absence.

This is a new evil that should be treated differently by society, not like watching the news on television, but rather with a caring and unifying eye. So, I had to leave the house, go here and there in the hope of finding my father. Every year during the holidays, I continued to do my research wherever I went. One fine morning, thanks to a lot of willpower, we finally found ourselves on the path of adventure. Our hearts were tight, but the overwhelming joy we felt proved that we were right. Joy is, in my opinion, a sign of success. We had the intuition that something mysterious and important was playing out there. In the trunk of memories, everywhere, at any point of the globe, we find the same gravity and the same quests: human beings separated by thousands of kilometers who believe they are strangers to each other.

Fortunately, there are trips to teach us that the community that saw us born is larger, more colorful, unique and infinitely more captivating than all the regions and villages of the world. Unfortunately, I had to stop my trips. I was young and financially, I could not afford to go on an adventure. I would have liked to continue, but I had to adopt another alternative. I went to meet young children. My goal was to help them bear the pain humbly. At the same time, it was an opportunity for me to continue my research with amazingly simple actions.

I spent time at the restaurant drinking tea. I wrote again and again in my journal about the absence. It is that my father's absence had become the theme of my novel, a novel of silence. Her name became the real prayer of my dreams. The days of setbacks and suffering seem to be linked to his absence, these days of heart pain. I was writing and it was as if I found myself again in the cradle that had welcomed me after my birth, this Thursday in June 2008. In front of the little bed, he was there. When it's gray and I'm bored or misunderstood, I think of that memory. In all this silence, the images of these

The first days will remain forever in my memory. Just like this birthmark placed slightly below one of my shoulder blades. This spot looks like the map of an island. These stories followed me into my nights, when the nightmares came to haunt my sleep, making me prone to insomnia. I lived in a world quite parallel to the normal life that I was supposed to live ... Another memory ... An omnipresent memory in my mind.

This is how I went to join a clear source, the drums of rivers, the orchestra of birds, the look of flowers, the smile of the waterfall. I walked into a dreary country and now go to bed. I am not walking anymore, and yet it's as if I follow the shadow of this inert figure in a corridor that separates us. I write my poem with the genesis of his gaze and the madness of being a novelist. Under my pen, the horizon, full height, is adorned with a thousand colors. These verbs dedicated to existence are eloquent. I have already said your name in the language of silence. With a last glance of embers, I remember this flawless Thursday when my father let himself be overcome by emotion. Dad was there, in front of my bed. He put his hands on me and gave me a welcome kiss.

Hope was there. And ... And ... And I would like to write books without an alphabet, poems without words. If ever I was asked why my poems are not long, I would kindly reply that there is truly little light in my life. Dad is not visible in this room that the universe is. I could not speak, but I could feel the movement all around me. I remembered the arrival of a friend, his gaze fixed on me. Then the doctor came. It was, of course, the midwife. She was smiling and calm. I heard him speak with my father. Writing this book and talking about my father changed me.

To always be looking for something or someone is to play the comedy of life. I am not ashamed at all. I only regret one thing; it is the time spent away from dad. Being around him would have been a great asset. Even when I am by the children, I cannot fill this void. I've experienced a lot of suffering, and yet ... I was not a year old, not even eighteen weeks old when my father disappeared from my life. Today, I feel like I have spent a long century waiting for it. The hard part remains to be done. Without my father's advice, I am afraid. The future worries me. I don't trust this man that I have to call daddy.

The pain of living without a father who is still very much alive is my shackles. I want to want to live. I spent days, weeks, months, and years away from him without knowing why. I am considered a puppet. I live in a saturated and corrupt district. I feel the pain of living without a father who is still very much alive is my shackles. I want to want to live. I spent days, weeks, months, and years away from him without knowing why. I am considered a puppet. I live in a saturated and corrupt district. I close my eyes so as not to see the others. Although I often want to communicate with them, I have never had the chance to speak to them. I watched my mother every morning at sunrise. She was young, beautiful, but also a little pale and very lonely. She was aged with misery. Shame strung him every day. She never told me why, but I imagine she had a lot of courage. I try to keep in mind all the times when Mom has shown the courage to become as strong as she, too. She fought every day for our survival. Our neighborhood echoed the surrounding misery. I do not want to name the name of this neighborhood, and you know why. It is because you probably have this same problem within yours.

You must take the time to understand life if you want to find answers to your questions. In each vision, in each thought that we share with others, there are elements of the response. When your heart gnaws at you from the inside, it is not easy to trust the one who tells us the truth. Where are you? It's as if I saw you on the way to Latin America, in front of the pyramids, on the Indian route, on the Maya route, in the Caribbean garden, on Duarte peak, during climbing Morne-la-Selle. A great way to take together. Life is never as simple as you think. Its complexity sometimes lies in the ideas that we have, especially when they are negative. In some cases, it is the lack of self-confidence and the lack of credibility that one gives to others that makes it difficult. No doubt we cannot give a precise definition of existence. No one can explain it.

Dad, it is no secret, I know you are somewhere. Mom complicates while hiding you from everyone. I want to get involved and tell everyone who wants to listen to me that I decided to meet you. My mission: to ensure that two dreamy people can finally exchange and live under the same roof. You are there, wherever I go. I keep wondering if you are safe. In what corner of America do you live? How do people look at you?

How do they talk to you? Are you looking for me in the eyes of the people you meet? How do you imagine that I am? What is the conception of a good father for you? How do you see the future?

I am in the imaginary world, of course. My goal is to find you to fill you with joy and meet your expectations. You haunt my dreams. You are the air, you are the breath, you are at the heart of all my conversations. What worries me is that I do not know what you do with your days and nights. You are a plant in my garden. Time passes. I see you pass by the door of my room, behind the curtain of my window. Believe me, Dad, when I tell you that you are the mirror that captures my reflection. I will leave after you.

I feel that my destiny has always been to find you. It is thanks to this mission that I started all my adventures. I learned to travel alone. I wanted to discover nature, listen to the birds, watch the flowers, serve others, and find my father. The need to travel often manifests suddenly when sometimes I had something else in mind. I'm here and suddenly I want to leave. In these cases, I don't even have time to prepare my research to find you. The absence, the lives of others, the existence of everything in everything and nothing ... Each of us is marked. More than a coincidence, each life scrolls in its way. A new birth always serves to revive this tired and doubting world. The days pass and the sufferings continue. In the morning, everything is lost, and no one is ever responsible. This other one that you look for everywhere is behind this mask that you wear. The people who accompany you are there only to listen to you cry. When everything changes around you, you don't have much time to think. You can just continue to travel in the void or choose to hear this little voice running through your head. I hear the voice! This voice echoes my adventures.

I feel like it goes with me wherever I go. The passage of time is a weight that you carry with you all your life. I imagine a smile ... With each beat of my heart, the volume of time increases. In the crowd, I search everywhere around me who could be my father. In each face I meet, I try to find the sublime features of my father.

I hear the sound of drums, accompanied by a voice that sings like a bird in my head. Sometimes the rhythm is light, sometimes it is gentle or insignificant. In this case, it is that the look I met was insensitive to my pain. I am tired, stressed. All that means nothing.

On my way, a volcano is erupting, and I must be careful not to walk in the invisible lava. I'm going through the days like I'm in hell. Living for me is as difficult as crossing a raw river.

When I look for my father, I try to find his smile. The people I meet every day represent the demon. This demon has made my feast of my life.

I do not despair of finding it one day. I am in joy, waiting. My attitudes and the expression on my face agree with everyone: welcome! I am not a stone or an inert piece of wood. You could rather compare me to a flower that opens its petals, revealing its 265 perfume every morning. I try to understand things without commenting on them, without making a speech.

Every day I look at myself in the bedroom mirror with a tender look. I smile at myself to encourage me to take the road, the path, to cross the future. It would be more accurate to compare my pain to a volcano still erupting. The hope of seeing my father one day coexists in my soul with the hatred that I feel. These emotions put aside, only me remains a victim who has suffered the choices of his parents. No one sees it, but everyone believes what they want.

I have no answer for anyone who believes gossip about my father. Dad is not a bad father. Even the sun, in each spark of its light, shares my pain. He warms me and watches me grow like a wild plant with no mark. I too want to be a sun to share and transmit all the positive vibrations that surround you, dad. And this despite the distance and the fact that I do not even know where you are. Until now, I have always managed to manage my suffering and transform it into a basin of purity in front of others. Time has transformed me to think of you.

In memory, it feels like you are living just to find a physical, feel a breath, hear a mature voice. There is a time to look you in the face, watch you sleep, watch you eat, watch you produce like in a vegetable patch. I am the fruit of the seed that you planted and that allows me today to grow, gain weight, climb, run, and dance. I always hope to see you again and again ... I imagine how, together, we could transform existence.

This is a life lesson that I can never forget. Naivety plunged me into a pearl of wisdom that eats into my heart and causes more suffering than years of prison could have imagined. I never wanted to file a complaint, but I am in pain. When I sleep, my eyes may be closed, my tears always end up flooding the pillow I'm supposed to rest on. Obstacles after obstacles, a pillow drowned in tears, a tortured memory. Me, desperate? No! Never!

When climbing the mountain, it is always good to look up without asking others to have mercy. Climbing the ladder requires a lot of courage; catch each bar, one after the other, calmly and with love to move forward ... My love still exists ... To forget you would be to sell my faith. I can never, ever, lose the faith or exchange it to forget you. Never...

Do you know that you direct my actions and my steps day and night? In front of me, I observe the shadow of your holy presence every day. If you are not with me, it's because ... I do not need an answer to this question. Again, and again, mountains of accusations ... Finally, it is impossible to understand this pool of lies.

We are like the stem of bamboo that stays flexible against the wind. We are still on the same path. We go back and forth and thousands of kilometers day after day, always on the same journey and always with the same love. Obedience to serve teaches me a lot about my ability to withstand the adversities of life. Without gambling, the existence of everything is a true witness to my cause. Life is not what you look at, but what you transform and what you protect to make it happen. The days pass and the silence is still there. With hope, I am convinced that God has placed a crossroads on our way so that we will meet one day, papa. On several occasions, I saw you in my visions. We had in mind the same objective: to meet one day. "Hello!"

This voice does not disturb me, because it is not unknown to me. The will that I have to find you has always been symbolized in my mind by an air of music. This melody that resonates in my heart is your voice, dad. The chords are right, I like to compare your voice to a symphony of flutes. Each sigh is short of breath. This voice is there in everything; it's like a relentless presence that welcomes me every morning.

You are the original door, the best entrance to come to this earth. I would first like to thank the powerful force of the Creator who has given me this courage. It allowed me to turn this inner suffering into the light on my path. Thank you again for giving me the opportunity to have this experience which clearly explains real life to me.

Except that I will never have the privilege of meeting and knowing my beloved father. The steps I have taken with fervor have all proved unsuccessful. In the name of freedom, I just hear your voice on the big road. Dad's life is closely tied to my life story and my career story. It represents the eternal flame of my heart. There are so many things all around us that we can appreciate or refute. One cannot remain confused when one becomes aware of all that one observes and absorbs each day. The family and the multidimensional existence of men, whether physical or spiritual, evolve daily. Each passing day resembles the previous one. These are funeral days. I had confidence in the future and still saw it as an opportunity to get back on the road by walking in my own steps. From a family development perspective, it is better to separate from one another and move forward successfully. Wanting to preserve at all costs a marriage where trust has been broken is an idea that probably comes from carefree people. It is not enough to have a family; you have to communicate your spiritual vibration to people. The good father who works for his family is the one who, through humility or silence, has received within him the power to create, transform, protect, and love. This is the dad I want to meet.

Since the one you are looking at reflects what you are, that means that he has the same aspirations as you. He wants to be able to project a better picture of existence. The presence of each person must be a source of life and love for others. Life sometimes demands that we stay in front of the first door, hidden behind a dark curtain. It is only so as not to miss water from the right source. We all have specific expectations regarding life. A bit like a traveler who knocks on each door with magic kindness to revive love. Listening is a gift, a great mission, and a search for oneself. It is always a subject of prayer and meditation. The little man who represents my father sings constantly in my head. No matter how young I am, I take the time to listen and look far into the dark, to the horizon, expecting nothing in return.

For some, it is not easy to understand that there is a girl somewhere who only sings to find her father. Even in my sleep, he is there. Her fiery shadow and sweet voice haunt me. People stare at me from all sides. They are not bad people; they are just weak people tired by life. Like big dreamers, they want to transform my father's sensitivity by using a source filled with foam, forming a transparent bouquet. While watching others evolve in their daily lives, I come to understand different lifestyles and what determines the power of each person in their own dimension. Throughout the day, my father's voice seeped into my sleeping vertebrae.

While moving behind this curtain of shame, I managed to take a few seconds to meditate. I'm talking about seconds because I don't really have time to fully enjoy the time that goes by when dad's voice is in my head In my imagination, I observe each movement of passers-by strolling in front of me. My father's unique voice keeps humming in my mind. It's hot, powerful and even fun. On each stair step, the concrete of disappointment builds up second after second and there is no way out of it. A month after I was born, everything changed, and nothing was ever normal. Some people say my father is a criminal. These people live among us, I meet them every day, I watch them ... I did not expect all that ...

I feel like I am being murdered psychologically for something I didn't do. I have no words to explain the fact that my father was taken away from my life. I have no idea what is going to happen, but I have the feeling that by having to fight, my life is ruined. Where am I going in all this? Nobody knows. I wander aimlessly! I'm waiting, alone. I don't know how, but I'm sure the truth is out there somewhere ... I'm waiting for the good old days of maturity. I'm waiting ... Everyone sees me as a painless little girl. Those who make me suffer even think I'm happy. I live in a paradox ...

An excessive and traditional paradox. People do not even have the shame to be responsible for their unfaithfulness to the rules. But I believe that every war exists so that in the end, we can heal the wounds of the combatants. A dad lost in the arrogance of a wizard with infinite power ... I remain prostrate in my miseries. It's for when? Like everyone, I have a father who lives somewhere and who loves me. I live in a world of extreme poverty. This world is engaged in a quest for a life without thinking of the sufferings of others. However, we are all equal and we have all inherited the same land. The day I was born, I remember that my father watched me with bright eyes of emotion: it meant that he loved me. All his images remain forever in my memory as a mark on the walls of this city where I live. I feel his breath, I seek the trace of his steps and the rays of his gaze everywhere. My dreams are like a journey through space. They are the array of questions I ask myself. I know my father wants nothing but my happiness.

If paradoxically, I have the right to speak today, it is to ask for permission to live with the one who gave me life. I want to be entitled to his marks of affection, to his protection. I want to bring out the truth from a bin of lies and thus offer my memory the possibility of forgetting everything ...

My father loves me and scans the street every day from his window in the hope of seeing me. Each morning, like a tired butterfly that continues to forage the flower, it launches into a fight to regain its dignity. Regrets knock him out. If you take stock, his life is only suffering. As for me, no one is trying to find out if I am suffering ...

This dad is my life, my pride. When I see children alongside their father, I cannot stop hoping for his return. It is a nightmare that has haunted me painfully forever. Since I am a humanist girl, I also ask for these same things: a dad to pamper me and accompany me. I recognize that for some it may seem a bit odd: wanting to find your father first and then living for me and for others.

After spending my time finding my father for a long time, I experienced many disappointments in the community in which I lived. If I had had a father, I would never have experienced all these ups and downs. Seeing children smiling at their father is mental torture for me. I feel like I'm in hell, I'm in a hallway and no one sees me. I feel like I'm transparent. I returned in complete anonymity, like a tired storefront or a towel that would be used to dry her tears. I am an open person, and anyone can enter my life. It gives me the illusion of existing. I'm dying, a paid slave, but no one protects. People whisper on my way, make comments without even knowing me. All this is unfair.

You can never know for sure if a window will open fully tomorrow to pin life. We all hide the real side of things. My door is open for anyone who wants to enter. In front of me, the big challenge is to move forward in this lonely corridor. The opportunity to cross the great barrier is there. The steps are already calculated, I have no time to waste. Everyone who watches me cries today will be surprised to see me smile in the future. I can only conjugate one verb: to find. Find my father, my dad.

I look at the poor people who pray in front of the cathedral. It looks like they want to put an end to bad memories. Nothing is simple. Everything has a reason for being what it is, to operate as it operates, to be at such a point in space, to exist in such a period of time. My story looks like a fable. I tell tiny stories that no one takes seriously.

My father seems to have always been available to serve others. Here is an extraordinary attitude, but one that causes pain. Each of us should be fortunate to have a father to find the strength to see life in a different way. Appreciate each life, each breath like a drop of water in an ocean of complementarities.

Not talking to anyone thus awakens our sense of observation. We absorb what surrounds us, we remember things to better transcribe them then. It is like sowing stones in the path of consciousness. When I am judged, I try to keep my eyelids closed like clipboards, but I can't forget. One cannot remain polite when one lives a life like mine. It is a bit like a fairy tale, nothing is real. The fact that some people knowingly choose to turn their backs on human misery cannot be explained by a simple word of courtesy. Everyone is lying to me, no one has the true version of the story.

I suffered too much, like the wrinkles on my face show. People think I'm simple and look at me like I'm a child like any other. However, I am one of those who are dying of hunger, who have had parents absent, have suffered abuse, and live in lies. I look here and there. I watch rivers flow without knowing where they come from. I live a life without interest. I am a child like any other, but I feel like an orphan because my father is not there to protect me. My spine broke under the weight of this pain because of other people's cunning.

Through my experiences, I have learned that life is never as simple as you think. Staying polite is a sacrifice. I speak in an affable tone, turning my back on my sadness and mental suffering. Everywhere, I am chased by the reality of evils. Really, I suffered too much! I am drifting on a sea of despair; the swell is driving me away from the coast at full speed. I use all the movements of the vacuum to pass the time.

I'm hungry, but I don't want food. I rather want to spend a moment under the courteous gaze of my father. I imagine that we are following the same path and that by force of circumstances, we will eventually meet. People are all looking for someone dear to them. The reunion always brings intense joy. I see them every day on my way. Even those who do not speak seek the approval of a father or a mother. Through words, I try to find an explanation for the problems I am having, but I cannot find it. What does this word look like? I do not know. A namesake or a synonym, I do not know really ...

When the war is quiet, the bodies and the minds are inanimate, I feel lost in a sea of suffering that others prefer to ignore. My father's picture in court comes back to disturb my sleep at night. Passion, silence, annoyances, pressure, and indifference are my daily lot. I am a doll that nobody sees.

Morning and evening, I repeat the same prayer. I see my father in every shade I tame. An epistle, repeated day after day. The years pass, the weather changes, but my adventure remains the same, always as monotonous. In the desire to never despair, I suffer.

People see me outside their door. I have been looking for my father's face for years. However, I had never left my neighborhood. I never dared to walk away from the house. I knew, however, that there were other people further away, but I had never seen them. I did not know if the community was good or bad. I did not know the neighborhood itself even. On the other hand, I knew that you had to hate those who made the decision to get away from my father. Even if my parents had decided to separate long before. They made this decision when they were still living in a wealthy country. This is the country where I was born, you must have heard of it.

No One Can Ever Take My Place

IT IS UNFORTUNATE TO FORCE A father like me to separate from his daughter, but that is no reason to slander or accuse me. I get rid of my regrets, my anger, my fear, and my resentment. I wrap myself in bold new skin that looks like God. A God who loves and forgives, but not a God who judges and who condemns.

I am unique, utterly unique! You can judge me and accuse me of all evils, but you will never be able to equal or replace me as a dad; never, never will anyone ever be able to slander my fatherly virtue. In this role, I am the most powerful even if apparently, we would like to deprive myself of it: nature would not allow it! Nature does not allow it! Nature will not allow it! No one can ever take my place. This is the main foundation of my victory. I will never forget the day of my daughter's birth and I will always greet her, from the top of any mountain, the look protector of the holy sun who witnessed my revelation as a father.

What is the king's child protection system? "Let us protect the children," they say. "Give us a few minutes to study the matter." But they don't take the time to see if what they are reading is true. Let us be realistic, the verdicts fall without any form of trial. Yet they swore to protect us, but alas! With the very large number of cases they have to deal with, they only have a few minutes to devote to us, and despite the laws which, in the books, are supposed to protect innocent citizens, they make decisions that will have a devastating impact on these same people they should protect. So many innocent people suffer because of this. And people bear the grave consequences, their pain being worse than that of hell. I have come to the sad fact that in this country where justice for all should prevail, fathers are often found guilty, victims of outrageous accusations.

No one takes the time to seek the truth, except perhaps those who have the time and the money to defend themselves, which is not my case. After the sentence, you have to forget everything. Come back in a year, as if we were just old clothes relegated to old cupboards, just to be forgotten. However, it is not easy for someone like me who was raised in the unconditional love of a mother and a father. I was lucky to have them both. I am the fourth in a family of six children. Together, they raised us in a gentle environment. They taught us to love, sharing, understanding, peace, self-respect, the community, and the world. When I started working with children on the streets of Port-au-Prince at the age of twelve, one of my older brothers bought me a bench so that children did not have to Nevertheless, I know that when we are together again, and because I love you so much that the meeting will erase all the pain, all the pain. I promise! Our reunion will be a real celebration.

I am sure you're asking yourself these questions: "Where's my daddy?" When will I see him?"

I was raised in a family where discipline and respect for the laws of the Earth were part of my heritage. I never thought that I could find myself in my current situation, accused of mistreatment, and without the opportunity to explain myself because I am convicted without the benefit of the presumption of innocence. I never had a chance to say a word. I have never been given the benefit of the doubt. I was found guilty and was forbidden to see my daughter again. This decision marked my life and I am convinced, that of my daughter too.

What I am sure of is that I will continue to fight for the rights of children, as I do for those of my daughter and my son, including risking my life if necessary. Unfortunately, today, life decides otherwise by inflicting this ordeal on myself, even though I have started to defend the rights of children since I was 12 years old. Who could have imagined that I could find myself in such a situation when I have been working with children for over 22 years?

I lived in a place where the rights of the child have always been taken for granted when they were violated. Many were homeless in Port-au-Prince, others became "rest with" (restavèk), little slaves who suffered the worst treatment without ever being paid. If I can remember, I have always fought for them, for their dignity, to protect them from all kinds of abuse. This incredible story of my life is a base that gives me more strength to continue the fight. I want to be the voice of other fathers who found themselves in my situation, and who suffer in silence. Yes, our fathers also have the right to be with our children.

The way these fathers are marginalized from society is completely shameful. If at least I had money, I could have hired a lawyer, and I could have made myself heard. Alas, I did not have the means, and I'm sure many like me have been silenced and have become invisible. Truth be told, no one cares about us.

About the same time a year ago, I was about to welcome you to this world. I want you to know that your dad was there, with your mother during the entire pregnancy and that I went with her to all the visits to the doctor. And it is with your brother that we chose this name which was yours at your birth.

I was there when your mother endured the pain of contractions and after several minutes of suffering, you were born. Immediately, I held you for the first time in my arms. There are no words strong enough to describe how I felt. I want you to know that I am ready to make all the sacrifices that a father can make for his daughter he loves.

Today, as I write to you and cry, I wonder where you are. You entered my life, but I could not cherish you until the first month of your existence. The last time I saw you was on July 29, 2008. For some time now, I was already in the crosshairs of the authorities, falsely accused of having abused you and your mother.

Horrible comments have been made about my account. I was accused of beating your mother every day and she was waiting for the best opportunity to run away. One day, she managed to escape to save her life and yours, she said. I had not weighed the seriousness of the situation and had not taken up a lawyer when I was summoned for the first time. I never had the opportunity to express myself and expose my version of the facts.

Throughout the interrogation, there was a policeman next to me, ready to handcuff me. I kept praying to God that I would not end up in jail. I am writing so that those who read me understand the tragedy that occurs when it is said that preventive measures will be taken to protect the complainant. A woman can simply go to court and pretend that she has been the victim of domestic violence if she wants to hurt you.

And without any physical evidence being provided, without a police intervention record, you can spend the rest of your life in prison. It was my case that day. I was alone at sit in the dirt. For several years, I have become the voice of street children, the children of the community and of those around the world. When you are raised by loving parents, you are the result of a seed sown to give love and give it unconditionally, to protect the dignity of the divine source.

This is what I am in the eyes of all those around me and who recognize me all over the world. Therefore people come from Canada, Switzerland, Sweden, France and the United States to learn with me to love and support street children. How could I have abused my own daughter, my own blood? My daughter, not a moment goes by without me thinking of you. You are my blood, my life, my past, my future. You are in my heart; your thoughts fill my soul like water fills the cup. One day you will find out the truth. No more lies will live in you. And when we look at each other in the eye, you will know. How can I forget the connection and the love we already shared when you were not born yet? We are going to make up for a lost time, I'm sure. I have to tell the world that I was taken away from you, without a trial. Instead of protecting you, we finally hurt you. Time has passed without our eyes meeting and we have lost sight of each other.

Court, in a court of justice without justice. I remember that barely speaking English and not having the means to hire a lawyer and a translator, I had been condemned mercilessly at first sight. But I know the truth will come out. My daughter, my love, you will then know that your father is a man who does not have the slightest ounce of violence in his body. How I have always been against injustice and the abuse of all human beings, especially children! How can I abuse my daughter, my daughter I love, the one who has my blood in her veins and bears my name?

My dear daughter, you must know I adored you and cherished you, even before you were born. One month after you were born, your grandmother Yvonne, who was sick with cancer, unfortunately, died. She was the most loving woman on earth. With the whole family, we went to Haiti for the funeral. It was the last time I saw you. It was July 29, 2008. In the same amount of time, I had lost two of the most important people in my life: you and my mother. There are no words to describe my pain.

I returned to the United State and make sure I am treated well. Then, in November 2008, I received a document from the police stating that I had to appear in the Boston court for domestic violence on November 14, 2008. I barely understood and expressed myself very poorly in English. I didn't have a lawyer. I discovered that I was accused of abusing you, even though you were not yet born! Then came the terrible verdict, I had to stay away from you. I did not even know what would happen next. I had no recourse. So, I wanted to pour my resentment and to cry out my love to you through these writings, hoping that one day you would be able to read them and learn the truth about the circumstances beyond my control that had us separated.

It is important for all little girls like you to know that their dad loves them. I love you my beloved daughter and I would have given my life to be with you when you became a teenager, as are, with their father, all young girls your age. I hope these words will transcend the limits of space and our separation, and that they will be whispered in your ears while you sleep so you know how much I love you and how much I miss you. These words will wait the time necessary so that you will know, when that the interior of the cathedral is released from your beauty. What does this life of tension look like?

A silence that memories, predictions, indifferences should have masked. A father who, morning and evening, takes the same route, is bored, exhausted, exasperated. The path of anguish remakes day after day, for years. An always a new adventure, although always started again. So, on the bench, I am still looking at this man and I am doing this calculation thinking of a thousand things that I may not have time to explain, to write ...

And I hear it every day in my sleep. Rarely, she is not there. This bed looks like a village. We don't have time to sleep. All spaces have been converted into a path, a path that leads to the mill to circumvent fate. A night trip that has not been defined by a road map. It's like this story was written for me; he presented himself to me on a special scroll. And when I read it, the benchmarks are defined by luck, and that luck will manifest itself to me in broad daylight. Voluntarily, I let time pass, just to reap the fruits of silence, because truth has no other virtue than the simplicity of time. My life would probably be much simpler if I were more discreet if I stifled all of this in myself. But it was not in this torment that it manifested itself to me, despite the wrongs that this marriage could have caused me such as accusations of domestic, physical or even psychological violence.

Even worse, after going to court, it was this endless shame that never left me. I never intended to abandon my daughter. I have had the opportunity to appear in court several times to discuss this whole matter but have never managed to get an answer that could have reassured me. I decided to stick with my instinct, rather than the opinion of others on this story. My instincts tell me that all of this is neither an empty testament filled with illusions nor the usurped charge of an interrupted fate, but rather a fruitful spiritual action simply justified by a life of solid commitments.

Oh, I meditated on all of this! Then, I made my bed a sacred refuge inhabited by the mind of a little girl whose heartbeat resonates every night in my head. She was my muse. She cried, she laughed in my imagination, because she is always where I am. She speaks to me with glee to never lose a sense of humor. And life, she told me, is full of surprises. She permeated my pain. It warmed my heart. I imagine how strange this may seem to many fathers who, like me, do not have the chance to share what I love to hear me tell about my communion with my daughter and how she transformed me.

From then on, I knew that this story was intended to be told to everyone and that it was my duty to explain how I was nourished by spirituality and how it was necessary to yield to this force that makes you smile... Because it's a chance that luckily you take the doubt away, especially when you find yourself in a situation where others judge how you may feel like a biological father and may not understand your enthusiasm. You then discover the wonderful role that you play in the life of all those who really seek to know your true face. Of all those who decide to find the answers in the face of taboos. Of all those who are really interested in the questions that lead to the truth, of all those who have started their quest for authenticity.

Creating close synergy with all those we love has always been an inexhaustible source, like the one we can find in fairy tales where there is a magic wand to open the sacred doors. And that is why, a large part of my life, I will dedicate my time to this story to treat most of the slain fathers. My speech must be able to counter the cheating of most questions, not to say all that we ask ourselves when we take a winding path. I know my daughter trapped in this wild, materialistic, and contagious land when we could live freely on one of the islands of the Caribbean Sea, between Cuba and Jamaica. Now in the middle of the mad rush, I am taking my first flight of stairs to a hopeless goal ... My stomach buzzes with concern at the idea of rubbing shoulders with people while preserving a holy naivety. Materialist and selfish love should not be confused with that dominated by sharing. With each step, the concrete of disappointment builds up second after second and there is no way out. It was an hour after my arrival that everything changed. Nothing was normal anymore. I listened to the

Haitians who arrived before me and used to the almost legendary rhythms of the Latinos or the Caribbean.

The torments begin halfway between dream and reality. We play with the shadow of worries, the highest mountains in the world being in front of me. However, the main goal was to move towards sustainable development. Unfortunately, intentions are not actions. Disappointment is the reward I get, or all the steps are taken to improve social conditions. As soon we got there, we just had time to catch our breath and the war started without anyone knowing why. The enemy is the fruit that feeds friends.

The neighbors play several roles at the same time in the communities. The most important is to protect ancestral cultural traditions. It is the strangers who eliminate the desires of protect our wealth and seek other alternatives to improve life, although we have already made good progress in terms of natural health, ecology, the economy to sell what we produce and to guarantee development safe and durable.

We know that the outside is important for the safeguarding of good international relations, but Communication is the key to keeping them and to orienting them towards a strong intercultural organization, in optimal working order, without forgetting to stay in permanent contact with the daily life of the world.

It is important to avoid unnecessary altercations. The ideal is to transform adversaries and allies into tools of change so that poor ideas become rich ideas and take the lonely road to success. However, some people within the community can also be responsible for a deterioration of social life, like the visitors who arrive and behave like gods, engorged with grudges to make the rich town, a property of human conflicts. For nothing, in a single second, you can lose an entire living and healthy community.

In these cases, we have the right to privileged communication. Alliances often emanate from ideas that do not consider the action of each person who acts in complementarity for a development centered on the common interest. The enemy is the fruit that feeds friends and is good in the balance of good community communication. I've heard this many times! But I don't really believe that others will succeed, without us, in healing the wounds that affect our values. My father and mother sacrificed almost everything they had to pay for their children's education, but they couldn't figure out what tomorrow would be for the world.

Mom and dad did everything they could to age together and happily live in their community, staying in tune with community culture and tradition. Yet they found in another space where they couldn't understand anything. Let us work hard, we mustn't have an artificial behavior dominated by our pettiness. Everyone's goal is to ensure survival for both customers and employees.

All those who are lucky to travel through the eyes of the people who work all around them, tired, thirsty for words, for a new look, for hope, only silence is the response of this shy woman, reserved, laborious. Imagine a woman who never spares her strength. She works tirelessly all day. Somewhat similarly, to many who leave their country of origin, she leaves Jamaica to come and work in a foreign country. Their day begins early, an hour or two before many others who already have financial stability.

Day after day, she faces difficulties, high-stress levels. It is commendable to work alongside such a courageous woman to achieve worthwhile goals. She is a reasonable woman who makes decisions that do not harm anyone. His break time is spent in the kitchen enjoying talking about the history of the Caribbean countries or simply the history of black peoples. She shows maturity, she is a lady of great character, great knowledge, a reasonable person who can make noticeably big decisions. Despite the fatigue, we play together daily small scenarios on the common life of peoples.

For some people, the fact that we are in the kitchen, we have nothing in mind than pictures of kitchens or food, dishes. At first glance, this woman seems to be inhabited by a responsible character, she always talks about her daughter, her only daughter. In some ways, this woman symbolizes the flame that circulates the energy in the house. This flame of the kitchen like this stone obedient to the passage of time, to have its warmth and its power in the wisdom of the contempt of others. She has a very advanced intellectual capacity on certain subjects.

What does she expect from this work?

She wants that despite the difficulties of her life, she does not want to live her separation from her country and her family as an abandonment. Like her, many immigrants entrust their destiny and their future to miserable or joyous adventures. Family and friends close or distant do so for the sole purpose of preserving their dignity despite the harsh conditions in which they live. She dreams that other immigrants like her will be able to obtain security while facing difficulties. A woman or a man who engages in just and worthy causes for life. It is only as a last resort that they entrust their objectives for other purposes. These people pay a high price: they lose the status dear to them. Everything that happens at work can influence an individual or collective character. Small unconscious or thoughtful gestures can build up or completely damage.

The friendship developed rapidly during the first year on the job. I have been in this position as an assistant cook for over a year. I carry food and do the dishes. Each new workday is a new battle to endure the stress more often in the emptiness of a time filled with discriminatory looks from the work colleague who shares the same exercise space as yourself, inferiority to what we are like To be human. We encountered all kinds of situations, from the simplest to the most complicated.

For a year and a half, we have experienced a relationship of trust. We move in a space with reduced traffic, limited to sharing words and everything that exists. Music, gaze, whispering in the corridors; as a refrain to the game and dramas mingle in their daily life. We create relationships with clients, families, workmates and the institution. We consider the will and experience of each person serving the participants. Like cathedrals, people parade behind the curtains of our obligation. However, in the event of illness one no longer distinguishes the real character. Frequently, illusion prevails in the home of these tired people. The house in which we live with reduced conversation could adopt a horizontal channel communication system going from the one who wipes the door to the one who manages the tired files of ephemeral keys.

More than a thousand kilometers a day in the corridors of this house to give the best of ourselves, by serving the participants. These are made up of rich past of production, fulfillment and a present filled with frustration, they are both solid-like cathedrals and metamorphosed like a butterfly. At this point, they reach their last stage of transformation before becoming this light and fragile butterfly.

The inner strength of these cathedrals is incomparable. Almost everything in a vacuum, the dream, the objectives, the projects, the memories, has a color invisible to any one of us who wishes to make the analysis or the comparison. The originality, or at least the authenticity of these characters is the only note that persists.

I remember a young man from Liberia, this young man is not afraid to explore the world of the victims of this disease. He approaches residents as family members do. He defies indifference and adorns his working time with a tickling look and an incessant smile where pleasure flows. He does his homework of approach at the first steps of his hours with a decisive movement that leaves no chance for others to read a tired face. Passionate about his work, he has the art of creation to adapt, he becomes a teacher of himself and continues his routine with pain and pleasure. A small gesture of benevolence can forge ties with patients of a very lonely nature.

People move around, without knowing that it is impossible to live at the same pace as in their country of origin, so they make a forecast of their own, unsuited to reality. They come from America, Asia, Europe, Africa, and the Caribbean. They are of a different culture, different nationalities, and different languages. The most important thing remains the personal strategy of the traveler to achieve his goal. As immigrants, they act every day to reduce exclusion in all its forms: social, economic, cultural. The challenge is that people from all walks of life can meet, find meaning in their lives together and mobilize for a just and noble cause. We realize how important the presence of each person in their respective place is for the well-being of everyone. And when we are in the corridors to share the look and the work, trust is an essential element and this trust must be reciprocal to balance everything.

We have never asked the question of whether certain families can be on this path of suffering where all the precepts of their family life are to be recalculated concerning the situation presented to them. In their lives, there is a feeling of poverty that is suddenly introduced into their journey of existence, highlighting the ability of each person who surrounds them and supports them in their daily lives. Going to conquer their origin will undoubtedly give another reason to exist without thinking of the simplest attitude which trivializes the depressed look. This journey will give the power to act while fighting and the traveler commits when necessary. There is no special method to work with these people sick when we already know that everyone has a behavior of its own. What their illness represents is in every glance that meets them.

One more reason to become invisible. None of those who were there in the corridor, none of those who attended me could feel my pain and transformation. I did not react to what is happening around me, I do not blame myself, as if I were poor or stupid. And I know that I am the winner of this natural happiness. And the more time passes, the more I realize that no one can give birth to my daughter. I am the best father in the world. I do not waste time-fighting for a cause already won by the blood that girl is mine. Rather I am born again into a realm of silence to absorb the pain of my daughter looking day and night to face his real dad. I learn to be present to its spiritual vibration, I learn to be a supporter of my responsibilities. At each moment, I rediscover new seeds for new seeds to open new paths to the quest for success, in each act a new response comes to life. I thought of all those who lived yesterday and saw with me the birth of my daughter. One month after the birth of my daughter, the death of my mother. But despite all that I'm a lucky man because the eyes of the judge wanted at all costs to throw me in jail ...

And I had just thought why the judge did not throw me in prison and allowed me to remain free to find my boy because out of all consideration the prison looked at me through his eyes and that day then I looked other fathers like me who left the courtroom and entered a strange door.

I looked in front of me where I was on the bench, without smile, without strength, a man, a father, a defendant without help, drowned in the fatal offense of his wife, who passes by the big door of the courtroom number two; he is looking for a person to defend himself. I look at it, I do my math like a so-called lucky guy that I am! I'm trying to minimize the severity of my case. What does a man look like when a nightmare is constantly watching him? I can't sleep and I decide to write a letter to send to any girl:

My dear daughter, where are you?

Do you agree?

Did I miss you?

I know you can't answer all of these questions. Just to let you know that despite being wrongly accused and unable to see you, see you smile, call me grandpa, watch you take your first steps, there is no anger in my heart. My heart is full of love that I am currently able to share with my son and the rest of my family. There is no room for hatred or revenge. I only have a room for peace, love, a celebration of life, making the world a better place, giving voice to those who don't have it, using my gifts to empower for serve all those who are looking for ways to improve their lives: this is what I am, my purpose in life.

There are many other children who suffer because they do not have a father. But you have a father. Although you and I are suffering from this separation forced upon us by an imperfect system. A system which, under the guise of protection, does more harm than good. People are thrown like dolls, nobody cares about the consequences, cares about those who suffer. He cannot go on like this. This imperfect system that must change. Innocent people cannot be abused like this, they need to have a voice, a fair trial, and cannot be punished if they are not found guilty, don't worry, be patient, time goes by and provides a solution to unresolved problems. I love you, Your grandpa. The first few times I started going to court, I felt like I was starting a special mission. A duty to clean up a bookish creed manifested itself to me, I knew that I was going to speak of the voiceless, I was going to speak everywhere in the world. And also, I realized that a little girl was looking for me somewhere.

The answers arise one after the other. Yet I do not sing about victory, because I already know human nature does not tolerate paternal separation. My life and the life of my daughter tolerate the pain of this separation for a time since the existence of this girl was not designed to separate her from her father in her early childhood. She may not be aware of such an event. I feel chained since the first day of my trip, my tears flow freely and travel in the void of these sad times. I remember on August 17, 2007, at Haiti's airport, in New York, we spent part of the day normally before joining the other family members. On the plane, I remember that there were three people on my right - another Haitian family - we shared different views on how to settle in another country. A West Indian sitting not too far from us joined the debate.

He said: with us, we never worry about what we will meet elsewhere. Moving to another country is like adapting to musical rhythms to dance to the sound of the drum of life. The pleasure of this trip was the meeting with this West Indian. However, more and more men still want to settle in the United States. We seem to have left the powerful dreams of our existence behind us to go to reinforce the vision of the other who relies on immigrants of all kinds. Five or six generations of my family have been paid slaves throughout their lives. Do not judge anything, everything has a meaning, do not joke ...

Little by little, those who accept slavery move away from the bowels of their maternal roots. Only a few victims fight to the end. And some continue to cling forcefully to their hard lives while feeling nostalgic for their homeland. However, this way of life has nothing to do with the suffering of a father who, morning and evening, hears the voice of his daughter in his head, and imagines his figure passing and passing. Sometimes this tired, rejected father turns to smoke to kiss his daughter's shadow. For a second, a minute, a day, a week, a month, a year and whole days, millions of thoughts strike his memory, and no one doesn't understand. With all his might, he waited to hear from his daughter, from a part of himself.

Anxiety is a terrible feeling that appeared on the first day. The shame felt in front of everyone, and the hope of receiving good news was always there. The days pass and pass again, but the anxiety persists in the face of the uncertainties of the future and the thousand unanswered questions which assail it daily. The hope that nothing can be worse, and that makes you live. This life of opposite feelings is extraordinary.

It is a path of an unparalleled spiritual dimension. Life in itself is a great meeting project which evolves, and which does not end socially. Logically, the population is changing economically and technologically, but without ever taking the time to hear the evolution of its heart. This is something very rarely discussed, even though it is even imagined in the most advanced meditation centers on this planet. This proposal to hear the beating of the heart is made in relation to the desires we have: always chasing after others without thinking of ourselves; destroy a good part of our life to associate it with that of any dreamer. As a tenant on the planet, no one is better placed than you who are reading this book now. Already, our existence on earth confirms that we are the key to the final decision to create a better life. For all those who feel neglected: our advice is focused on research around a more humanistic world. No matter what physical choice we make, spiritual existence will not condemn us, but it questions us about the length of our path. He will show us the way. It will not force us, however, to accept the impossible.

I find the real palliative to this endemic problem in our environment: it is the social commitment of each of us by opening doors that are both captivating and disgusting. One elementary thing to our survival is the captivity of all those who are corruptible catalysts living among us. However, the scale that this evil becomes is the name at all levels of society.

Fear of filing a complaint is considered an offense. And it is the degradation of each small moral patch which becomes giant, and which, one next morning, is likely to destroy parents and children at the same time. What we must reflect on our children is not the image of revenge, but rather a heritage, mixed with compassion and passion in this beautiful life that we must spend together in the purest harmony. One can very easily and without worry acquire the honorary inheritance of a family without destroying the initial structure.

Before talking about others, denouncing what they are doing wrong - and evil they imagine because very often they do not know what they are talking about - it is better to talk about your ability to transform and create life again without sticking to a specific subject because life is never precise. Knowing how to live with others does not mean that you are winning and having the control to make things go right, because you always have to take risks. Putting others out of your life puts you in loneliness very often associated with this scene that you are currently experiencing. It is this marriage that prevents you from fully grasping the problems and clearly understanding what it means to live in communion with oneself. This infinite evil goes back and forth in your life. When we keep human qualities, we rarely find ourselves in the perspective of two beings inevitably aspiring to live together with their unhappy acts and their happiness in the same equation. People who judge you clearly understand the outrageous aspects of your life, but they limit themselves to the physical understanding of things and this aspect prevails, regardless of the other aspect which is spiritual. It is therefore not surprising that this results in a completely distorted perception of what you are as an individual. It must, therefore, be understood that your case, like any other case, cannot be fully understood by a simple observer who imagines and gathers the facts without making a permanent study from two distinct points of view: in men and in women.

I mean, of course, from the physical point of view and from the metaphysical point of view, from the social point of view and from the family point of view. These four views are vastly different and diverge from each other. But they are not contradictory, although they may appear to be for a shallow audience. I saw the real illustration. Four fathers erected as guilty actors for an unreal cause: a pastor, a teacher, a social worker, and a medical technician displayed the same disappointment with their lives. This misinterpreted theme can make people's lives that were initially peaceful difficult. They are deeply affected, but nothing can change if the silence surrounding the facts is not broken. And if one day we simply reverse the roles: consider the strident parties in the same way as the fathers who are in a perilous situation. No one has ever approached this view of tortured fatherhood, while the other part, speaking of mothers, never forgives the one who allegedly bears responsibility for their bruised life.

However, at first, it is the story of a man and a woman who live in perfect harmony, and who know that they both share the different aspects of the great river whose source is their truth. Everyone around them believed them to be as harmonious as one could imagine. But some people did not understand it. I remember one day a father said to me, with great perplexity: I do not understand anything! When we were two indicators who had decided to talk to us, to put us together and to look together in the same direction to build a real-life, we found ourselves at two opposite poles. I then understood that married life represented problems which caused a great number of difficulties in the physical or spiritual life of many people who nevertheless dreamed of honestly establishing a solid and lasting base. It's as if two friends are going to drink from the same source and go forward together following the same current, to celebrate in a unique environment the same events; build projects that they would then undertake and that would be the fruit of a perfect adventure, enriched by ambitious dreams.

And yet in a period which sometimes does not last longer than the time to say hello, the dream has already failed. One went to the north side of this story, while the other went to the south side. The first steps begin with cooing on the red carpet. This love is constructed in such a way that no one can guess in any way that the passion will die out. If I had been asked before if certain currents of harmony could be destroyed, I would have said: no! But afterward, I perfectly understood that this immense world was endowed with foresters and carpenters who both work with wood, but cling to time at different times. And this time is available completely free. It's up to you to use it, and divide it up between the responsibilities of these two men, both driven by passion and patience, because time requires patience and to have a good piece of wood, you need passion and patience.

As life can tell, this description is the basis of a true couple based on mutual respect, until death does it. Imagine that we are going down the river and that the reality is on both banks, a man and a woman can easily decide to descend the river bed in the middle at the same time and therefore find themselves caught in the speed of the river which advances to the end or to the total confusion of the great ocean. Once reconciled, but exhausted, the ocean receives them without having time to explain anything to them. As clearly a possible, then, what is the vision of these two DIY enthusiasts?

This is where the problem is! I'm going to show you how not studying the case of each of these two exhibitionists will create an imperative gap for the child who was born in passion but becomes a mercantile object. By joking with the chance, I would say that the authorship of man is an act of trust, advised by God in his works. We can immediately see the contradictory difference between these two people from a physiological point of view which is however not apparently visible.

Contrary to popular belief, the integral development of a child takes place in the accuracy of palpable and unique facts. We must think before making decisions, ramshackle dilapidated by divine power at the risk of carrying the stuff of shame that we would not be able to bear perfectly. For the happiness of everyone, in any good cause, we must openly contemplate together the work of perfect and glorious unity, devotional to the mirror of God like a mutant gaze.

We must be transformed with each humiliation so that we can leap from an aphasic image to a gladiatorial appearance anemic with memories of a given time. Serenely, we must transform ourselves into a responsible

254

nurturer. Normally, all the duties performed must be transparent and form the uncompromising renewal of this power which is never in your favor. The secret of a life charred by unhappy talks gives no chance of discernment. What is good is to accept and seek to understand what is the will of the partners confronted with the dilemmas.

When the sun warms the earth, it is not the idea of owning it, but rather of rendering a simple service to the simplest plant that needs it every day. When the sun gives its heat, it is common to find rest in return thanks to light rain. The source is always the end of another source that begins again in another direction with another, more thoughtful dimension, to combine the maturity of a seemingly invisible long road. And yet, the space of land occupied by the perimeter of the water wisely gives its dust so that it turns into a terrace of traveling mud.

Again, it's about giving and still giving! Like giving to giving. Water gives the earth its limitless source. And it is the trust of the people who live there that confirm the existence of this inexhaustible source for the thirstiest men. The willingness of each person to serve others is a possibility to discover the creative side of the latent state of a person voluntarily engaged. Before the power of the will, creation can take place to balance emotion and sensitivity during social events. The chance to volunteer does not mean that you are the chaplain or the benefactor who deserves salvation.

Whoever wants to speak is silent and lets others speak to understand the meaning of the conversation and maintain liaison between those who want to discuss good causes and maintain memory to cope with demagoguery. And sometimes silence is the answer of everyone who believes in a savior. You do not pretend like you're a merchant looking for customers. Besides, if you were a trader, you would offer your products without giving anything material, but rather the word, the look, the haunting perceived in the different facial expressions, the gestural paintings of daily reality, through movements of your simple body. The resonance of the gaze is one of the elements that always give this possibility to the other to appreciate and keep the product that he appreciates.

The politician gives his speech to collect voters in return. The priest or pastor who delivers their homily for the sole purpose of having more people in the church are destroying the gospel predilection to bring people together all over the world. What does the gospel represent for these men of the Church? It must be the fundamental basis for calling hearts. Seven days a week, the volunteer is there to offer a smile to everyone regardless of color, origin, religion, and gender. The volunteer's gaze must provide an answer, or the hope of providing an answer, such as when you look for the answer in the eyes of the person asking the question.

The volunteer, through his words, his look, with a happy look, must share peace. In this life, if you go through the front door, you are received by a mother and it is she who gives you the keys to play this game of patience that is life. Despite the pressures, this woman most often always managed to manage the smallest details despite the disrupted schedule of her days. The mother's experience will be useful to all who are preparing to become a quality volunteer. In addition, the mother gives you strength and teaches you principles that will be useful in your everyday life so that one day you will become a person who will want to learn, identify or learn. Use good manners in the service of others.

Your mother is not a teacher, but in each look, she shares so much with you! It transmits you full of positive vibrations, and all around it, the space it manages turns into a pool of purity. In front of her, there is no time to think about the waste of bad thought. With her, one has the impression that one lives just to find time to serve others and turn one's life into leisure. Smiling is the most important thing in the life of a volunteer. This is what the volunteer can clearly demonstrate by receiving people with a blown smile on the face of each person facing him. The look of a volunteer should never bring despair, but joy and welcome for everyone.

In terms of voluntary service, young boys and girls play an essential role in the survival system of people in the community. Their creative skills can save lives. Even at a high level of ingratitude, one cannot forget this youth of the community who has great qualities in terms of communication with others. The volunteer must always be available to listen and plan the time necessary for everyone. For some people, being in a poor country only reflects images of poverty. However, being rich or a foreigner means absolutely nothing. You are a human being who attends the same school as everyone else: this world.

Confidence is another dimension of the wealth one has within oneself. To restructure, create an organization centered on human values, never uses the force of money, but rather the power of thought, the wealth of the heart. When you work with wealth from the heart, it's an amazing story. An opposition that appears is a positive point for the organization. To adopt a project against the opinion of the population would do more harm than good. Work to make opponents think and gradually come to convince them that they are becoming a module of change. Cultivate and give respect to whoever works with you so that he becomes your friend and the defender of your ideas, ideas which are at the base of the philosophy of the organization. This is how we manage to find collaborators, and not to be forced to do everything ourselves.

Make everyone, even the weakest, feel their value and what they can bring to the community. Explore the country, starting with its area of origin. Each person in the community will observe what they discover with the idea of coming back and applying what they have learned to build their own environment. Often people in the area are reluctant to meet around a project. They are shy or uninformed. It is about establishing and cultivating relationships with them, to understand their conception of things and help them build their thoughts.

Organizational development work should not be limited to the walls of the organization. It must be practiced everywhere by observing, speaking, and listening to people. No one is a prisoner of his environment: you must not adopt the attitude of letting live and watch live without judging and questioning each fact; you must know how to live and advance your own ideas. Each circumstance calls for a unique attitude oriented according to the environment, people, and actions. You will have to know how to refuse what is bad by saying yes or no when necessary.

We realize how important the presence of each person in their respective place is for the well-being of everyone. And when we are in the spaces to share the look and the work, trust is an essential element and this trust must be reciprocal to balance everything.

In a community, we meet families who, through their family culture, give quite different educations. The evolution of the community takes place with the culture of the people who are part of it, during the three phases of their life: childhood, adolescence, when one is adult or elderly. Knowing the people of a community is not enough, it is important to understand them to recognize them one by one with their own family and personal culture.

Being in a family is not enough. You also need to know the behavior of each person and cultivate family friendship. Be friends of your parents to be able to share life and understand your role, your vocation. It is this role that allows everyone to be socially integrated into their community. Familiarize each person with the behaviors of the community in which they live, analyze the facts, master them, transform them according to the needs of the community.

Reflect on the situation of the people who live in the community, understand and make people understand that they are instruments of change and that they must necessarily be trained while taking into account the values and the reality of the environment. Work with all the forces of the community. Each within the limits of its capacities can take charge of its own development. To understand people, you have to study the environment in which they live. To be comfortable in a community, you have to know the culture of that community.

The organization is, therefore, a permanent pool of meetings which trains and informs people about their responsibilities, based on their values. It is through families that we know the community. It is a question of understanding this family organization before broadening its community vision, and this requires asking the question of what is necessary for it. In general, we meet families whose members have very different behaviors between generations. People do not develop at the same rate, and their level of understanding is very different.

To be a respected and responsible person, you must be able to understand the life of a community and to integrate it. The real goal is to give strength to families to make children happy by building the community. Go to people with all their spiritual and physical dimensions. Knowing a little bit about people's history is already a path to success.

Inform, train, participate and involve people in concrete actions. Keep people informed about what we are doing, and especially people who are interested in the cause we are defending. Talking without doing anything and doing without saying anything are dangers that can bring the organization down.

Act with an open heart and tell people what is being done, demonstrate respect for the opinion of others, and at the same time state their views and reasons for doing so. It's about being ready to listen to others: optimism should be the weapon of the host. The facilitator is not there to provide answers to the problems, but rather to listen, discuss, support, and always encourage creativity.

Discover people and their lives. Believe and make people believe in the value of man, give the assurance that we can transform everything. Each person has hidden talents that must be discover. Build a common destiny in the freedom and autonomy of each person in relation to other decision-making powers. You cannot develop yourself without working to understand others.

Each person has his reasons for living and he must choose his own principles to base his style and his personal conduct. Continuous research to find out why we exist and what meaning we should give to our lives; how we see the world; the people we meet all have the same goal: to succeed in their lives, even if they are not in the same direction. If we take the example of a plant whose purpose is to give fruit: this plant must go through several stages. Each phase has its own rules that give it meaning and allow it to arrive at real production. It is important to seek the goal of one's life to guide each action.

The joy of existing lies in the ability to create. You are alive, and your existence is an instrument to build the life you want to live, your capacities as a responsible man will mobilize your resources to build with others. You must constantly recreate your life so that it is adapted to the reality of your environment.

What you say, do, see, think is the product of your reading of things and the environment in which you live. The faces you see reflect your being. Your availability at a given moment is the product of a feeling of responsibility towards the elements that surround you at that moment.

The animator must refer to morality without being moralistic, and common sense to remind parents of the duties and rights of their children, and the possible consequences of bad behavior. Let us pose the problems of our society and seek solutions to these problems: it is important to seek what should be done to put an end to the recriminations and avoid the division because then it would not only be a family that would be affected by it but all a community.

The facilitator should be able to remember that he has a responsibility to make a difference in his world. His world rests solely on his shoulders. He is a leader in being a servant of this world, but he may be the most powerful, being the one who brings solutions.

However, there are things he cannot do on his own and he needs to meet, listen, share, communicate with others. Talking a lot can be good if you do so by listening carefully to the silence of those who accept the words. The facilitator must be able to recognize who is active among the liabilities ...

It is sometimes a question of recognizing a single asset among dozens of liabilities, this is not obvious. The animator is a walker between dream and reality, and often it is patience in the wisdom of his silence that shows him the way. He does not need to do any major studies, if he has acquired experience in the field and has carried out internships, in particular in animation techniques.

Crafts, music, theater, painting, agriculture are still the basics required to be a facilitator. From there, he can exercise his creativity, his natural talent, his originality, and give free rein to his ideas. Of course, his professional training allowed him to develop his skills. The leader must follow in the footsteps of the community to be aware of reality. The most important thing for him is to be recognized in his work. There is a long way to go because it is a matter of making people recognize that this work is selfless. You must, therefore, be patient and not give up.

By carrying out artistic activities with the children, the animator trains himself. Indeed, through these activities, he will discover his limits and his qualities: is he able to teach a group a simple work method, activities centered on each person as a kind of therapy? When you have a project, you should rather live in the future and believe that you will succeed in imposing what you want to do, in the community as in the whole world. And this, despite the nature of prejudice in societies, despite the risk that this profession of animator entails being accepted for what we are not.

Critics are scary. At the start, we dare not venture into any project, for lack of self-confidence. Keeping your own style will make you feel stronger. We can take as a reference all those who have succeeded from nothing, who have given themselves and struggled to be at the level where they are. We must meditate every day on our dream. The main concern of a facilitator is to bring to life and enhance the community where he evolves, through what he is, but not with what he has. We do not build with what we have, but with what we are.

So, this way of becoming invisible manifested to me. And I literally put it into practice in a book that was written with you. It manifested to me and when you think of me, the spiritual power that binds me to you is my guide. I feel it manifest in me every time I think of you.

My life would probably be a lot easier if I had kept it all to myself. But it was not for this purpose that this power of invisibility manifested to me. Despite the inconvenience, this way of living could cause me, it is no longer possible for me to stop my trip. Nor is it my intention to stop.

I have had the opportunity several times to move away from all this powerful and fragile business to imagine something else, another road to see you, but I have not found other easier ways. I feel more comfortable in this adventure where I enjoy full powers. I decided to stick with the fact that your existence dictated this incomparable lifestyle to me.

Sacrifice my normal life to live another life for my daughter, divorce the opinion of others, and get as deep as possible into the content of this adventure. This invisibility tells me that life is neither a territory where men live or the surface heated by the injustice of justice.

Oh, I thought about all of this in detail. Then, I chose this uniform way of life without registering in the torments caused by anyone. Trying to juggle the inequalities of the world, I silently enter an invisible universe. There are other factors of instability: ignorance, poverty, disease, exclusion, illiteracy, lack of values, desertification of the imagination, unemployment in addition to this separation. I am exasperated by the socio-economic imbalance, by injustices and humiliations. This is how the techniques to become invisible are born and developed while retaining the moral concepts of normal life.

The world has remained indifferent to all these phenomena for too long, in which many of us sometimes seem to have taken part. The invisibility of a man in the physical world is seen as a dangerous phenomenon; all this arouses distrust and fear; we lock ourselves up; we barricade ourselves; we veil. A father like me has no confidence in this justice system or in certain people who are not shy about using trickery out of interest.

It is very important to know what you are looking for otherwise it is impossible to find the unity of objectives. The conditions for obtaining the result is therefore clarity of mind, otherwise, it will be very easy to disperse.

It was like a measure beat party with your voice you were in the middle of the music and a shadow song opened the doors to the world.

The movement of people all around you tosses the bright space of nuance and joy until the day when permission is ours to leave the door of the hospital.

A Beautiful Job

THE PART WHICH MAKES THE PHILANTHROPIC base in the man, it is the family, even in the countries strangled by differences. Existentialist philosophy always combines life as a verb and uses it as a subject of sharing to form the sentence of a world without borders. Everyone's active participation is more than giving voice, it is more than giving what we have. It is not a gesture of pity or a gesture of favor.

Speech, words should not be the basis of the love you give to others. Never believe in the crowd. The crowd is nobody, yet the person represents the crowd. Man is never complete without the community providing him with what he is continually looking for. It is important to know the behavior of the community in which we find ourselves.

Volunteering at CODEHA is a question of full commitment that is gradually taking shape. The existence of everything is not just a coincidence, one is the complement of the other. Life is not what you get from it, but what you give it. Anyone who knows and accepts his value is free. We realize how important the presence of each person in their respective place is for the well-being of everyone. And when we are in the spaces of sharing of look and work, confidence is an essential element. This trust must be reciprocal to balance everything.

It is important to describe the social evolution of the CODEHA in the suffering communities since its creation in early 1992. This evolution also affects the transformations of the society where it evolves through practical actions of visible representations among the communities.

The work of CODEHA is based on daily value research and focused on the existence of studies and research for integrated development, both national and international. The CODEHA is available for a faithful listening to society without housing from an ideological point of view. We obtained documentation totally focused on the cultural study of the inhabitants of the area, because without these social studies, we cannot effectively be operational. It is deeply exhausting for a giver of community development to invest in the universality of an entire population directly involved in their own social destruction for hundreds of years. To respond to this failure, culturally fragmented social orientation workshops for the social and human community are to be recommended.

To work on new approaches to social classes and movements for social and individual promotion in contemporary communities, the CODEHA has brought together a generation traditionally very controversial. She has had the courage to publicly rally around the contradictions that have arisen and attract the incredible interest of everyone in sociologically important work.

We are present in society as in a flooded river following an unknown downpour. One of the first points to characterize community development is people's lives. It is a question of values and beliefs for generations. We must not forget that society is relatively new since the concept of social life had completely disappeared in recent years. Years of natural disasters in the country.

You who are called to volunteer, listen to the instructions of silence, and listen to your interior. Accept a traveler's advice and follow it effectively. Thus, you will come back through the work of self-esteem and obedience to the one from whom the uncertainty of your ability has alienated you.

This philosophy is for you, whoever you are, you who give up your selfish feelings and take on the very powerful and unlimited weapons of community engagement, in order to create, transform and produce for others and for you - even true happiness.

If you are looking for others, do not look for the crowd, rather look for the one who forms the crowd. A good worker is never in the crowd if he is not the one leading the crowd. A people without novelty is a people without shield, it is a breathless people who are called to work and who renounce their human value. It is then considered as a retarder to social progress. What is the secret of a man who loves life and wants to see happy days What will be the result of harvesting a day of celebration? Who finds an answer to this question? And if you answer, it will be your answer and not that of others. Imagine everyone coming from these poor countries remote and underdeveloped. There are most certainly people who have long agreed to let their country of origin to go and contribute to the development of another country. Parents or single beings have granted me their confidence to organize and trace together a way of destiny and choose me as a guide for to advance the magical value of their existence.

I must sharpen their talent like a craftsman of historical perfection which cuts the fabrics of communities and where engagement finds a place without excess for development tools. At the same time, we never suspected that people, millennia later would remain attached to their sacred ideas like polished stones. We had fiery people in their thoughts that passed so fast that it looked like lightning streaks ripping through the clouds in the sky. There were a lot of affinities, but these things didn't last that short moment and their audiences with ideas of crystal gave nuances to their duration. It was like lightning fighting in meetings community-based and those who remained as deaths for decades, hampering walking of a whole century.

At the same time, people worked on their ideas and transformed them until come up with real symbols of communities. They fraternized resources that gave them a natural power to lay the foundations of a foundation solid. Community members have become residents of one house, and this house, it is their solidarity that protects them from the misery of underdevelopment. Young people of all categories carried the flames from which sprang the light of their charms without limits, and we popularized their know-how using these talents as a lucky charm of their own lives, until the accomplishment of their 18, 20 years.

We focused on one point that is fascinating: these creation legends, demonstrating that it is they like people who have the responsibility to work to create the world by generating significant capacity for everything simply produce dynamic wealth and alive. These can give life to all those that are born and exist in us and around us. This youth is remarkable, after having matured in she trusts her, like fruits of new hopes. Our inkwells can be filled to write the methods of new theories, and that is how all the black ideas fell into the trash.

The young people were inhabited by trust and this trust becomes a protective god. If the referential person in a community does not have this trusted guide, we consider it a raw and passive matter. However, this same person, referenced with confidence for their values and his ability to create, is considered a stone cut by God to participate in the construction of the world. For men who inhabit it, it can indicate and trace the passage of a road. Thus, volunteering becomes the brand in which the commitment of every citizen serves to ensure respect for the rights of each individual. The founder of the CODEHA himself took to the streets to go to remote areas to meet the people of all categories. The nascent movement kept these unique secrets here and there in populations, content to assimilate them, keeping the precious and sacred values of each person in a particular and symbolic way, marking them so of his social works.

Our campaigns teeming with examples for the construction of a modern and prosperous world. To reach their goal, the movement saves everything acquired the potential of the people with whom he works and accompanies it. The organization has a pyramid of proper functioning. Identify by the community culture where it is found while respecting the basic standards, that is what we can also call the philosophy of CODEHA (Haitian Child Rope). We are against rumors of community spells, well that we are not ignorant of manners and beliefs people animists. A person who has great human values has an open door of a size comparable to that of a big barrier to let people in and the news. In the mode of compared dolphins to that of men, it is always the man who is the first place of living beings, a being capable of reason to recreate his world in his own way. For some people, a vision is just a disease psychiatric devoid of analytical sense to understand that the great thoughts that may create and change come from the poor. Without us realize, we live every day with stars to destroy the black life in which we swarm daily.

The star, which we look for shines already in the night that was our millions. Volunteer at CODEHA, this is the response that life has given when we believe in this creative power that lodges in you and all around you, whether it is wealth, opportunities more numerous than ever, of a life formed by people from the community and transformed by your creative force. Those who have waited all their life for happiness - for some it is the first time in their lives - will discover the solution because they were convinced that life should be transformed by themselves and that their creative ability could be this transformative response.

I also dream of being a promoter of human value in all societies. Extend the name of each one, as sons and daughters of a single homeland, recognize the cultural source of each one to act according to their origin and the intellect of their training, to understand ancient peoples and modern peoples within their limits.

I dream of receiving lessons from everyone and having common sense, to express a value judgment without the barrier of stereotypes, whether it is color or race. Walking in righteousness does not mean that one is perfect or the best. Before comparing yourself to others, you must give them permission to discover yourself through simple everyday actions.

Always have time to listen to others, and this will increase your chance of finding your true path and knowing where you must start walking to complete the race with your own steps. All those who are against you will be sparks of light on your passage as well as for all those who will remain faithful to you.

Accept everything and you will find the art of dominating everything to manage your environment well. Take the time to grasp the meaning of everything around you, and one by one: watch observe, travel, verbalize everything to find the true meaning of your being as the energy that keeps each existence, words and boundless gestures to make new decisions.

The fear of starting is the beginning of the end, a departure without a trace. The incredulous despise the words and the gaze of passers-by, sometimes wise, sometimes aggressive and misunderstood in their appearance. The biggest method is to listen to them as you would listen to a brother or sister. The education of your father and mother is not necessarily the education you received to fragment the teaching of your method, because each of us is a gift reserved for others. It is a race accomplished each time we have the grace to find ourselves through others. Each new morning on this path is a new bet won in your fight.

Souvenir

My one and only power are to create. I had to suffer to create the infant movement and hold out until the end! My heart has always been for sharing and for charity. I have always had the strength to continue my mission, First of all, I would like to thank the passion and the spirit of commitment that has always lived in me to take the right path and follow others in their difficult trajectories. Thank you to everyone who made this dream projection possible. Those who have provided me with the means to satisfy my passionate search for this sensational connection between man and nature, and for the confidence they have placed in me on the high road I would like to warmly thank my parents for their success in agriculture which gave me the desire to join this natural corridor to better understand their passion and continue to cross the infinite passages they have traced. I also congratulate all those who from morning to evening take any path to go everywhere where there are men, women, and children to meet them one by one.

I am talking about these anonymous herbalists, the pioneers of this profession, of a formidable culture. These people have contributed a great deal to the establishment of solid foundations for certifying the theories practiced today. This learning is the accomplishment of many obligatory passages taking the hook daily for a real accumulation of natural and spontaneous know-how. Through this study, I renew a sacred bond with the ancestors, they open up to me the rhythmic spaces of tired hearts and the secret channels of retirees.

At first, I started to panic thinking that the profession of herbalist would be a primitive, isolated, unknown profession, impossible to understand by the contemporary world, but at the moment when I began to read articles and books corresponding to the evolution of this profession made up of natural panacea, I gained confidence in what I was doing. If I had to move forward, I would have to widen my field of knowledge myself. Go to the villages, meet the oldest, share with them new ideas, understand the stories, follow the paths that we should find from their vision and deeply feel the spiritual blossoming that binds us to plants.

Although sometimes physically, I felt a little lonely and tired in the race, I always felt myself floating in pools of great surprises. Many innate, anonymous, self-taught herbalists in these remote villages of different countries like Haiti, the Dominican Republic, Peru, Guatemala, Venezuela and of course those of other countries like Switzerland, the United States, Canada, and France allowed me to take an observant and unusual look to be able to understand today my responsibility as a new insider of this sum of knowledge of which I am very proud to present a passionate literature in a vital and inseparable culture between human and all of nature.

In general, my first goal is to mix formula and design in the natural rotation of a magical daily herb.

I think that becoming a herbalist today requires a whole disposition and a little time so that all the elements that form this profession really connect in order to have the possibility of remaining open on the horizon of an endless mission to meet what we are through the real bases of an existence created on the communion of natural forces without being manipulated by men. Above all, passion is an important phase in the exercise of this modest profession. The largest and most accessible school for learning in nature, the real home of plants. In a simple way, the world of plants always opens its doors to all those who want to explore the secrets of Mother Nature.

The absence or presence of a plant in a garden does a lot in human culture and in the evolution of life in general. The existence of each plant is not a coincidence, one is the complement of the other. It is the pluralism of everything that forms the great helix of the systemic and circulatory development of the diagonal growth of humanity. Nature is for me a basin filled with love that makes me kneel before the wonders of the world and gives me the true vision of a traveler.

Haiti must follow the process of rapid and sustainable development. Poverty reduction and rural development are part of popular thinking. The remote regions of the country have a huge economic vocation allowing us to enter a form of revolution for a total transformation of community life through agriculture. Strong agricultural potential is justified by an adequate climate and suitable soil. However, they are among the regions that offer strong economic potential to both national and international investors. We can be sure, research on a new way of working the land and using natural energies can change the future of the world, especially Haiti. I assure you that a good use of land and energy could help many countries to cope with the hunger that gnaws at them. For lack of having found a good answer to the lesson of which we exploit the livable spaces, the environment dropped our hearts, and this earth took speed by going down the path of nothingness where man has exhausted all the resources available as trees, mines ...

For a few years now, the CODEHA (Corde Enfant haïtien) has focused its research on culture and agriculture, a way of recreating a whole new dynamism in the territories occupied by men, women, and children. And for good reason, CODEHA, this organization composed mainly of young people, aware of their way of life, has just married the idea of producing more food, by bringing together the skills in art and agriculture and by renewing energy to have a better life.

The activities, that were unusual to say the least, took place in communities in the Valley of Jacmel, in the southeast of Haiti, on the most remote mountains and hillsides. If we have the necessary funding, we think that in less than five years, we will be able to start all the resources and in less than ten years we will be able to obtain a profession of earth and energies renewable to be able to train people by becoming professionals in the field of agriculture and energy which we so much need to save, not only Haiti but also all humanity. Let us hope that these professions arrive at their notoriety so that we put again the man in his place of greatness and capacity to relive life in the energy, food, and financial security.

Several thousand hectares of land can be cultivated, several thousand natural resources can be transformed and we will be able to help an entire community survive without waiting for several years for assistance from the state or recognized national and international organizations around the world for their food assistance. The CODEHA organization finally decided to choose a safe route for sustainable development communities in terms of food, renewable and economic energy. . . And here is our proposal: to have a school of earth and renewable energy trades, which means a school mainly focused on agriculture.

Trouble Moment

I UNDERSTAND THERE IS SOME CONFUSION. Many are traumatized. Many confused about the timing of discovering the life connections that people experience. With concern for my life dream: what can I do to get my goal within this human salad of life, pleasure, work, disease, and death. It does not matter what people think of me they can never stop me. Did you accuse me or try to destroy my dream? It is hard to imagine that creating poverty can be a hobby of some people, those that promote misery and death. I have my conception of what life is. I am with the understanding that women and men should believe in themselves before all others.

Back in my community, there were ideas without formation that occupied my mind constantly. That is why I never seem to sleep well these ideas kept coming and coming filling my brain like a blank chalkboard. One by one so many images came to me like movies that filled my time. Family and friends living around me could not understand. When I got my first job as a social director in Haiti, I oversaw a project working with the children living on the street. When I started the job, it was necessary to move to Port au Prince. I remember being surprised by the way I see these children living in the street.

There is something about immigrant life. The road they make by others. The work they do, one job after another after another after another every job one more door to open and ask how where and anything just to bring food at home. Every job different but somehow the same. And the day goes on forever, given place to the year, make people old. Wherever you are, you could go to work, and if you follow your path, you would find the way you can fit.

There is another thing to know about my dreams. They are big and far to realize. Dreams are like life. You do not want to get in their way those dreams. My mom and my father left me they whole model heritage when my dad taught me how to have come to a farmer and a nature lover. That is another reason why I like herbs they connect me to him, wherever he is. You could say that my rail passion is almost the most important thing in my life. Inside of the nature with the people next to them. After meeting people from all over the world, I can safely tell you a thing for sure. The people you were meet, the people you meet today and the people you will meet in this life are not so hugely different from you. All of them felt they had something to say, a story to tell. Like it or not, you are a creator. Creation is a fact of existence. Everyone creates many things every day.

I am a quiet man, pretty much invisible except if you happen to notice me standing next to the people of my community. But if you ask me to envolve in active politics I can never do that even I am so popular there. I have never seen so many things in my whole life. In that country where the skin color has a big question marque (?).

I cannot understand the culture, I try to listen. I can catch only a few things. I am not sure what kind of things bothers me more than others. My full name is Godfroy Boursiquot but my nake name is Gody everyone on my family my wife **Marie Guetty** calls me Gody, usually when I meet someone for the first time, I tell them my full name but for the pronunciation of my name I say okay call me Gody. The most important cause to me as a human being is not my name. The most important is involve as tools to develop my community. I am never underestimating my power to change the world with my skills and my experience as a human being. Sharing ideas to the people, speak with hem to create the new alternatives of développements is my way to focus. My name is fit day after day like a plant in the garden where I make space for blooming flowers. I am from Haïti. It is a big adventure country in caraïbean south America. After sipping a cup of coffee with peace and honor at the hard of the house, enjoy the air supported by the politique sun in nature. Walk to the people of the village to explore the culture.

Now after the swimming ideas, we had a dream for support, illusion salad and omnipresent stress, all the stress people bring from home country. I filled. Every time It was time to go home. The responsibilities threw me into the water of this life it was like the last time. But we splashed a long time on this water. In the past few years, I was the director of a Humanitarian Organization. I was responsible for the staff and coordinates daily reporting and activities to ensure overall objectives and strategies are achieved. I also supported the development of program strategies and annual plans and Coordinated with all levels of management to gather and analyze information. I prepared monthly, quarterly, and annual performance reports including management. Also, I possess outstanding persuasive and follow up abilities. I have worked efficiently in a challenging position. I also process strongly organizational, managing institution and development programs. I identify and resolve problems promptly, develop alternative solutions, work well in a group problem-solving situation.

I, upon my oath, do depose and say, I am the Plaintiff in the above-captioned restraining order complaint. I have known my husband for about five years and have been married to him since December 2006. We have one child, a daughter, born in June 2008. Around August 2007, on about three different occasions, my husband attempted to hit me while he was drinking. I was forced to leave the house each of these times to keep myself safe.

Also in August 2007, my husband made plans for us to come to the United States from Haiti. We stayed for a while with his sister's family in Connecticut. In November 2007, while I was pregnant with our daughter, my husband's brother-in-law sexually harassed me by trying to engage me in inappropriate conversation, asking me questions about my intimate life and talking to me about sex. When I told my husband about this, he said I was trying to start trouble for the family.

We then moved to Boston with my husband's mother and brother. This family made me uncomfortable and accused me of bad behavior with men.

When I tried to defend myself, my husband's brother said he would "kick my ass" and send me back to Haiti. When I told my husband he again accused me of practicing voodoo and of putting a spell on him.

While receiving prenatal care at the Mattapan Health center the staff at my doctor's office noticed that I seemed very sad and asked me what was troubling me. I told them about my life at home, including the fact that my husband was making me sleep on the floor between the living room and kitchen where I got very little rest. The doctor's staff was concerned about my living conditions and offered to help me with services including finding better housing.

I told my husband about what was said at the doctor's office and he became very angry and said I was not allowed to accept any outside help and that he was responsible for me and that if I continued to talk to people he would divorce me, keep the baby and send me away. Because I didn't speak English and had no one else to turn to I didn't think I had any way to improve my life. On the night of June 11, 2008, I was thinking about my situation, became very upset and went into labor a few days early. my husband refused to call an ambulance to take me to the hospital. He said it would be better if I stayed home to give birth and died as a result. I was in labor all night and in the morning, he finally called the ambulance. I gave birth to our daughter immediately upon arrival at the hospital and suffered badly tearing because of the delay.

Shortly after our daughter's birth, my husband's brother arranged to have someone come to the house and do DNA testing on the baby to make sure it was my husband's. I didn't want such a thing done and even thought about calling the police but my husband's brother said he would "put his foot up my ass" if I didn't cooperate and he grabbed the baby from my arms to have her cheeked swabbed. My husband went along with all of this.

Around this time my husband's mother died and he said we needed to return there with her remains. I did not want to go because the baby was too young, she hadn't had her shots and the doctor said she shouldn't go. My husband insisted and again I didn't think I had a choice.

In Haiti, my husband left me with my mother for two months while he returned to the U.S. after a few days. He took my immigration documents with him. I called him to send me a ticket to come back but he refused to say I was trying to "get rich off of him". My family told him they were prepared to call the police about my documents, and he sent them back and my aunt helped me return to the U.S.

When I came back to this country, I sought help from domestic violence services. I am staying in a safe place with my daughter and trying to start a new life. I am afraid of my husband because he has threatened me with violence and has said he will take my daughter and keep her from me. he has been calling my relatives asking where I am. I fear that if he sees me somewhere, he will hurt me and take my child away from me. I am seeking the court's protection so that this will not happen.

My daughter and I are currently residing in a confidential location out of fear of suffering further abuse at the hands of my husband, Godfroy Boursiquot. On November 14, 2008, I obtained an abuse prevention order against my husband for one year. At that time, I feared greatly for my safety and I still do today.

Since November 14, 2008, some of my relatives and close ones have reported to me how they received calls or visits from my husband, Godfroy Boursiquout, asking about my whereabouts and making threats. To preserve confidentiality around my past and present locations and also out of fear of putting these persons at risk of further harassment by my husband, I cannot give their names here. At least one of these persons changed their phone number and moved to avoid my husband contacting them.

On at least one occasion, my husband talked to somebody within my circle of relatives/close ones and tried to find out if they had seen me or knew where I was. When he did not get a piece of information from them, he warned them not to complain to him later if something bad happened to me. My husband also called my mother in Haiti many times. She Warne me several times and, on one occasion, she told me my husband called saying he needed to get to me some important documents related to my immigration status or I would be in trouble. I am a permanent Resident of this country and so that was just an attempt to get my mother to give him my address. My mother was very afraid of me and for herself.

My husband harassed her with calls so much, and she was living in such a state of fear and stress that her health, already delicate at the time, deteriorated quickly. I can talk about this openly now because nothing I can say can put her at risk any more, my mother suffered a stroke and passed away last August.

Since obtaining the Abuse Prevention order on November 14, 2008, I have had to change residence 3 times because of my husband's constant search of me and my daughter.

The Phone Rang

ON FEBRUARY 3, 2011, THE PHONE rang and a female voice on the other line asked if they could speak to Godfroy. When I asked who was calling, she said that it was Manoucheka. I was so shocked not expecting to hear from her. I thought that it was strange, first, she knew my voice and second, she was the one who put a restraining order against me to stay away from her. Having been through the legal system and being found guilty without being given a chance to defend myself, it even scared me that she was on the other line. The thoughts of her concocting a plot came to mind.

She said that the reason for this call was to ask me if I wanted to see my daughter. "What are you talking about? You are not supposed to be calling me on the phone," I asked her. "Are you trying to have me put in jail? You were the one who went to court saying that you were miserable when we were together and that I beat you up every day, even though you were pregnant with my daughter and that you know very well that you are not supposed to call me."

"I never said all these things," she said. "I went to court to prove that she Mayud was your daughter." "How strange," I thought, "you don't go and said all these false accusations for that. This can be proven only by a paternity test."

When I realized that the reason for the call was for her to know if I wanted to see my daughter, I told her that indeed I wanted to see her; any good father wants to see their children and have them in their lives. She then said that she wanted to go back to court and withdraw all that she had said about me. How could I go to court, I have already spent money that I did not have with this affair, am presently unemployed and it is only with the help of family that I can support my son and me as well as paying the child support to pay for a daughter that I have been forbidden to see for life.

If you go and ask me to go to court and I have no money to pay for a lawyer, is this another one of your plots to put me in jail?" I asked her. "If ever the charges are withdrawn, I want to see my daughter but with someone else around because I don't trust you," I told her. She again reiterated that she never said anything bad about me. I could not sleep at all, not trusting her, not trusting the whole legal system? At least I knew now that my daughter was doing okay. I must go now. Do not worry, be patient, time heals and brings a solution to unsolved problems.

To My Daughter

I WAS RAISED IN A FAMILY where discipline and respecting the law of the land was part of my heritage. I would never think that I would find myself in this present situation, being accused of abuse without the opportunity to speak and in the name of prevention found guilty. I never had a chance to say a word. I was never given the benefit of the doubt. I was found guilty as charged and told that I could not see my 5-month-old daughter and to not return to the courts for one year. That decision has impacted my life and I am sure that of my daughter.

What I know is true, is that I will continue to fight for children's rights. My fight includes the rights of my daughter Mayud and my son Madyuf even though I find myself unable to defend my own daughter's rights I remain focused on this quest.

Unfortunately, at this juncture of my life, this is what life has brought to me. This pain and suffering have come to me even though I started defending the rights of children when I was 12 years old. Who could have imagined as I have been working with children for the past 22 years that I would have ever found myself in this situation?

I lived in a place where children's rights were nonexistent. Many lived in the streets of Port-au-Prince, others called "restive" meaning indentured servants. My daughter, if I can remember I always fought for them, for their dignity, I fought to protect them against all sorts of abuse. With you currently not in my life I have been given an unbelievable strength to continue.

I want to be the voice of other fathers who have found themselves in my situation, suffering in silence. Yes, we the fathers also have the right to be with our children. The way society has set it up is completely wrong. Maybe if I had money and could hire a big hotshot lawyer, I could then have a voice. But I do not, and I am sure that there are many like me who found themselves silenced. It seems that no one cares.

About this time a year ago, I was getting ready to welcome you into this world. I want you to know that your dady was there, with your mother throughout the pregnancy. I went with her to her doctor's visits. Together with your brother Madyuf, we chose your name. I was there when your mother was in labor, when you were born and when I held you for the first time in my arms, there are no words to describe how I felt. I want you to know that I am ready to make all the sacrifices that a father does for the daughter that he loves.

Today, while I am writing this I am crying. I am asking myself where you are. I had the opportunity to have you in my life, cherish you, the first month of your life. The last time I saw you was on July 20th. It was the day I was in the court of law, being falsely accused of abusing you and your mother.

Evil words were said. I was accused of beating your mother daily when she was pregnant for you. She said when she had a chance, she escaped trying to save your life and hers. Not having a lawyer, I was not given the opportunity to talk and explain my side of the story. Throughout the ordeal, there was a policeman by my side, ready to handcuff me. I just kept on praying God that I would not end up in jail.

I am writing this so those who read it may understand the tragedy that occurs when in the name of preventive protection, a woman can just go to court and say that she and her child have been abused. Without physical evidence, or any police intervention or record. I am alone in the court of law, barely speaking English with any translation being offered. I was condemned without pity.

But I know that the truth will be revealed. Mayud, my love, you will then know that your father is a man that does not have a cell of violence in his body. That I have always stood against injustice and abuse for all human beings, and especially children. How could I have abused you my daughter, the one I love, the one who carries my blood?

November 27, 2009, by Gody
Life circumstances are keeping me away from you. I promise you that one-day we will be in each other's lives.
Your father Gody

June 11, 2009, by Gody
My dear daughter Mayud:
Where are you? Are you okay? Do you miss me? I know if you could answer all these questions.

Just to let you know that in spite of being wrongly accused and unable to see you, see you smile, call me daddy watch you make your first steps, there is no anger in my heart. My heart is full of love that I presently able to share with my son Madyuf and the rest of my family. There is no space for hatred or revenge.

I have only room for peace, love, a celebration of life, making the world a better place, giving voice to those who don't, using my gifts to empower those looking for ways to better their lives. This is what I am about, my life purpose.

There are many other children who suffer because they do not have a father. But you do have a father. We are both suffering from this separation forced upon us by a flawed system. A system that in the guise of protection, his doing more harm than good. People are tossed like dolls, no one cares about the consequences, no one cares about those who are suffering.

It cannot continue like that. This flawed system must change. Innocent people cannot be abused like that; they need to have a voice, given a fair trial, and only be punished if they are found guilty. I love you, Your Papi, Gody.

P.S. Writing these notes to you has been very healing. Sometimes, I ask myself what other fathers like me who cannot write do? I hope to hear from those who do too.

June 11, 2009, by Gody

Today I am thinking of you and the many other children who live away from their daddy, not by choice. Many children are suffering because, by law, they have to stay away from their children for their protection. The only thing is that those who create those laws did not take into consideration whether the facts that lead them to make that decision could be flawed. There is no consideration that some of these fathers could be innocent. Therefore, these father's children end up being abused by the system who is supposed to protect them. While away from their fathers, these children are missing something important in their lives.

As someone who has always fought for children's rights and a law-abiding citizen, I would have never imagined that one day a faulty system would have kept me away from my daughter. This only gives me the impetus to learn how the system can work better. The decision to take away the rights of a father to see his child for one year simply because the mother accuses of abuse is abusive to the child's and the father as well. Should you, my daughter suffers because of a flawed system?

There should be a system in place that indeed does protect children and their mother when they are being abused. But there should also be an opportunity for the accused to defend himself. My daughter was taken away from me because her mother falsely accused me of abusing her while she was still pregnant.

I have never abused her – neither have I abused anyone in my entire life. I did the best I could as a husband who had recently emigrated in this country, barely speaking English, and trying to start a new life.

There were marital difficulties like those that many new couples have, but she chose to punish me by taking away my daughter from me. Most probably, because she knew that by crying wolf, falsely saying that she was afraid for her life and the life of our daughter, she would get away with it.

However, I am not bitter. I must see this experience as an opportunity to grow. If life gives us all that we need, all will come to a standstill since there would be no opportunity to create.

For a while, like everyone else I thought that only children in third world countries, and those living in the ghettos in rich countries were poor. However, I have soon realized after traveling abroad while leaving in Haiti that it is far from the truth.

Children from all walks of life, whether they live in rich and poor countries, they are poor whenever they lack a voice that would represent them fairly and not making decisions for the sake of protecting them and in the confinement of an unjust system.

My daughter Mayud happened to be born in America, the land of the free, and the same justice system was used against her. This would have never happened if we were in Haiti living in my community. Such lies could not have been perpetrated in the name of vengeance since in that system, who would have judged us would have not depended on the justice system, or the law, but by the society where we live in, where everything is transparent, because everyone lives in proximity of everyone, so there is no place to hide. Whenever one lives in a community where everything is on the open and where they are held accountable for their actions, there is no possibility for one to be abusive, neither for another to commit crimes out of their selfishness and the need for revenge and get away with it.

But, unfortunately in big countries with advanced systems and no time for everyone to come together, seek the truth, one will be punished not because they had gone against the norms of society, but judged without fairness. When this happens for the sake of expediency, then we all lose. With time, this society can only be doomed for failure.

Children who live in this kind of society are even poorer than those who lack food, shelter, education. It does not matter how much materials things they have. Fortunately, I was not born and raised in such a society. I had people around me who loved me and protect me, and that is what I am doing for my son Madyuf and was planning to do for my daughter Mayud. But destiny had other plans.

I know that it was not in vain that I cared for so many years for children who were orphaned and lived in the streets and cemeteries. I took it upon myself since the age of 12, recognizing how fortunate I was to start working with those of the streets with no one to protect them.

The only thing that I have found is true is that regardless of our race, gender, religion, and country of origin, we are all the same. We are all connected through love, justice for all, giving, sharing, and working together to make this world a better place.

I know that in the end, justice will prevail. My daughter will grow up and will be asking for her daddy. With technology and the many people around her who know the truth, she will eventually call me and asking me to come to see her. That is my birthday wish for you Mayud.

June 5, 2009, by Gody

As my daughter's first birthday approaches and the last time I saw her was when she was barely a month old, I am invaded with pain. Writing what is my mind and my heart has made the pain somewhat more bearable.

I try to tell myself that I should not get discouraged. I think about many others who are in my situation but are not lucky enough to have a way to vent and try to heal their pain. I thank God that I am using this instead of using substances such as alcohol, cigarettes, or street drugs to mitigate my pain.

Yes, I am lucky to realize the gift of life that I have received. It is a duty one has to protect their mind, body, and soul. See it as a temple where God resides. I am healthy and have to find the strength to remain healthy while hoping that my situation will eventually come to an end and I will be able to see my daughter.

The pain is even unbearable with June 12 approaching, especially when I see other children, those hanging around with their dad and calling them daddy, daddy – papa, papa, – papa, papa. It does not fair to know how she looks like and where she lives.

I can't help thinking about her every moment of the day. I cannot help asking is he is being taken care off, does she go hungry? Is there someone around her to fulfill her needs the same way I am doing with my son Madyuf? Why cannot she be with us so all of us can share the love my heart is filled with.

The pain of a father being separated from his child is no less than that of a mother. Fathers have feelings just like mothers. I want the world to recognize the harm being done to my daughter and me. Decisions were made to protect her, does keeping her away from her father good for her? Is this true protection?

What kind of child protective system is this? Let us protect the children they say. Let us spend a few minutes reviewing papers in front of us, not taking the time to see if what they are reading contains the truth. Let us be judges and hand verdicts without trials for the sake of expediency.

They have sworn to protect but with so many cases in front of them, they only have few minutes to look, and then according to the laws that are on the books to protect innocent citizens, they make decisions that will impact adversely the same people they are there to protect. So innocent people suffer because of this. These people have to bear the consequences of these senseless actions, carrying a pain, worse than being in hell.

I came to the sad realization that in this country of justice for all, fathers are being found guilty when the world "abuse" is summoned. Everyone immediately assumes that they are guilty and in the guise of protection, their rights are trampled and they suffer, as well as those in the system that they assume need protection. No one takes the time to find out the truth unless the father has time and money to defend him, which is not in my case. After the sentence is handed down, it is all forgotten. Come back in a year, like if those involved where old clothes that they place in old cabinets with mothballs and just forget about them.

However, it is not easy for someone like me who was raised in a loving environment with the unconditional love of a mother and a father. I was fortunate to have my father **Duclerc** and my mother **Yvonne.** I am fourth of a family of six children. Together, they raised us in a gentle environment where we learned about love, sharing, understanding, peace, and respect of oneself, the community, and the world.

When I started at the age of 12 to work with children in the streets of Port-au-Prince, my oldest brother Hughes bought me a bench so the children would not have to seat on the dirt. At the age of 18, my father called me aside and told me that he had noticed that I was a special young man. He made sure that I had my room, a place to put my books because I loved to read, and the capability to have friends coming and going whenever I wanted.

At the age of 22, he took me to the village where I was born called Au Tuff, in the county of La Vallée de Jacmel in the southeastern portion of Haiti. There, he gave me a piece of land adjacent to the house where we were born, where eventually a center for children – CODEHA – Corde Enfant Haitien was founded. I have been the voice for children of the streets and the children of the community and the world.

When a loving mother and a father raise you, you are about love, giving love unconditionally, and protecting the dignity of the underserved. This is who I am from all that learning and recognized around the world for that. People come from Canada, Switzerland, Sweden, France, and the United States to learn from me about loving and supporting children from the streets. How could I ever abuse my daughter, my blood?

Mayud, my daughter, not a moment goes by without thinking of you, you are my blood, my life, my past, my future. You are in my heart; your thoughts fill my soul like water fills a cup. One day you will learn the truth. No more lies. Also, when we look into each other's eyes you will know. How could you ever forget the connection and the love we had even when you were not born? We will make up for a lost time, I am sure.

I have to tell the world that keeping you away from me, without a trial, instead of protecting you is only hurting you in the end. Because the time we spent apart is lost forever. Nevertheless, I do know that when we are together again, I will love you so much and it will erase all the hurt, all the longing. I promise! I am sure you are asking yourself these questions: where is my daddy? When am I going to see him? How could anyone treat my daddy as a criminal without a trial in the guise of protecting me?

Tired, exhausted, humiliated, exploited in the rain as in the sun of the day, even at night, the time is imperative to be with everyone and I never rest, whatever happens. My main concern is that being called to help others means nourishing life as you keep up the joyful crowd; it is to value the beauty and kindness of each one like a flower hiding its perfume.

Develop society through what I am, but not through what I have. Besides, we don't build with what we have, but with what we are. The child that you are represents the silent power that you possess and the future of your life, itself silent. You have all the secrets to becoming invisible to yourself and saving this world from false judgments.

You are for me a basin filled with love, and I bow on my knees before the world, because you give me real life, pure. The world is unable to separate us. In my invisibility, I am there to see you and see you smile again, see you and see you again grow like the flower of this invisible garden, like the river that pours into an ocean.

You are the title of my book, the name of my doctor, the words of my conversations, the speeches of my lectures, the music of the turtledove that sings in my cornfield and the sigh of my last day, it's you again. As in a playground, I watch you walk, swing in my memory. No one has this divine power to inhabit my life! You jump in my heart and you keep jumping, you trot in my head and you keep trotting. Like a prayer that is recited, like a stone that is thrown into a bowl filled with water, you dance in my blood and shake it. The liquid in my veins irrigates a body that grows for you an unparalleled love, transparent flowers, and jasmine in abundance.

All the kilometers that blood - my blood - travels through my veins are dedicated to you and it will never stop. Unlimited sharing, you are my blood and my life. A rope connects us and the middle separates us at equal distance. Everything else is ours and no one will ever have the power to set boundaries and erect barriers. You are the lighthouse at the bottom of the ocean, which indicates the direction to the boat. We are not separated by the waves of this azure blue sea; the same wind takes us to the same place. Big as the ocean, my love is the boat that carries you. I only have a rowboat; there is no room for hatred. Space is yours; I govern the boat while observing the water that supports us. I scrutinize the transparency of the waters that take us; I enjoy the beauty of the canvas that invades us. I row and at the same time scoop to make the canoe and our trip more luxurious.

The same gestures, the same reflexes draw us in color a sparkling white diamond. With each small twist, an explosion of bubbles accompanies us and our little wooden shell in the shape of a diamond spreads behind it a long trail of varied shapes, which testifies to our crossing.

The rays of the sun do not remain invisible and are radiant with radiance. Patience serves as an invincible guide. Navigation is safe and awakens on the cap of each drop of water. It's like we're in the middle of a room with doors open to all directions. The blue world belongs to us and caresses us with its breezes. Our eyes open on the turbulent capes of the great vault. Our memory grows in a perpetual back and forth of untenable points. Almost invisible water droplet dust veils the space occupied by the confession of a whitish cloud.

For back and forth, we are two witnesses, or better yet, two friends, who delicately oscillate on the thread of life: a little good forward and a little good back, once to the left and once to the right, we cross the vital alley. We enjoy this natural gift together, in the midst of aquatic species whose agility serves us as a spectacle during their dive, establishing a brotherly game with the boat and the spiral movement of the waves. The relentless divers escort us: special service throughout our trip. The currents cross each other as our eyes meet on the highway. The reef barriers cannot trap us on the waterways thanks to the saving bounces of these small animals that serve as our guide. They seek nothing other than to create a close bond with us by escorting our undulating track race: it is a duty of bravery that they want to accomplish by following us.

You are my companion and you are in the foreground in the boat. In this adventure, life for you is just a mixed card game. The rules of life are quite simple. The least protected like you and me are those who respect the natural rules of the timeephemeral.

And consider each image of this journey as a message that can bring you closer to the goal. You are immersed in a hopscotch game for a life of pure utopia. Thanks to the smallest details, you reinvent your goals, you animate each object in your image and you can even challenge the power of metaphor.

The right to rest is trivialized. You are always in a deep search for the truth. There are many other children who suffer because they do not have this divine power that you have to dare to have the audacity to have an invisible dad, and that the end of suffering is often the result of a transcendence which forces time to stop. But meanwhile, nothing has changed yet, we are in the vision of new birth.

Today, still on the boat, I see another syllable floating in time. A pendulum that oscillates in your existence and turns the hands of the watch. I am looking for you in the shadows and in the city. You walk as if to cordate life.

I have been, on many occasions, the victim of very violent crises of stress that have really troubled me, but I have always recovered thanks to my extraordinary force of meditation. Far, we are. We suffer, far from saying no. Everything is there, the heart, the thought. Time passes, the world, the future, everything is there. You arrive like the wind, with your voice like your voice, your beautiful voice ... On the chair, I am here. A song, a melody, everything for me. Tell me again your words, again your prayer, your word. Your name is the way; a part in you is common to both of us.

Oblivion, words ... I'm at the door. This is your door. The door is closed. I want to come in. You are not here, I'm listening. Your Heart beats in my bed, in my Heart, in my imagination. Good day, you will still be here soon, tomorrow.

My Son Telling Me

A DIFFICULT TIME FOR ME WAS when I first came to the United States when I was only three years old and my Majorie Celestin in Haïti. I also had to get over the loss of my grandma who passed away. I also had to adapt to all the cultures, foods, buildings, people, scenery, religions, etc. for a long time I couldn't get over my grandma's lost, every day I would wake up and ask my dad all these questions like: "where did grandma go", "is grandma coming back", "why did grandma leave", and "where's grandma".

But he would only say to me "Grandma's not with us she's in a better place" and "Grandma's gone". Then I would go to school and ask my teachers and my classmates if they lost someone and how they felt. As time passed, I got older and I read some books and watched some videos about death and why people die and do it happen to everyone.

I found out that death happens to everyone at a certain point in their lives, the most common causes of death are diseases, natural causes, and old age.

A difficult time for me was going to middle school. In the fifth grade when it close to being the summer they gave us school recommendation papers for what school they recommended us to go to. Everyone got the same school (Mary E. Curley) so I was really happy about that because I was probably going to be around all my friends. I was nervous... and Excited at the same time. I wasn't sure if I would fit in. I was so nervous that I would be the outsider, the kid who sits by himself at lunch, the kid with no friends, and the kid no one likes. I was excited because I wanted to have a good experience at middle school, I wanted to meet new people, get good grades, and improve myself.

The first few months or so I was getting bullied by kids in my grade that I didn't know that well. I didn't try to change myself or do things to try to fit in or to be cool I just kept being myself and hung out with my friends. They kept bullying me but didn't change or do anything about it. My friends didn't care but at times they would joke around and bully me but I knew they were just kidding. **Madyuf's**

A difficult time for me was going to middle school. In the fifth grade when it was almost summertime, they gave us school recommendation papers for what school they recommended us to go to. Everyone got the same school (Mary E. Curley) so I was really happy about that because I was probably going to be around all my friends. I was pretty nervous... and Excited at the same time. I was not sure if I would fit in. I was so nervous that I would be the outsider, the kid who sits by himself at lunch, the kid with no friends, and the kid no one likes. I was excited because I wanted to have a good experience at middle school, I wanted to meet new people, get good grades, and improve myself. The first few months or so I was getting bullied by kids in my grade.

Sometimes my friends would bully me a little bit and sometimes they would play around with me. Sometimes I questioned my friendship with them, because what kind of friends bullied each other but I stayed with them. I did not try to change myself or do things to try to fit in or to be cool I just kept being myself and tried to hang out with my friends. They kept bullying me, but didn't change or do anything about it, I did this because of what all my teachers said to me or someone in my class "if someone is bothering you ignore them and they'll soon stop".

My friends kept on a little bit but Over time I just got used to it, and my friends stopped bullying me, the only time it felt like they were bulling me was when they were joking around with me around about my lineup. But the bullying didn't stop it kept going. Kids, I didn't know we're coming up to me and saying mean things about my lineup. But I just dealt with it and stayed true to myself. As time passed, the bullying died down and I didn't hear anymore bullying.

My friends never bullied me. For that whole year, no one bullied me anymore. I got a new experience. I liked and disliked that experience because I realized that all great successes have had to have something like this if it is bullying, torture or anything they disliked that hurt their feelings or hurt them physically. I got honor rolls two times that year, I made a bunch of new friends that year, I always sat at a full table with all my friends at lunch from then on.

The Speech of my Nice Kaytelle

First, I want to thank everyone for being here today to pay respects to my grandfather Duclerc Boursiquot. He would be so happy to see everyone here together today. If you knew him as a father, grandfather, uncle, cousin, or a friend I know everyone probably has the same amount of respect/appreciation if not more for him as i do he always made his children and grandchildren know the importance of family and being together, spending time together no matter what happens between us, when we were spending time together he was so happy and loved seeing us laughing eating dancing talking just simply being together.

I if you only met grandpa once and had a conversation with him you will know that grandpa loves to talk and thankfully for me I had it all the time him giving me advice, guidance on life situations and a lot of lectures when I didn't listen. He truly was never shy of giving a little advice to anyone who would listen.

My earliest memories with my grandpa are me visiting Haiti at the house in la Vallée playing in the yard while he is working in the field or giving me the stuff to go feed the pigs. Yelling my name when he heard a coconut fall so I can run and go get it or when he told me no to riding a horse that day I cried like crazy cause I wanted a ride with him so bad.

A few days went by and before I left to come home, he finally let me ride with him. I was so scared I was going to fall I screamed, and grandpa simply says idiot I would never let you fall never. But my all-time favorite memory is when grandpa and grandma came to the united states to stay.

I remember them coming up the stairs and me being so happy I get to live with them and spoil me as they did in Haiti.

I am losing more than my grandfather I'm losing a father. a man I respect and love so dearly but I am so happy that you are in a better place and you are not suffering anymore but I'm so happy you are with grandma now.

Grandpa remember when I always use to make fun of you because you would always ask her, oh Yvonne get some coffee, oh Yvonne get me some food, oh Yvonne get me some juice. I know that day you left us you did not drink coffee and that is not like you. It's causing with your wonderful smile and the love in your eyes for her you asked grandma again Yvonne get me a little coffee and she finally answered again yes Duclerc.

Grandpa, I cannot describe the words of how much I will miss you. But I have so many memories to hang on to. You were one of my biggest role models that I look up to and adore. All the advice you gave me I will keep them and your love to the end of my days. I love you, Grandpa, until we meet again. Duclerc Boursiquot was born in 1934 in Duré a small village of La Vallée de Jacmel he was one of five children to the late Normal and Valérise Boursiquot and was the beloved husband to the late Yvonne Boursiquot for over 40 years.

They both moved to Tuff where they started their lives and family together. Duclerc passed away peacefully at his home in Roslindale, MA where he spent his last days with all his children. He will forever be remembered and cherished by them Marie Lourdes, Hughes, Wanses, Godfroy, Loïque, Armelle, Andrea, Wilson, and Wanio and treasured by his grandchildren Kaytelle, Aïsha, Rajhamina, Yvlydnie, Jefferson, Naëva, Niajah, Walens, Cedrick, Madyuf, Mayud, Chloe, Liam, Fallon, Lorissa and one great-grandchild Thomas along with countless other friends and family members who were blessed to know him.

Duclerc was also a father figure to many others throughout his life as well as a counselor to everyone in his community in Haiti where he provided support, guidance, and wisdom. Duclerc worked as a farmer on his farm in Haiti to provide and to send his children to school. Once his children grew up and moved on with their own lives he stayed in La Vallée de Jacmel with his wife and continued to work and provide for his family and a counselor for his community.

Then in 1997 he and his wife moved to Roslindale, MA where they established a new chapter in their lives in the United States where he met more people to adored him.

Duclerc loved being with his family and friends cracking jokes and laughing. He enjoyed going to church every Sunday and praying daily. He also enjoyed playing lottery, dominos, and when he went back to Haiti he loved being on his farm, horseback riding, and going to hen fights. Duclerc touched so many lives with his smile, personality, wisdom, and strength. He maintained his sense of humor to the end with his children, grandchildren, and great-grandson and for that, he is truly happy to finally reunite with wife and watch over them all.

The Unknown

I AM THE UNKNOWN MAN, UNKNOWN on my way. I know so little about myself that I sometimes must beg another stranger to teach me things about myself. I live at random; I look for myself among the abandoned: I was born Haitian and I will die for my cause, I am a poet and I will die for my words. I expect all this because the criminals are there, and they live among us.

I expect it all ... Let me kill me for my creation and my words, I expect it all; let me take my life for my ideas, I am like that! I am waiting, alone, and I don't know when, but I know that death is there and ... that it is waiting for me, too. Everyone knows it; even those who already violate my confidence know it.

I come from a country ... an extraordinary country of incomparable purity, a country of war without reason and end; a country lost in the dust of its miseries; a country of extreme poverty which is engaged in a struggle without me and you; yet he has been calling us for a long time, under this sun which has shone for centuries in this land of dreams; a green nature, a country of happiness and peace, a country of law where speech is free; right to housing and life, right to actions, right to promotions; a country where life appears like a vision that is reflected in a beautiful painting offering power for all ... A country that awaits us all, for a new morning, all for a new life, a new fight in a thirsty country: thirsty for justice, thirsty for life and peace. And if one wondered what is this country...

This country is Haiti and I cannot stop believing in everything that painfully inhabits us, since I am a lonely man, an unhappy poet. I recognize that for some it may seem a little odd: wanting to live first for art and others.

I have, after having devoted my time for a long time to art, to children, to the community and after having suffered many disappointments, experienced the adventure of several pages of history. But now I am going back to the other homeland as we would go to a hospital supported by people, like a prisoner.

I cross a corridor like an invisible. No one sees me; I go into the rooms and sit on the illusion beds I find there. I lie on the sealed back of the reunion. The white walls of life, the gray curtains of uncertainty on the glass windows of doubt hide from me the real nature of things. The door is open. In front of me, the big corridor, the opportunity to cross the big barrier, is there. Passersby watch me cry and laugh at the same time. I combine the past of my verbs where my suffering nests, but where chances smile at me.

I look at my eyelids closed like windows, like forgotten days. By simple politeness, I speak in an affable tone turning my back on my fundamental doctrine that is to be reserved, and yet I do not smile! I have suffered too much. Too often I lie to myself, mocking the emptiness of these sad times.

I look here and there, without smiling, without strength: children and orphans without help bent by hunger pass in the large corridor, set out on the same path as me. Everyone is looking for a hand to get bread. I look at them and they too cast their eyes on me. I have a nightmare in broad daylight. What does a man look like when a nightmare is constantly watching him?

A suffering, which others ignore, is inscribed in me to return in the evening to disturb my sleep. What does this life of sensations look like, this power to bring about a silence that worries, haste, indifference should have masked? A poet who, morning and evening, takes the same route, is bored, exhausted, exasperated.

The path of anguish, redone day after day, for years, remains an ever-new adventure, although it has always been started again. So, on the bed of my adventures, I still look at children and orphans. A story that I may not have time to explain, to write. ...

My imagination makes me discover the other nature of things; another sense of life in this homeland, where I wait like in a waiting room. I reduce the world to despair and let it be ruled by memories. I look at the world and it hates me, I become ashamed of myself: I have too many friends converted into enemies. I want to be alone, alone, without friends, without anyone by my side; because nobody in this world wants to understand me, I wonder why...

Finally, I realize that I ask too many questions in a single life, silence is always the answer to my hell. Isn't it silly to seek life in the various ways of living it?

I said to myself yesterday in the silence of the night - but no doubt, I may have known it long before childhood - "All we should know today is that we have no power if you are not able to look in the mirror. " Forms of life behind each of us, crippled, with laws from a pyramidal source, cross the threshold of our thoughts.

I strive to be myself, a man of firm character, but adopting a simple attitude as always; an insider who allows others to easily find a new path, without savoring the pleasure of being in the first place, but rather that of being able to stay the best.

There is something that we can always do better than others. To get there: stay yourself, listen to your inner voice and above all never stop on the way when you are facing obstacles. Have the courage to measure your limits and do the things in which you feel great. Never want to impress anyone in his life to avoid living an arrogant life.

It is the way you throw the ball that gives you the opportunity to reach the goal you dream of. No one will make you happy before you decide to take the first step yourself which will lead you to be happy. You exist to find the path you want to chart for yourself to lead the life that will make you happy. It is the existence of everything around you that creates the life you seek. This life manifests itself in looks, forms, movements, attitudes, formulas, and ways of thinking to form, transform and define every morning the parameters of a power that will make you live sumptuous days and evenings.

It is not the skill of your hands that forges the performance that others admire, it is rather the quality of heart that produces the embalming spark of perfume that makes you become similar to those with which everyone wants. to foil. Do not give another image to what you need to develop, rather paint a partial picture of reality. Joy is a mind game to score points.

In this entertainment, you must paint yourself the picture of what you aspire to while remaining within the prescribed formula. You yourself are a transparent board that must be repainted day after day with a motivation that you must support until the end. And you can do better than everyone you look at, and people applaud you. Do not grab the big head when you're in the limelight.

(*Conquer without danger, we triumph without glory...*) If in your space ritually occupied by your spirit of creativity, you are already qualified for again without having had to face a rival, that you reach the objective without having to ever lower your head in front of the door, you will always have the boon to sound the alarm to break in a door in addition to the one opened by this crystal clear picture, visible to everyone. Surround your name, your character, and your personality with secrets to finally find what you feel valuable or elegant in your social connections.

Your expectations will never be fulfilled if you do not remain like an empty container ready to receive the new morning with all that it contains. And never forget that you have the hook in your hands to catch your seconds, minutes and hours of joy, a chance that everyone hopes to have in their life. Always stay happy without forgetting that, even if the joyful river is on the road to your heart that does not prevent it from mixing with the quicksand of your daily life.

What you are is reflected in your skills and especially in the motivation you have to achieve the goals you have set. What you want to do does it now and with determination as if you were accessing a simple staircase that would be one kilometer from your room. When you get there, make the world see you in a different way, prove to the world that you are unique in everything you do, and don't hesitate to worship every new thing that brightens your life every day.

Motivation is like the amount of water you can get. Let us say it's like a river or a river from which you must receive powerful water, but which flows drop by drop. If you want to live a productive existence, the source will not dry up, and you will transform yourself day after day into the creator of your own life.

It is how you think and acts that will determine how successful you are. If you do not change the way you see things today, you will be the barrier to your own development yourself and tomorrow what you expect will not be yours. Never be afraid of being an adventurer in life because life itself is a great adventure that should not be taken for granted. The people who promise you the moon never hope you can be free for one day to do what you want with your life. Those watching you now are not the insured protectors of tomorrow. You are stronger and more intelligent than all those who accompany you.

Support is just a temporary chance to guide you in your actions, but it makes you dumb and dependent. Like me ... What I have become today stems from voluntary missions carried out since my childhood. Each of the faces I meet increases my knowledge, all the poor neighborhoods, and each of the people who are part of it, all the young people and the children were, first of all, a source of imagination and creation.

My life is shaped by physical and metaphysical adventures. Everything I do is a success. I've never experienced chess in my life, so adventure is a safe road for me, a school without a rival. Adventures train me. A great man is one who meets nature in an impossible world, without a family circle and who runs daily after time with ease.

I cannot let my dreams die; I feed and protect them by internal and external journeys. I feed them in my sufferings and my rejoicings. I always have a positive image of my travels: trips often to unknown places and without a road map. I always cherish the madness of reaching the goal...

I do not believe in chance, but in the fulfillment of a commitment. Everyone has a gift from somewhere, you just must guide and feed it with the madness of being happy and natural.

I never drop a commitment; I have a vision of things that I do not give up easily; I don't let anyone make decisions for me like I never take someone else's place.

I do not pretend to say that the ideas of others cannot complement mine and that what they think is not right. On the contrary, it is important to consider the opinions of others.

When I was younger, I always wanted to have my own space, it was one of my first goals: to be lonely and free. I always had the spirit of a traveler, always had an image to discover in my head, whether it was a celebration or distress.

I seek to live in depth the mystery of my existence, that of others too, as well as the full reality of things. Thinking back to the story of my childhood and my life of adventures, I realize that for a very long time, the Supreme Being has staked my life with experiences that prepared me for the different activities that I would have to exercise as that of motivator with the most deprived.

I have no special words to speak to young people; I just speak to them like a friend, like another part of my being. The need to travel often manifests suddenly when sometimes we had something else in mind; I'm there and suddenly, I want to leave, without preparing anything; whereas two minutes before, I didn't even have the idea to go for a walk. The beauties of nature, the music of the birds, the simple things, the accompaniment of others: this is above all what drives me to travel. At home, the need to work arises especially in front of nature shows. I feel that my job, my mission since I was 12, is to simply throw myself into the world of children. I learned to travel alone, no doubt thanks to my thirst for discovering nature, listening to birds, watching flowers, serving children, playing with them.

For me, a traveler is not only an adventurer, but also a dreamer and a motivating messenger, but above all, he is a human person in touch with nature and Man to weave bonds of human solidarity and foster a deeper understanding between adults and children in their environment. During his travels, one has the feeling of reality, of space that changes, of time that moves and of society that changes every day. There is the song of the birds, the music of the water, the growing plants, the transforming flowers, and the clouds dancing in the sky. Children who play and transform themselves into real creators of another world. We have everything we need to be happy on a trip without having anything: a hat, a pair of boots, a bag, books, a pen, and sheets of paper. Nature is your gain and your endless playground. So, I focused on the children so that they become full actors in their own natural life.

I wanted to make them speak as well as all those who have no right to speak. It's a great experience. I have been fortunate enough to travel and meet many children. From them, I learned a lot. I think it will help me later, even after I die, to exist in some other way. I do not know how many times I can say it, but they are exceptional.

Most of the time, when foreigners think of Haitians, they think of voodoo, not as a religion, but as it was defined at the source, as witchcraft; they think of poverty too, yet each of us has a wealth to share, a unique, original wealth. If you come to my house, you must not believe, because you are rich, because you are a foreigner, that you are going to be accepted as a god.

Being rich, foreign, means absolutely nothing to me. You are a human being, a student in the same school as mine: this world! And we drink this atmosphere from the same glass wherever we are. That is all! As my way of working is not very formal, often people think that I am not a classic educator and yet, sometimes, after several weeks spent with children, the parents consider me as a parent, as a member of the family. Confidence and the creation of existence is another dimension of the wealth one has in oneself.

One of the temptations that I have always tried to avoid is not to destroy this stable wealth that is the heart, it is the power of money and never to undermine my dignity. You can really welcome someone when, humanly, you have established a contact, a friendship, a mutual, sincere interest.

In this life, we often work in the shadows, silently, ignored by public opinion. I sometimes go to a group on the street, in the countryside or in the Bateys in the Dominican Republic to offer entertainment with a few children. It's a spontaneous action that comes from the heart. I play with them without necessarily belonging to a group or an organized movement.

I usually meditate alone every day, but I have many opportunities to meditate with others when I play with street children, young people and during meetings. My job as a motivator has allowed me to experience extraordinary moments. I suffer from loneliness too; it is part of this job. Family is my strength, my balance, and my energy. His moral support is essential to me.

My father and mother's advice reassures me and gives me the energy I need. I use the richness of the heart, which already pays off in the underprivileged when they acquire the certainty of wanting to succeed in their lives. Many people come to me and ask me what my secret is for being so calm. At first, I did not know what to answer them, because this calm side is natural in me, it is I. I understood one thing: you cannot be motivating, reinventing movements over time without finding harmony, balancing with yourself and identifying your wealth. I am motivating because above all I like to practice self-mockery, to look for myself in another way and to find others. I always dress very simply, and I have a positive outlook on everything around me.

Many people think that I am a rich man. In fact, yes, they are right, because having a heart awakened to everything around you is not understandable to everyone. I believe in the richness of the heart, in the power of thought, in human value. For me, the most important wealth is in the one in front of you. I never understood these people who say: "I want money to live", without ever saying: "I want love, attention, human value, spirituality and I want keep this spirit of sharing to exist ".

The children are sincere, intelligent, and frank, honest and mysterious, creators also of their world, always occupied by the adults. And the most important thing is that they have a family. Unfortunately, many of them do not live with her, or at least live in an incomplete family unit.

We work, we are tired of the judgments sometimes made about us, but when we are with children, we receive tons of love all at once. Now, so many children who love you at the same time, it is something huge!

I'm hiding, it's true. I mostly hide what I think deep inside because I never wanted to tell anyone what I felt inside this heart that is sometimes pierced with insults and violations. I'm a very reserved person.

I remember the first risk I took was when I started working on the street with the children. I slept outside with them so that I could understand their inner life. This is something I cannot explain; it is too sensitive a subject.

There are powers that families attribute to this movement. Imagine all those who come from these poor, remote and underdeveloped areas. Among them are most certainly my own family, and long-time minority people. These have accompanied me in my first eminently positive gestures during this long journey that I have undertaken to get the world out of the doldrums and offer it the purest life possible. This is the very genesis of this organization of which I am the founder: CODEHA (Corde Enfants Haïtiens).

Gody's Friends Talk About Him...

GODFROY BOURSIQUOT, ALIAS "GODY", IS A warm, engaging man. An exciting and humorous speaker, he is also a recognized thinker in the field of education. Born in Le Tuff, in La Vallée de Jacmel, he moved to Port-au-Prince at the age of 12 and began teaching children who were homeless and in cemeteries. He holds a degree in communication and journalism, with an option on children's rights.

Activist, he goes underground at 22 and hides in the woods for two months to save his life, but this episode only strengthens his commitment. He will then write an educational program that will include a sustainable development plan for children and adults in any community. A year later, he created one of the first Haitian non-governmental organizations - the NGO CODEHA (Corde Enfants Haïtiens), to disseminate his revolutionary approach.

He then became a guest lecturer at many American universities, including Harvard, and spoke at the UN for the rights of the child. He also worked for foreign NGOs such as UNICEF and mediated for armed children on the streets during conflicts. He ends up working with the Haitian people to build a community center in Tuff. Able to facilitate exchange programs, he works with street children in France and Venezuela, while children and young adults from other parts of the world come to train at the center. He has also studied and worked in Peru, Venezuela, Guatemala and the Dominican Republic. As a journalist and radio host for Radio Haiti, Gody developed and ran a weekly radio program on the rights of the child, the first of its kind.   **Dr. Carolle Jean-Murat**

GODFROY BOURSIQUOT, KNOWN AS "GODY," IS a gifted leader for children. He is a multidisciplinary teacher, but in fact, he is much more than just a teacher; he may be a leader, but much more. He is, in fact, an artist, an enchanter, a model, a source of inspiration. In an instant, he can get from a group of children that they laugh, shout, play, learn, and, thanks to the prevailing hilarity, that they support each other. For adults, too, there is a phenomenon that marks them with his ideas, his writing style and especially his poetry. Gody represents the best of Haitian culture, optimism, joy, and human affiliation expressed primarily through his vigorous art. Cordial personal greetings. Good Zanmi "w, **Dr. Robert Belenky (Bob)**

My statement is simple: "I have never encountered such an altruistic soul who is as concerned about children and their well-being as God. **"Mr. Henry Darby"**

An authoritative voice in the social milieu: Godfroy Boursiquot has dedicated his life to the quest for community empowerment. **"Mr. Olivier Lamothe.**

Thank you to **MICHI TASSEY** for the picture she made."

Godfroy Boursiquot